STRATEGY toward the CONQUEST of HUNGER

Selected Papers of J. GEORGE HARRAR
President, The Rockefeller Foundation

1967
The Rockefeller Foundation
New York

THE ROCKEFELLER FOUNDATION

111 WEST 50TH STREET, NEW YORK, NEW YORK 10020

Contents

In 1963, on the occasion of the twentieth anniversary of The Rockefeller Foundation's Operating Program in the Agricultural Sciences, President Harrar's colleagues prepared a selection of his papers which, as was said in the Foreword, "eloquently set forth the philosophy and policies which have guided the evolution of the Agricultural Sciences Program from its beginnings in Mexico to a globe-encircling network of cooperative ventures to help the world grow more food for the millions of people who do not have enough to eat."

During the five years that have passed since the publication of these papers, the somber realities of hunger and malnutrition have increasingly engaged the attention and efforts of the world's leadership. Today we stand at a critical point. Hopes of feeding the world's hungry people by sharing our abundance or by transplanting intact our own technology have shown themselves to be largely illusory. Yet the principles proposed and practiced by Dr. Harrar over a quarter of a century—principles based on the fact that lasting gains come not from help but from self-help—are only beginning to find general acceptance.

This revised and updated edition of the selected papers of J. George Harrar is published by The Rockefeller Foundation with the hope of further stimulating the application of techniques which have proven themselves effective in highly divergent parts of the developing world.

WILL M. MYERS
Vice-President

Strategy Toward the Conquest of Hunger

Science and Human Needs

We are told that "man cannot live by bread alone," which emphasizes that there are other basic human needs. These have been variously described, but in the world today it is obvious that the classical statement that the basic human needs are food, shelter, and health is incomplete. To these must be added education and opportunity, and without opportunity the others have little meaning.

We are currently living in a time when many opposing forces are in operation. These confuse and alarm and tend to cause us to look backward rather than forward. In times such as these we are prone to complain that the world is in a sorry state, our youth are going astray, our leaders are failing us, human morals are declining, and the good old days are gone forever. These statements are made by each generation and simply reflect a defensive social reaction to change.

The fact is that we are the victims of rapid technical evolution, much of which is our own creation. We cannot have and enjoy all the marvels of modern science in communication, transportation, medicine, and entertainment and still retain all of those conditions which existed in the past only because these benefits were unavailable to our ancestors. It is impossible for the world to retrace its evolutionary path; we must look toward the future, attempt to adjust ourselves to a developing society and technology, and use past experiences—good and bad—for material from which to fashion future gains. The very rapid development of modern communications has completely reversed the relative importance of national and international problems, and today we clearly understand that

Nellie Heldt Lecture given April 30, 1953, at Oberlin College in Ohio our own future is dependent on global peace and prosperity. Therefore, it has become apparent and important that unsatisfied human need in any significant sector of the world's population has a direct impact on the rest of civilization.

There are two major schools of thought with regard to current human problems. The first holds that population pressures are rapidly increasing and, unless curbed, will lead to world chaos; that science and technology are responsible for this situation in that they are responsible for reduced mortality and increased longevity; and that we are rapidly exhausting our nonreplaceable natural resources and thus progressing toward economic collapse. The second believes that education and the application of the benefits of technology can keep pace with a growing world population and human needs; that science is responsible for the rational development and utilization of natural resources for the benefit of mankind; and that society, although demanding technological advances, has failed to face the fact that population and resource balances must be attained with human species just as with plants and animals.

Probably the truth lies somewhere between these points of view. Certainly it is true that scientific research has produced in this country human comforts and opportunities and a standard of living which were inconceivable a few decades ago. Scientific progress is not responsible for wars, but in wartime science is largely diverted into defense channels and we beat our plowshares into swords. It is, of course, inevitable that technological advances will permit a more rapidly increasing world population, and if man does not learn to stabilize population with reference to available resources, then war and famine will be the uninvited stabilizers.

I think it might be of interest to discuss certain aspects of food production as related to modern social problems. Most of us are only vaguely aware of the facts of agriculture, even though we are all dependent upon the success of agriculture for our own well-being. Fortunately for us, we have never had to worry about food supplies in this country, but there are areas in the world where every individual is highly conscious of the fact that conditions which may adversely affect wheat, rice, or corn production will directly affect his life and well-being. Here we worry about excess calories in our diets; in many other countries the problem is one of sufficient calories to sustain life.

4

The greatest human need is still "bread," and in spite of all of the technological advances of the last half century, population pressures on food supplies continue to increase. In simplest terms, agriculture involves domesticating plant and animal species and producing these in large quantities under more or less controlled conditions. This, of course, has resulted in developing communities of food plants and food animals and has created problems of plant and animal health and management parallel to those which exist in human communities. Technically, food production is the conversion of solar energy into food substances through metabolic processes, and since plants are the only organisms which can transform solar energy into organic food compounds through photosynthesis, we have been restricted to cultivated plants for our basic food supply.

In view of the importance of an adequate food supply for normal social progress, it is interesting to note that the practice of agriculture is today essentially similar to that of centuries ago. Although new principles have been developed and tremendous progress made in such technologies as transportation and communication, food production, which is strictly a biological process, has not changed fundamentally. Moreover, in many areas of the world it has not changed at all for centuries. In these the planting stick and wooden plow are the principal agricultural tools exactly as they were before the time of Christ, and power sources are still men or oxen. Modern agriculture is the result of the application of results of scientific research to problems of plant and animal production. And even this is a most tedious and inefficient process from the standpoint of utilization of energy. In terms of production figures, modern agriculture has been highly successful as contrasted with the yields of decades ago or current yields in those areas which the benefits of agricultural science have not reached. In this country the devoted efforts of a large body of agricultural scientists and farmers working together have resulted in the production of crop yields which would have been considered impossible as recently as 25 years ago. Agricultural scientists have learned to combine the best characteristics of food plants, and similarly of animals, through breeding to produce more vigorous and productive varieties. The improved management of soils and maintenance of soil fertility have had tremendous impact on increasing yields. The effective control of pests and diseases has reduced mortality in domesticated plants and animals with commensurate reduction in annual losses. And the application of engineering to agriculture through the development of a vast array of farm machinery, the extension of rural electrification, and expansion of irrigation systems has played a major part in modern agricultural progress. If these improved techniques could be applied effectively to all of the agricultural areas of the world, it would be possible at least to double the world food supply without bringing new land under cultivation.

Not only is the practice of agriculture conventional in the sense that it still follows a traditional pattern, but the basic materials of agriculture are little changed. Nearly 90 per cent of the world's total food supply is derived from a single plant group: the grasses. Wheat, corn, sugar cane, rice, sorghum, barley, oats, rye, and forage grasses are the chief economic species of the grasses, and ever since man has learned to domesticate plants and animals, he has depended primarily on grasses for his food supply. Other plant families have been domesticated and are important sources of food, *i.e.,* the bean family and the potato family, but the grass family is many times more important than all of these together. It is therefore obvious that grasses are the most effective known converters of solar energy into organic food through photosynthesis.

In the foreseeable future we are going to have to depend upon conventional agriculture as the primary source of human food. We must then make every effort to improve conventional agriculture on a worldwide basis for maximum production compatible with good management. In so doing, the first obstacle is lack of available arable land. In the United States of America there are approximately three and one-half acres of farm land per United States citizen, and it is calculated that under present conditions three acres are needed to provide an adequate standard of living for each citizen. In contrast, Japan has approximately one-quarter of an acre of farm land per citizen, and the effect of this situation on the national standard of living is at once apparent. It is, of course, possible to increase to some extent the amount of land now under cultivation. It is also possible to continue to increase yields per unit area to a level which is not now known but which obviously is limited. And finally, it is possible and extremely important to bring into cultivation once again areas which have been eroded through improper cropping systems, overgrazing, or forest destruction. Nevertheless, if all of these are carried out with maximum efficiency, they will not suffice to provide food indefinitely for a growing world population.

In the United States less than 12 per cent of the population is engaged in agricultural production, while in certain Asiatic and South American countries this figure exceeds 85 per cent, leaving less than 15 per cent of the population to produce other goods, to teach, to enter professional fields, and to engage in cultural and social activities of importance to the development of the nation. An under-fed nation is an uneasy nation and a fertile field for the sowing of undemocratic ideologies. It is not enough to provide such nations with surpluses from more fortunate neighbors; rather, assistance must take the form of aid in developing their own economies for national stability and increased production. Only in this way can the so-called underdeveloped nations take their rightful places among the nations of the world and contribute to world peace and prosperity.

The organization which I represent has for many years concerned itself with human problems throughout the world. Something over ten years ago it was decided that greater attention should be given to international problems of food production in response to urgent requests for assistance. Accordingly, a beginning was made in Mexico through the establishment of a cooperative agricultural research program in that country. A team of outstanding agricultural scientists was carefully selected by The Rockefeller Foundation and sent to Mexico to work with Mexican colleagues on the basic problems of food production in that country. It was clearly understood that the members of this team were embarking upon a career in Latin American agriculture and that each was perfectly willing to live abroad, learn a new language, adapt to new cultures, and place his technical skill at the service of Mexican agriculture. This group grew from one to 15 families and the number of Mexican colleagues from one to over 200, plus some 50 Latin Americans from other countries who came to work and study with the group in Mexico. Now, ten years later, there are improved varieties of corn, wheat, and beans widespread throughout Mexico. Potato production has increased, sorghum and soy beans have been introduced and are widely grown, and vegetables are becoming more commonplace.

More important still are the results of the training program which has been in progress during these past ten years. Many of the young Mexican scientists who have been associated with this program have now had training both in Mexico and abroad through Rockefeller Foundation scholarships and have returned to Mexico to accept positions of responsibility in the fields of agricultural research, education, and extension. These young men are expanding the work in agricultural improvement into new areas and are training younger men for future responsibilities. As a result, it has now become apparent that The Rockefeller Foundation can look forward to the day when it will be possible gradually to withdraw from Mexico and to transfer its staff to other areas where the need is greater, with the assurance that Mexico itself will effectively carry on with the further development of this sector of its agricultural potential.

In 1950, in response to a request from the Government of Colombia, The Rockefeller Foundation undertook a cooperative program similar to that in Mexico, and there are currently seven Foundation staff members and thirty-odd Colombian scientists associated in an agricultural research program in that country. This project has already produced material benefits to Colombian agriculture, with others in prospect for the years to come.

The agricultural programs in Mexico and Colombia have attracted attention from other American republics and from abroad. This interest has made it possible to begin to attack certain fundamental agricultural problems on an international basis through international meetings, the exchange of personnel, information, and material with the hope that progress toward the solution of certain of these problems may soon be more rapid and widespread. Projects in progress include the control of black stem rust of wheat and late blight of potatoes, the improvement of average yields of corn and beans through the development of improved varieties, the preservation of corn germ plasm in the Americas, and an international testing program involving various crops and leading to increased food production.

It is believed that the more fortunate nations of the world must provide this type of assistance to other nations if conventional agriculture is to keep pace to any reasonable degree with a growing world population and its demands for food. Fortunately, there is still great possibility for increasing annual world food production through conventional agriculture. In many areas crop yields are pitifully low and poor in quality due to such factors as inadequate systems of land management, poor seed, ineffective disease and pest control, lack of mechanization, absence of agricultural credits, and inefficient methods of storage, transportation, and marketing. These can be improved, and there is little doubt that world food production as we know it today could, as previously stated, be at least doubled through the application of known techniques to all the important agricultural areas of the world. And, as agricultural science progresses, still greater yields may be expected.

Regardless of expected improvements, conventional agriculture must necessarily have its production limits. On the basis of present calculations, population pressures for food will outstrip these improvements soon after they can be realized. Therefore, we must begin to seek for ways to expand the calculated limits of conventional agriculture as well as supplementary sources of food supplies. This might be called nonconventional agriculture, and several of the potentially more important types of nonconventional agriculture merit mention.

Since photosynthesis is the major factor in food production, it is desirable to examine possibilities for the greater exploitation of solar energy from thus far relatively untapped sources. One of these is the sea, which covers seven-tenths of our planet and represents a photosynthetic potential ten times as great as the world's land area. It seems absurd that present marine food resources are limited to those which man can capture blindly, and that we have not yet learned to domesticate or control more of the vast resources of the sea. Greater attention to oceanography and marine biology will undoubtedly result in techniques for multiplying currently available marine food supplies by an enormous factor to greatly supplement that now produced by conventional methods.

The sea is also our greatest potential source of irrigation water, and in view of rapidly depleting supplies of ground water, there is a growing interest in sea water for agriculture. Eventually it may be possible to convert sea water into fresh water economically with resultant benefits to agricultural production.

We think of rain as being an agricultural blessing, whereas in reality it is a capricious phenomenon upon which the farmer must depend for normal crop production. In more than one-half the world, rainfall is frequently inadequate or maldistributed, and this fact is responsible for greater annual crop losses than all other factors together. Thus, we must at last "do something" about climate. We

9

must continue to support research on cloud physics, air movements, temperature variations, humidity, and all of the other interacting components of the atmosphere. From a greater understanding of these phenomena we may one day be able to affect the timing, distribution, and quantity of rainfall for a better agriculture.

Today we are largely dependent upon conventional sources for work energy, *e.g.,* coal, wood, petroleum, and water power. These are relatively expensive as well as exhaustible. If, however, cheap sources of nuclear energy are developed and these are applied to agriculture, a new era will have been reached. With readily available nuclear energy, agricultural production could be immensely increased at a greatly reduced cost.

Finally, we come to solar energy, which we now tap through plant metabolism, with a loss of more than nine-tenths of the available total. We are steadily approaching fuller understanding of photosynthesis, and it is entirely conceivable that man will learn to utilize solar energy directly for food production. At that point conventional agriculture will undergo radical changes and food production will be vastly increased with resultant release of agricultural workers for other constructive tasks.

Although there is evidence that the world can produce vastly greater quantities of food than is presently the case, this does not imply a solution to the long-range problem of population. Actually, the problem of food, acute as it is, is less alarming than the social problems which the world must face and solve if it is to survive. Man's greatest enemy is still himself, and he must gradually learn to reconcile personal and national ambitions with universal fraternal principles. Only through the blending of moral and ethical values with material progress can society hope to survive. Society will also have to learn that it too is subject to biological laws and must stabilize itself in reference to production potentials if world stresses are to be eased rather than intensified. One of the most immutable laws of biology is that the unrestrained multiplication of any species within a given space leads to its ultimate disappearance, and from this law man is not immune.

Meeting Human Needs Through Agriculture

Basic human needs include food, health, shelter, education, and opportunity, and the most fundamental of these is food. The rapidly increasing population of the world is continually putting greater pressure on agriculture to supply adequate quantities of food for human needs. While agricultural science has made great strides during the past half century, it is being hard put to meet current demands for food, and this demand is increasing daily. Therefore, in an attempt to satisfy growing world food requirements it is necessary to apply all known techniques for agricultural improvement on a wide scale and to develop new techniques and new sources of food production. These two approaches might be termed conventional and nonconventional agriculture.

Conventional agriculture has reached a high degree of development in certain areas of the world, principally in the Western Hemisphere, but for the world as a whole there still remains a wide gap between actual and potential levels of food production. Indeed, if it were only practical—economically, physically, and in terms of power requirements, for example—to apply to all the arable land of the world the presently known facts of agricultural science, then surely the world's total food supply could be increased by a factor of at least two, and very probably a larger factor. To do this it is not necessary to depend exclusively on bringing new land into production but rather to increase the yields of land already under cultivation to figures approaching the potential production capacity of the soil and crop plants. Present average world yields of basic food crops are pitifully low, and these could be greatly increased by the appli-

Address made at the Eighteenth North American Wildlife Conference,
Washington, D.C., March 10, 1953

cation of known techniques. These include more efficient utilization of available water as well as more efficient measures for making water available, soil improvement and conservation, use of appropriate varieties of crop plants, the application of organic and inorganic fertilizers, the establishment of rotation systems, and the control of devastating pests and diseases. Mechanization is of great importance when feasible. The more strictly technical improvements, moreover, must be supplemented and supplanted by correlated improvements in storage and transportation of foodstuffs and in landholding systems.

If agriculture is to be improved throughout the world, then agricultural science will have to be placed on a truly international basis. Each area of the world will have to exchange material, information, and personnel with other areas for mutual gain. A large share of the burden must necessarily fall on the U. S. A. However, certain social problems must be met if international agriculture is to succeed. These include cultural and language differences, in addition to those of race, creed, color, and tradition. Before agricultural science can become truly internationalized, these differences must be rendered unimportant and an atmosphere of mutual understanding and respect established. If this can be accomplished, then it may be expected that world food production through conventional agriculture will substantially increase with resultant improvement in world economy and harmony.

Efforts in this direction are already being made by certain worldwide agencies such as UNESCO, government agencies such as the Technical Cooperation Administration activities under U. S. auspices, and philanthropic organizations such as the major U. S. foundations. The sum of these efforts can have great and useful impact in increasing world food production and will undoubtedly do so if care is exercised in the selection of personnel and if there is adequate and stable support to permit maximum accomplishment.

Although the improvement of conventional agriculture on an international scale holds great promise in the solution of current food problems, it is unrealistic to assume that such a program will alone solve food production problems of the future. Of course, it is essential that mankind take a rational attitude toward both basic aspects of the food population problem and begin to do something to curb the continuous and rapid increase in the numbers of persons who are doomed to be hungry and miserable. A discussion of population control is outside the limits of this paper. But it is within the present topic to emphasize that food production by present conventional methods always involves the process of transformation of solar energy into food through the medium of plant metabolism. This is an uneconomic and time-consuming procedure, and is extremely inefficient in terms of the ratio of available solar energy to the ultimate food energy product. Therefore, it is essential that a continuing and increasing effort be placed on researches leading to production of vitally increased quantities of food by what are presently nonconventional methods. Certain of these may be described as follows:

One form of unconventional agriculture which should become rapidly transformed into a phase of conventional agriculture is the utilization of marine resources for food through management. Marine resources today are essentially limited to those which can be blindly captured; and, with rare exceptions, little effort has been made to gain sufficient understanding of the sea as a great organic entity which can be made to produce diverse types of human food in great quantity and these regularly harvested. The great potentiality of the sea for producing food plants is little understood and has not been exploited; neither has marine biology been developed to a point at which techniques for the increased concentration of plant and animal products can be economically applied. It is generally agreed that the sea offers one of the greatest convenient sources of additional food supplies for the world, and unquestionably greater and greater emphasis will be placed on the rational utilization of this almost inexhaustible source of direct or indirect human food.

The problems of marine resources are too complicated to be summarized accurately in one or two simple figures. But it is worth remembering that some seven-tenths of this planet on which we live is covered by water. And this figure is not as illuminating and impressive as it should be. For the more important fact relates to the overall conversion of solar energy, through the photosynthetic process, to stored chemical forms which are potentially available to man as food. And here the ultimate argument for the sea is a much stronger one. For several times—perhaps as much as ten times—as much photosynthesis goes on in the sea as is carried out by plants on land.

There are also great possibilities for food production through the mass culture of microorganisms, but to date little progress has been made in this direction. It is well known that certain algae and fungi are important sources of vitamins and other elements of great significance to the human diet. It is also known that certain microorganisms multiply with almost incredible rapidity and under certain optimum conditions can produce greater tonnage of dry matter per unit area than ordinary food plants. Therefore, it is desirable that greater emphasis be placed upon research on food-producing potentialities of microorganisms, with the object of developing techniques for their mass production and subsequent utilization.

Weather still remains an agricultural enigma and an agricultural handicap, and in most of the areas of the world the farmers have to be content with minimum quantities of natural rainfall at the times when water is needed for normal crop production. Probably greater annual losses result from the irregularity of rainfall than from any other factor. One solution of this problem has been the increased use of irrigation water, but this, of course, has definite limitations. We certainly do not understand, as yet, the factors which combine to produce the phenomenon which we recognize as weather. It is true that there have been attempts to induce rainfall, with varying degrees of success, but these attempts have been limited by our very partial understanding of cloud physics. It is conceivable that with an increasing body of knowledge of the atmosphere and its components, it may be possible eventually to influence the distribution of rainfall to produce a much more effective pattern.

Since water is of paramount importance in nearly all forms of agriculture, and since sources of fresh water are not only limited but are being depleted rapidly in many parts of the world, the possibility of the economic conversion of sea water into fresh water, or at least into water of low salt content suitable for agricultural purposes, is of major importance. If this could be accomplished at energy costs which would be economically feasible, then there would become available an unlimited source of agricultural water which could be transported great distances for irrigation purposes.

The direct transformation of solar energy into food offers enormous possibilities for the solution of food production problems in the future. As stated before, no matter how efficient conventional agriculture may become through research, it is still true that the transformation of solar energy into food through the medium of crop plants is a highly inefficient process. Therefore, as the mechanism of photosynthesis becomes more clearly understood, it may very probably be possible in the future to utilize solar energy directly for the transformation of inorganic substances into metabolically useful organic compounds. If this were possible, the quantities of food produced by conventional methods would doubtless be supplemented by, and conceivably largely replaced by, those quantities resulting from direct utilization of energy from the sun.

Finally, utilization of sources of energy other than solar may be brought into play in the years to come. Thus, it is conceivable that nuclear energy may supplant that now derived from conversion of fuel into heat or conversion of water power into electrical energy for domestic purposes. Heat, light, and power for agricultural purposes should become cheaper. Fixation of atmospheric nitrogen would be much less costly, with a resulting decrease in the price of fertilizer. Farm machinery costs would be reduced and farm products would be transported more cheaply. The possibilities here are necessarily vague and uncertain at the moment since security issues conceal the knowledge of known uranium resources, as well as the possibility of recovering energy from other nuclear reactions.

In conclusion, there may be a question whether Malthus and others of his fraternity were too pessimistic in their dire predictions concerning the ultimate effects of population pressures on food resources. If conditions which they knew were to remain unchanged, their conclusions might be reasonably accurate. However, advancing technology should begin to enable mankind first to supplement and eventually to supplant a very large sector of conventional agriculture by new techniques which will produce very much larger quantities of food than had been believed possible. This should also result in significant reduction in the number of individuals engaged in agricultural production and free them for other constructive tasks of importance to mankind.

A Pattern for International Collaboration in Agriculture

INTRODUCTION AND PRINCIPLES

During the past 50 years it has become apparent that isolation of any part of the world is no longer possible. Modern improvements in communication, transportation, and other branches of science and technology have continuously tended to bring the countries of the world into closer and closer juxtaposition until today essentially the only barriers left between them are linguistic and political. Intercontinental travel, which was once limited to explorers, traders, missionaries, the military, and a few of the wealthy, is now practiced by thousands of ordinary citizens every year. International travel is today looked upon with the same nonchalance with which local travel was viewed two decades ago, and businessmen, professionals, and tourists representing almost every nation of the world can be found in any great capital city.

Unfortunately, but perhaps understandably, technical progress among the nations of the world has far outstripped social progress, and as a result many misunderstandings and difficulties have occurred. We are prone to think of the benefits of civilization as being synonymous with machines and tend to overlook those moral and spiritual values which should take precedence over the material ones. Consequently, major world progress today is manifest in the machines for modern living as well as in those for destruction. If it were possible to make similar rapid progress in international education and understanding, then perhaps the necessity for the development of the machines of war would disappear and it would be possible to concentrate intellectual, moral, and physical forces on

Article appearing in *Advances in Agronomy*, 1954

making the world a better and more peaceful place in which to live.

As the world's population has increased, the problems facing society have gone through considerable evolution. When there were sufficient land and adequate natural resources for all, it was believed by many that the greatest and most pressing problems facing society were those of public health. Today, however, it must be realized that one of the foremost problems confronting the world is that of an adequate food production for all of mankind. At the same time, the fact must be faced that the world itself is growing no larger, although its population is increasing by leaps and bounds each year. The solution of this problem lies in two obvious directions, namely, increasing use of technology which will enable the world to produce more food more efficiently and take care of the growing population, and the application of knowledge which will lead toward the stabilization of the world population in order that it may not outstrip the world's resources.

In recent years it has become apparent that not only for humanitarian reasons but for reasons of self-interest as well, it is essential that those nations which have been most fortunate in their natural resources and their national development aid the other nations of the world to utilize their human and natural resources for the benefit of all. As this idea has developed and crystallized, a considerable number of diversified efforts have been initiated by governmental and private agencies in an effort to help those nations which are presently underdeveloped to take maximum advantage of their own resources and potentialities so that they themselves may assume a respected place in world society. As implied by the title, this paper is intended to discuss principles and to describe one type of pattern which might be applied in helping certain nations attain the stated objective.

In seeking to aid the underdeveloped nations of the world through technical collaboration in agriculture, in other natural sciences, or in social sciences, it seems that there are certain principles which should always be kept in mind. The world obtains no benefit from ill-advised, abortive, or poorly planned programs of international collaboration, and it is therefore essential to establish sound principles for the planning, organization, and execution of such programs and to embark upon them only when there is evidence that they may be successful and have mutually beneficial results.

One very important principle in planning any sort of technical assistance for a nation is to distinguish between need and opportunity. Important human needs are easily recognizable and readily demonstrable in many parts of the world, but real opportunities for the intervention of foreign agencies to alleviate these needs by the application of technical knowledge are not always so clearly defined. Compassion and good will are laudable virtues, but they can become dangerous if allowed to blind one to the fundamental problems which present themselves. It is dangerous as well as odious to talk about know-how as being the solution to the world's problems. Most commonly demonstrated human needs in a given area cannot be resolved simply through the application of so-called know-how by other nations, and when this is done without attempting to determine the true possibilities for useful technical assistance and without attacking local problems at their roots, either no benefits are obtained or they are only temporary and provide no final solution to these problems.

When need and opportunity have been clearly defined in relationship to each other, then it should be possible to develop sound programs and patterns for technical collaboration with lasting benefits. Unfortunately, too often there may be a sense of urgency involved in such programs and heavy pressure to make maximum accomplishment in a minimum period of time. In principle this aim is laudable, but in practice it is often quite impractical. The same factors responsible for the lack of development of the country in question mitigate against the rapid solution of its problems. Only through a careful study of these factors and a program designed to take them into consideration in carrying out technical collaboration is it possible to produce accomplishments which will bring about continuing benefits to the nation concerned.

It is logical that any foreign technical aid program should be framed in terms of the needs of the country under consideration. To establish these needs clearly it is necessary to spend both time and thought in preliminary surveys and in evaluation of current and long-range problems as well as possibilities for their solution. This means that competent individuals must travel widely in the country in question, consult extensively with leaders in the fields of agricultural science, education, extension, and production, and ascertain the thinking of the political and social leaders of the state. As this is done, problems become apparent and the desires on the part of the nationals of the country in question for collaboration in the solution will be expressed. Finally, there may be agreement on the over-all type of program to be initiated, those projects of greatest importance, and those of collateral emphasis, as well as details of organization.

In planning to provide technical aid abroad it is important to keep in mind the economic and technical resources of the country involved. No foreign aid program should impose upon the recipient country greater economic expenditures than its budget will readily sustain. Neither should such a program contemplate early attainment of such size that it will very rapidly outstrip available national personnel who can be trained ultimately to take over the entire responsibility. It is very much better to initiate technical aid projects slowly and permit them to grow only as rapidly as accomplishments dictate. These should then be reviewed periodically and modified to suit changing conditions. The entire program should fit itself into the cultural pattern of the country in which it has been established and produce trained nationals who will take greater and greater responsibility for the further development of the projects. At some point the effort should become such an integral part of the over-all scientific agricultural activities in the country concerned that foreign technical aid is no longer urgently needed, and it will be possible to begin to withdraw with the assurance that the work will continue and expand under completely national auspices.

In the past it has been the practice of underdeveloped countries to borrow information and material from more advanced countries. This is a logical and natural procedure, but often it is not a successful one. Conditions which maintain in one country are not necessarily those which exist elsewhere, and, as a result, the importation of seeds and other plant materials and of agricultural techniques and information from one country to another is not always the best way to increase national agricultural production. However, through foreign technical aid it is possible to evaluate local conditions and to decide both the needs and the possibilities for the utilization of materials from other areas. Careful studies of altitude, rainfall, climate, soil fertility, disease and pest problems, and plant and animal varieties used for food production enable the scientist to decide where to turn for material which is likely to prove useful.

Often he finds that it is possible to utilize, at least temporarily, varieties which have been developed elsewhere and to apply techniques for the control of pests and disease which have been found effective in other countries, as well as methods of soils management which in conjunction with these other activities make it possible to obtain immediate or early benefits to local agriculture. For best results agricultural improvement programs involve introduction and testing over a wide geographical range, as well as the early initiation of projects calculated to produce materials and methods of maximum utility under local conditions.

The true measure of the success of a program of international and technical collaboration is not in its accomplishments during the period it is in force but rather in what happens after foreign aid has been withdrawn. Unless changes brought about are both permanent and dynamic and unless benefits continue to accrue in greater measure after the termination of the program, it cannot truly be considered as having been successful, and there is real doubt as to whether, under such circumstances, it should have been initiated at all.

Stability of policy and of support is an essential quality for the successful prosecution of a program of technical collaboration. Assuming that adequate planning has preceded the actual establishment of the program, individual projects should be initiated on a sound basis and should be permitted to develop normally and in response to opportunity and for such a period of time that successful, long-range accomplishments are in no wise sacrificed to either haste or expediency. The fact that there are underdeveloped countries in the world which need assistance from other nations is the best evidence that there are long-standing deficiencies in education, technology, and development which cannot be resolved on a short-term basis.

In the final analysis, no program of foreign technical collaboration can possibly be successful unless the personnel assigned the responsibility for carrying on the work are of an appropriate caliber. Technical competence alone is insufficient and must be accompanied by an international viewpoint, a determination to learn local languages and customs, the ability to see local problems in their logical framework, and the willingness to work within this framework toward stated objectives. Recruitment of appropriate personnel is one of the most difficult tasks of technical collaboration in the foreign field.

If urgency and expediency are substituted for a careful process of selection, eventually the disadvantages of this system will far outweigh the advantages of rapid recruitment to get approved projects under way.

Since individuals assigned to foreign programs of technical collaboration are inevitably ambassadors for the country they represent, the success or failure of the effort rests largely upon their shoulders both as technicians and as individuals. Thus, it is essential always to seek persons who from the standpoints of training, experience, ability, and personality offer greatest promise of success in their foreign assignments. Since such persons are not in excess supply in any country, when they are found they can only be attracted by the assurance of an opportunity for real service in international development as well as reasonable guarantees of stability, opportunities for advancement, and agreeable conditions for family life.

The greatest contribution which any foreign technical aid program can make does not lie in the technical accomplishments themselves, but rather in its total impact upon the people of the nation concerned. They must first become convinced that the program is one of good will and of real value; that foreign operating personnel desire to become a part of the community in which the program is being carried out; that empire-building is not contemplated; and finally, and most important, that there is definite and sustained effort to transfer knowledge and skills imported from other countries to the nationals of the country benefited. Only then will there be general acceptance of the results obtained and will these be applied to the amelioration of local conditions.

The formal and informal training of young nationals of countries involved in technical collaboration programs is the most vital single factor in this type of effort. Admittedly, this must sometimes be started at a very elementary level, often with many delays and discouragements attendant upon the situation encountered. Nevertheless, every national who receives training through the application of technical collaboration becomes one more person who may devote his life and efforts and abilities to the solution of the important problems of his country. The number and the competence of such individuals developed by a technical collaboration program will in the long run determine the total success of the operation.

There are several ways of helping to train the nationals of those countries in which technical collaboration is practiced. The first and most fundamental is through the strengthening of local institutions so that they themselves may produce graduates with the best training possible under existing circumstances. A second method is through training within technical aid programs of graduates of local institutions. This overlays the academic experience of such young nationals with experience in the practical application of technical knowledge to the problems of the country involved. This process tends to sharpen the thinking of these young scientists and focus their attention upon those urgent problems of their own countries which they themselves can help to solve. It enables them to establish objectives and goals in their own minds so that if later they are given training abroad, they embark upon such a training period with a better knowledge of how to utilize this experience and how to apply it after returning to their own countries. A third training technique is the use of external fellowships or scholarships for the training of young nationals abroad, and an essential fourth technique involves the strategic utilization of their services after their return from a foreign experience.

The strengthening of local institutions may require operations at various levels. Frequently a major problem is the flow of farm youth to appropriate agricultural institutions and their ultimate utilization in the service of national agriculture. In such situations a first approach may necessarily be through the strengthening of vocational schools of agriculture and farm youth organizations. Coincidentally, superior schools of agriculture and agricultural research and extension agencies should receive support. This may involve aid leading to the improvement of staff, equipment, instrumentation, libraries, and curricula. The greatest single resource which any country can have is its youth, and their preparation for future responsibilities is of paramount importance in technical aid programs.

Often the most immediate need of an underdeveloped country is for the application of known and easily applied techniques for greater crop yields. Under such conditions concentration on farm management and agricultural extension pays great dividends. If, at the same time, the local institutions of agricultural education are strengthened, new methods, material, and personnel will begin to flow out and into the service of agricultural production. At this point it is possible to begin to take advantage of foreign training centers for the further development of those persons who may later become leaders in agricultural science for their own countries.

The in-service training of local scientists in operating programs is an invaluable method of training such personnel. If, from the outset, local scientists are associated with research and development projects, they gain great benefits from the actual participation and the association with specialists from abroad. It is through this type of activity that it becomes possible to select individuals for local responsibilities and others for future training abroad. Moreover, the number of persons receiving in-service training and growing into positions of responsibility is of greatest significance to the continuity and future success of technical aid programs.

The common and easy technique of foreign fellowships is one which can be badly abused, especially if the responsible agency makes the mistake of thinking that the award of fellowships and management of a fellowship system is an easy or simple task. The concept that the solution of all scientific problems is to select a number of individuals from underdeveloped countries and ship them abroad for advanced training is not necessarily a sound one. The abrupt transfer from an underdeveloped country to a large, modern, foreign university; inadequate program planning; the lack of the attention and understanding which a foreign student needs while in a country not his own—all may contribute to his confusion, discouragement, frustration, and in some cases even active resentment. The idea that all students who are trained abroad immediately become enthusiastic supporters of the way of life of the foreign country is an erroneous one, and there is considerable evidence that improper selection and handling of such students often does more harm than good. Too often fellowships are awarded on a quota rather than quality basis. A few carefully selected, competent fellows are many times as valuable as a large number of poorly selected ones who perhaps through no fault of their own are in no wise ready to take advantage of such an experience. Moreover, the indiscriminate awarding of fellowships without any plans for the utilization of these young men after their return to their own countries is a grievous error which can only lead to future disappointment and discouragement and often active discontentment. Rather than establish fellowship programs of this nature, it would be much better to use the same funds to strengthen local institutions which are set in local traditions and which cater to local problems.

Obviously the majority of fellows from underdeveloped areas come to the United States for postgraduate training. In many instances this has been both a useful and satisfying experience for the trainees, but not in all. Too often fellows are poorly prepared on arrival and are disheartened by their failure to make a satisfactory record. Others are overwhelmed by instrumentation, with the result that on returning home they immediately demand tracer labs, ultra-centrifuges, electron microscopes, and similar equipment as preliminaries to the establishment of local research projects.

It is not in the least suggested that the technique of fellowships be abandoned. On the contrary, this is a most important and significant way of supporting foreign technical aid programs and assuring their ultimate success. However, the same careful planning should go into a foreign fellowship program that enters into a technical aid arrangement. Carefully selected young men should be sent to institutions selected with equal care, and they should go with specific assignments, with the understanding that they will have definite responsibilities and career opportunities in their own countries upon their return. These young men can subsequently make real contributions to the solution of agricultural problems of their own countries, create opportunities for others, and generally improve the tone of science and education in the countries that they represent.

American institutions can be of invaluable assistance to under-developed areas through consistent efforts to provide the type of training most needed by foreign fellows. This requires some international understanding and some flexibility in the realization that the needs of foreign students are not necessarily identical with those of United States nationals. The sister-to-sister relationship between certain United States land-grant colleges and their foreign counter-parts has been a pioneer step in this direction and can have results of great benefit in the area of training in agriculture as well as in international understanding. It may well be that interested institutions should attempt to familiarize themselves with the needs of their foreign student guests, plan curricula with special reference to their needs, and award special recognition for their accomplishments. It does not seem logical that all foreign students should be

24

forced into educational patterns and regulations precisely the same as those designed for national requirements.

The more effective training projects are those directed toward specific objectives. Thus it is much better to train scientists, locally or through fellowships for study abroad, for specific subsequent responsibilities. One of the great contributions which a foreign technical aid program can render is in this area. Aid to the establishment of nationals in positions of usefulness in agricultural education, extension, and research is of maximum future benefit. And this alone is not enough; it is often necessary to continue to aid these young scientists both morally and materially to become established and to direct or carry out projects and programs of significance to the progress of local agriculture as well as to aid in the training of subsequent generations of agricultural scientists.

AGRICULTURAL COLLABORATION IN MEXICO

The operating agricultural program of The Rockefeller Foundation had its beginnings in a request for technical assistance from the Government of Mexico in 1941. Prior to this time the Foundation had limited its operating activities to the field of public health. However, there was strong interest in problems of food production and therefore willingness to explore the possibility of being of assistance in this area through an operating program. As a result, a committee of distinguished agricultural scientists was sent to Mexico in 1942. This group spent several months in travel and study, after which a report was made recommending the establishment of an operating agricultural program as the best method of helping Mexico to progress toward the satisfaction of its own agricultural requirements.

In 1943 an agreement was signed with the Government of Mexico, and the leader of the local project was sent to Mexico to organize the effort and get the work under way. The first move was a broad survey of agricultural conditions and potentialities in all of the different geographical areas of the country as well as visits to the several agricultural colleges and vocational schools, experiment stations, and farms of every description. During this period frequent conversations were held with farmers, students, teachers, scientists, administrators, and political leaders.

After several months it became apparent that greatest needs were for more corn, wheat, and beans, and that other important food crops were also in short supply. It also became evident that local crop varieties were inadequate, that soil fertility and management problems were serious and pressing, and that there were great annual losses due to the attacks of pests and diseases. From these facts it was decided to organize a program consisting of related projects in the fields of plant breeding, soil science, plant pathology, and entomology, and a search for staff was begun.

Since it was believed that staff represented the critical factor in the success of the entire program, the selection of staff members was accomplished slowly and carefully. Large numbers of universities and colleges and experiment stations were visited, and many outstanding young scientists were investigated as to training, experience, personality, and other pertinent qualities. In each case it was considered necessary to review more than just the qualifications of the candidate himself, since the abrupt change to a different country with importantly different traditions, language, and cultural patterns requires rather special types of abilities on the part of the entire family concerned. Dissatisfaction with aspects of life abroad on the part of either partner in a family has more serious implications than it might have at home, and it was recognized that responsibility for success or failure falls equally on both. This practice of extensive travel and investigation prior to the selection of staff, plus a visit to the foreign country by the candidate as a preliminary to a final decision, has paid definite dividends. At times it has seemed slow, but in terms of ultimate gain this has been unimportant. Both for the sake of the program and the individuals concerned, every effort has been made to avoid mistakes in the appointments of staff, and results have more than justified the time, care, and expense involved.

During 1943 and 1944 four staff members were appointed and projects in corn, wheat, and bean improvement were initiated. They involved plant breeding, soil management, and fertility studies relating to these three crops, and the investigation of those pests and diseases of major importance in limiting their production. In 1944 the cooperative program was organized as a special office of the Mexican Ministry of Agriculture, and the first young Mexican agricultural scientists were commissioned to the office for in-service training. From the beginning it was the policy of the group to minimize departmentalization in favor of a concentrated attack on important problems. This attitude has continued to prevail, and each scientist feels himself an important part of a total effort rather than the proprietor of a small area of one discipline.

From the outset it was recognized that efforts toward agricultural improvement in Mexico would have to be made in terms of the local medium. Not only were the climate, soil, pests, and diseases important, but available equipment, transport and storage facilities, and economic conditions were all of great significance. Prevailing customs and traditions had also to be taken into account, and it was therefore necessary to tailor materials and methods in such a way as to make them most useful and acceptable under local conditions.

Since corn has long been the primary food crop for the majority of Mexico's people, initial emphasis was placed on the improvement of this crop. Accordingly, collections were made of corn varieties from representative areas throughout Mexico, from the United States, and from Central and South America. These were carefully tested in the several important corn areas in Mexico, and the most promising material was selected for use in the improvement project. As might be expected, it was not possible to introduce improved varieties from the United States corn belt for commercial production in Mexico. The best genetic materials from which to develop improved varieties for conditions in Mexico were found in Mexico, Guatemala, and other areas with similar climatic and physiographic conditions.

As the immediate need was for more corn, selections were made of the best material among the collections, and the most outstanding were increased for distribution. These open-pollinated varieties both contributed to increased production and helped to convince farmers of the value of improved seed. At the same time, projects for the development of synthetic and hybrid varieties were initiated. As the synthetic varieties became available, they began to replace the various open-pollinated varieties and to set the stage for the acceptance of hybrids.

By 1946 the significance of the improved corn varieties had become generally apparent, and in this year the Government of Mexico established a National Corn Commission to increase, distribute, and promote the use of improved varieties. Thus, when the first hybrids became available, there was an agency prepared to undertake their increase and distribution to interested farmers. However, it was recognized that no attempt should be made to convert all of Mexico to the production of hybrid varieties or to produce hybrids the same as those used in the United States corn belt. Open-pollinated varieties are still of importance in many areas, as are the multiple top crosses or synthetics. Moreover, it was not practical to attempt to use hybrids produced from late-generation inbreds under Mexican conditions. It was therefore decided to develop hybrids from early-generation inbreds in order to retain a degree of rusticity as well as stability. This has proved practical and has in effect created a special pattern for the production of improved varieties of corn for areas with special conditions such as those which exist in Mexico. Currently, nearly a fourth of Mexico's corn acreage is planted to improved varieties with average increases in yield of from 25 to 30 per cent.

Wheat improvement proved to be as fascinating a task as the improvement of corn. The so-called native varieties of wheat grown in Mexico were found to be well adapted to local growing conditions but of fair to poor quality and completely susceptible to established races of black stem rust. In fact, wheat was traditionally grown under irrigation in the dry season because of the impracticality of trying to produce this cereal under conditions favorable for the development of stem rust. Previous efforts to introduce high-quality rust-resistant United States and Canadian wheats to combat the wheat rust problem had not proved effective, as they were not well adapted to growing conditions in Mexico.

Again, collections of varieties from important wheat-producing areas were made, and these now numbered in the thousands. Since, unlike corn, wheat is not indigenous to Mexico, it was necessary to draw genetic material from widely varying sources throughout the world. These in combination with native varieties resulted in the production of high-quality rust-resistant varieties adapted to conditions in Mexico. Over the years materials from such widely separated areas as Texas, Minnesota, Canada, Italy, Peru, Africa, Australia, and Egypt have been utilized in the formation of improved varieties for the several important wheat-producing areas of Mexico. Currently, over 75 per cent of the Mexican wheat crop is derived from them, and wheat may now be grown during the rainy season with attendant economic advantages. Yields from the improved varieties range from 30 to over 50 per cent more than the yields of those which they replaced.

The introduction of Race 15B of stem rust into Mexico in 1949 was a severe blow to the wheat improvement program, but, fortunately, resistant material was already available, and the new varieties which have been released subsequently carry resistance to this race as well as to the other major races found in the country. They are increased and distributed by a Wheat Commission, established within the Ministry of Agriculture. This organization greatly facilitates the rapid dissemination of new varieties, and the commission now handles several thousands of tons of seed wheat each year.

Beans are an important item of diet in Mexico and are widely grown. However, yields are low owing to poor stands and losses due to the attacks of pests and diseases. Quality is variable from very good to poor, and local preferences are strong. Accordingly, no attempt was made to substitute varieties, but rather to improve the yields of those commonly grown and widely accepted. Major problems proved to be seedbed preparation, soil infertility, anthracnose, root rot, virus diseases, bean beetles, and the bean pod borer. These were all given attention along with a project to produce healthy, uniform seed of selected varieties. Collaterally, a breeding program was initiated for the production of improved varieties for future introduction.

From the first it was clearly recognized that soil improvement was fundamental to any progress which might be made in increasing the production of Mexico's three major crops. Therefore, a broad program of soils research was initiated with the beginning of the collaboration, and this has been a major factor in all subsequent developments. The work in soils has been concerned with land preparation, rotations, the use of green manure crops, field crop introduction and testing, and the investigation of fertilizer requirements. The great benefits which accrue from rational soil management practices are readily demonstrable, and these practices have increased markedly since the establishment of the first demonstration in 1944.

The foregoing paragraphs are intended to illustrate the early technical phases of the collaboration in Mexico. At the same time other developments were also taking place. The small experiment station established on land of the National College of Agriculture in 1944 grew to one of approximately 300 acres and became a land-grant college type of agricultural experiment station. A field station building and greenhouse were constructed, and farm and laboratory equipment was increased as needs required. Other stations were added in strategic areas and projects were established at already existing Federal or State stations. Large numbers of demonstration plots were established with farmers in many areas and the program began to extend into the tropics. Field days for farmers were held regularly with steadily increasing attendance, and farmers' and technical bulletins were issued describing the results of research projects.

In the training phases of the program the number of Mexican commissioned personnel increased rapidly, and some of the first appointees left the office for positions in government or for post-graduate training through scholarships granted by the office. They were replaced by recent graduates of the local agricultural colleges, many of whom had worked at the experiment station during vacation periods. As the numbers of staff and commissioned personnel increased, the program began to extend geographically, so that by 1948 work was in progress in 12 of Mexico's 28 states. Laboratories had been expanded and improved and a research library established, and many scientists from other countries had begun to visit the project in Mexico. Some of these came as observers and others as trainees, who, after one or more years with the program in Mexico, returned to their own countries to engage in agricultural research.

Once the possibilities for the improvement of the three principal food crops of Mexico had been demonstrated, other opportunities presented themselves. One of the first was the necessity for a grain crop to replace corn in those areas where rainfall is insufficient for normal corn production. This need was responsible for the addition of a sorghum project, and various types are now planted on thousands of acres in Mexico each year. Forage legumes, grasses, and soy beans were added to the crops included in the research program, the former in support of animal industry in Mexico. More recently, a vegetable improvement program has been started, involving potatoes on the one hand and truck crops on the other. As a result, Mexico's potato yields and total production are increasing, and certified potato seed produced in Mexico is becoming available. The vegetable project involving tomatoes, onions, crucifers, cucurbits, and other table vegetables has resulted in the development of a number of superior varieties adapted to Mexico and the production of some seed for local use.

In all of these efforts the attack has been on a team basis. The entomologists have worked with insect pests of corn, wheat, beans, potatoes, and vegetables; the pathologists have worked with rusts, smuts, root rots, viruses, blights, and wilts attacking the several crops; and the soil scientists have studied the nutrient requirements of each crop in terms of major elements, time and placement of fertilizers, and other factors. In the meantime, the plant breeders have continued to improve genetic stocks. This work has not all been purely practical; on the contrary, considerable fundamental research has been continuously in progress. Results include: specially designed breeding techniques for corn and wheat to meet the needs of areas like Mexico, a study of the indigenous races of corn in Mexico, investigations of the transmission of virus diseases of corn, the role of clay minerals in Mexican soils, and investigation of the physiologic races of the fungi causing stem rust of wheat and late blight of potatoes.

As the research program developed, a growing need for agricultural extension was recognized. As there was no extension service in Mexico, efforts were made to get this type of activity under way through demonstrations and field days, but initial progress was slow. In 1950 it became possible to work with the officials of one state in the establishment of a testing, demonstration, seed production, and extension program. This developed rapidly and gained wide acceptance in the state, other states expressed interest in similar projects, and several began smaller programs. In 1953 the Federal Government of Mexico initiated an emergency extension service to aid in increasing production of the basic food crops, and it is planned to convert this effort into a national extension service in 1954. This should result in a more rapid transfer of the results of research to increased food production. Initial emphasis has been placed on corn, beans, and wheat, but other crops are to be added in the future. A large proportion of the young Mexican agronomists who are carrying on the actual extension activities have had previous training and experience in the co-operative program herein described.

By 1950 the collaboration in Mexico had become quite international in scope. Staff members regularly participated in international meetings in the United States and visited numerous other countries in Latin America, and many Latin American and United States scientists had visited or studied in association with the program. Seed and other plant materials, as well as the numerous publications on results of research, were widely distributed in response to requests. Two international meetings of Latin American agricultural scientists had been sponsored. In the same year it was decided that in response to an official request the work would be extended to Colombia through the establishment of an operating program in that country.

In the succeeding years a number of additional international activities were initiated, and those already mentioned continued. They included cooperation with the United States Department of Agriculture, first, in testing the world wheat collection for resistance to races of stem and other rusts in Mexico, Colombia, and Peru, and second, in testing the world barley collection in Mexico and Colombia. Cooperation was begun with appropriate centers in the establishment of a Latin American testing project involving study of resistance of potatoes to races of late blight existing in several countries. The programs in Mexico and Colombia both began collaboration with the National Research Council of the United States in the establishment of maize germ plasm banks in those two countries. International meetings were fostered, among them one of plant scientists meeting in Brazil, one of soil scientists in Mexico City, and a third of agricultural librarians from Central and South America meeting at Turrialba, Costa Rica.

Two types of scientific aides receive appointments to the efforts in Mexico and/or Colombia: one, the "Temporary Scientific Aides," consisting of postgraduate North American students interested in Latin American agriculture, who are sent for a year's experience in association with the programs, and the other, the "Special Temporary Scientific Aides," being distinguished North American agricultural scientists who would contribute to research in progress and obtain some familiarity with Latin American agriculture and research and educational institutions. And to the present, 49 agricultural scientists from Central and South America have received training and experience in the Mexican Agricultural Program.

Most recently, inquiries have been received from several countries in Central America regarding the possibility of some assistance in improvement of basic food crops, principally corn, in that area. These inquiries were stimulated by several facts, among them that a number of young Central American agricultural scientists had received training in the Mexican Agricultural Program and subsequently had tried improved seed from both Mexico and Colombia in their own countries. Several varieties proved superior to local ones, and not only has the area under cultivation to the new ones been increased, but interest has been created in a more active program of food crop research. Accordingly, it has been decided that a small project for the testing of improved corn varieties in several parts of Central America will be begun in 1954 with Rockefeller Foundation assistance, there being the possibility that it may develop into a program which will provide superior and adapted seed of corn and possibly other food crops to the farmers of the several interested countries.

The current situation with reference to the program in Mexico is quite different from that of 11 years ago. During this period approximately 220 young Mexican scientists have received training and experience in the cooperative program. Between 40 and 50 of these have held Rockefeller Foundation scholarships for postgraduate study in the United States, and three have had foreign experience in Costa Rica, Colombia, and Brazil, respectively. These past trainees are now scattered throughout Mexico, many in the national extension service; a number have become professors in the several Mexican colleges of agriculture; others are directing local experiment stations or specific research projects; still others are engaged in state agricultural programs; and several are employed by the national agricultural banks. A few have gone into commercial enterprise with canneries, agricultural machinery companies, insecticide and fungicide corporations, and cotton and tobacco producing companies; and a few have entered the field of agricultural production on a private enterprise basis.

The scholarship program for Mexican agricultural scientists has been most productive, and scholars have studied at agricultural institutions in Massachusetts, Pennsylvania, New York, Ohio, Michigan, Wisconsin, Minnesota, Kansas, Texas, Colorado, Iowa, North Carolina, and California in accord with their special needs. Each scholar has been carefully selected, as has the institution chosen for his training. In addition, every effort has been made to place these scholars under the supervision of leading agricultural scientists who have had some experience in Latin America. In a number of instances experience in Latin America has been provided for United States faculty members with a special interest in the training of foreign students. During their study period in the United States the scholars have each been visited by a Foundation staff member who investigated the scholar's program and social adjustment. At the termination of the training period the scholars are returned to Mexico, frequently by an indirect route to enable them to visit important agricultural centers, and upon their arrival in Mexico each has been placed in a previously agreed-upon position of responsibility commensurate with his training and experience. In a few instances these young men have returned to the United States at a later date, have successfully completed the requirements for the Ph.D. degree, and are again in Mexico rendering valuable service in agriculture. Six of the forty-odd returned scholars now have official status as regular staff members in the agricultural program carried on cooperatively by the Mexican Government and The Rockefeller Foundation, and others will be added to the staff as rapidly as they qualify.

Research projects of various types have now been established in all of the important agricultural areas of Mexico. Work with corn is in progress in the principal corn-producing areas ranging from elevations of over 9,000 feet to sea level and from temperate climate to both the tropics and subtropics. The wheat improvement program is largely concentrated in two areas, namely, the Bajio of the central plateau and northwestern Mexico, although there is a third center in the north central part of the country. Bean improvement is being carried on throughout the central plateau and extends into the Valley of Mexico and the subtropics. Similarly, work with other crops is located where they are most important or are best adapted. Projects in force are being carried out principally as part of the overall agricultural program of the Mexican Ministry of Agriculture, but collaboration has also been afforded to state governments in Mexico engaged in state agricultural programs.

The benefits of research are being rapidly extended to all interested farmers through the efforts of the National Extension Service and the Wheat and Corn Commissions, which are entities within the general structure of the Ministry of Agriculture. Great progress has been made in the annual increase in the quantity of improved seed available and in its effective distribution for maximum production. A modern seed-handling plant has been constructed by the Corn Commission in the state of Celaya and is rendering effective service to corn producers in that area. The use of fertilizer has increased enormously, especially since the completion of an ammonium sulfate plant constructed by the National Government. The increased use of both nitrogen and phosphate fertilizers has resulted in larger yields and in greater and sustained demand for more fertilizers. The use of green manure crops has increased, and various types of legumes are now planted in rotations or in association with food crops such as wheat and corn. The application of insecticides and fungicides for better crop yields has become more common in Mexico, and as further information is made available, it is expected that their use will increase. Among the food crops, beans and potatoes account for much of the consumption of these materials. The use of herbicides, unknown in Mexico several years ago, is gaining in importance, and they are now used for the control of weeds in large acreages of wheat and to a lesser extent in corn. New uses are developing rapidly, involving such crops as rice and sugar cane.

The importance of agricultural education in Mexico has not been overlooked. Not only has the cooperative program developed new faculty for the principal agricultural schools, but a number of the more mature faculty members have been given opportunities for postgraduate study. Additional support has been provided in the form of research grants and grants for laboratory equipment and library materials. Promising undergraduates have received part-time employment. As a result of these activities the research output of the schools has increased, and one or two are now extending their services to farmers through the establishment of short courses.

The role which Mexican Government officials and Mexican scientists have played in the entire development described herein is a major one. Not only has the Ministry of Agriculture over the years provided land, labor, the salaries of commissioned personnel, as well as contributions to construction, but it has also contributed direct subsidies to the operating activities. A major proportion of results obtained to date is directly due to the efficient and dedicated services of the commissioned personnel. These Mexican agri-

35

cultural scientists associated with the program have demonstrated fine qualities of industry, enthusiasm, and research ability. They have steadily accepted increased responsibility, and those who have moved from the office in Mexico to positions of greater importance have continued to contribute significantly to agricultural progress.

AGRICULTURAL COLLABORATION IN COLOMBIA

The cooperative program in Colombia, although less than four years of age, has grown with great rapidity. Experience gained in Mexico, as well as improved plant materials from the Mexican program, enabled the staff in Colombia to make early progress. The first staff members sent to Colombia were transferred there from Mexico, which was also a great advantage.

As in Mexico, the program was organized as a special office of the Ministry of Agriculture with both Rockefeller Foundation and Colombian personnel joining forces in conducting the various research activities. As corn, potatoes, wheat, and beans are of major importance as food crops in Colombia, these were the subjects of the first research projects. And since there are three distinct climatic zones in the country, work was begun simultaneously in each (at Bogotá, Medellin, and Palmira). Already the combined efforts of the Colombian and North American scientists have resulted in evident improvements in corn and wheat varieties, and these form the basis of a government seed increase and distribution program. Progress has been made in the control of potato disease, and much is being learned of the problems of bean production in Colombia, some of which are being overcome.

Recently, additional projects involving grasses and legumes, barley, and green manure crops have been established, and these are also being approached from the standpoints of breeding for varietal improvement, soil management, and disease and pest control. Approximately 40 Colombian and eight United States scientists are involved in the entire research program, and the first scholarship candidates are being selected for postgraduate training.

In Colombia, as in Mexico, the agricultural effort has been a truly cooperative one. The Colombian Government has provided a wide range of important facilities which have aided programs to date, has commissioned a considerable number of young Colombian agricultural scientists to the cooperation, and has directly subsidized the office during each year of its existence. The Colombian scientists associated with the office have worked intelligently and indefatigably toward the improvement of agricultural methods and materials leading to increased food production for all of Colombia's people. Their role in the entire operation is one of incalculable value.

SUMMARY STATEMENT

It should perhaps be repeated here that the present article is intended to describe only one technical aid pattern. The programs dealt with here have now been in operation for a sufficient period of time to permit an estimate of accomplishments, which it is believed have been both numerous and beneficial with respect to the established objectives. It is in no wise implied either that there is only a single pattern for operations in agriculture or that the method described herein is applicable to all of those countries in which technical aid programs in agriculture might be undertaken. In fact, the programs in Mexico and Colombia differ in numerous respects in recognition of differences in local situations. It is believed, however, that results in Mexico and Colombia serve to establish certain useful principles and a pattern which may be helpful in similar efforts. A summary of the procedures which have proved effective follows:

1. Foreign technical aid programs should be established only after a clearly demonstrated interest and enthusiasm on the part of the recipient government and the individuals most directly concerned and after a thorough preliminary survey of agricultural potentialities, local personnel resources, and economic possibilities resulting in the conclusion that a useful operation can be initiated.

2. Staff members assigned to foreign technical aid programs should be selected with extreme care and chosen on the basis of qualities of leadership, character, and personality in addition to unquestioned attainment in their special fields of agricultural science. The qualities of the rest of the family for foreign service should also be taken into consideration. Finally, it is highly necessary that staff members be assured of the stability of the positions to which they are appointed and that the posts offer sufficient career opportunity to attract individuals of highest caliber.

3. In any agricultural improvement program it would seem desirable to begin with those problems which are of major significance to the population of the country concerned, and these should be

selected in agreement with the appropriate persons in the country. It is believed that projects should be strategically located, started on a modest scale in an effort to minimize errors, and permitted to grow only as rapidly as accomplishment dictates. It seems only good sense not to make impressive initial announcements of what is going to be accomplished. If the actual accomplishments fall short of such predictions, then hard feelings and disappointment will result. If the actual accomplishments are impressive, then they will speak for themselves.

4. In the establishment and subsequent development of local projects every effort should be made to utilize qualified local personnel, either directly as partners in the enterprise or as trainees when younger and less experienced individuals are concerned. They should have opportunity to participate in every phase of a program and to acquire increasing responsibilities as their experience broadens and as they demonstrate capacity to accept such responsibilities. As rapidly as possible local personnel should be inserted into key positions which provide career opportunities.

5. Collaterally with any program involving research, extension, or education in agriculture, each of the other two should receive attention. In the last analysis a research program cannot rise higher than the level of the local personnel emanating from the agricultural colleges, and neither can it be more effective than the degree to which its results are transmitted in a useful fashion to agricultural producers.

6. Every attempt should be made to draw on other countries for methods and materials which may be useful to the program under consideration, and in addition such progress as is made which can be useful elsewhere should be made available freely to agricultural scientists in other countries. The exchange of personnel and information and the technique of small scientific meetings, bringing together the leading agricultural scientists of an area, contribute to the success of an operating program in technical agriculture. Regular publication of results in appropriate form is essential.

7. The ultimate objective of any program of foreign technical aid should be one of creating a situation in which the program is no longer necessary. It is a simple matter to state this as a goal, but in practice it is necessary that it be kept in mind always and that a continuous effort be made to reach it. This means that program planning

must take into consideration the requirement that the projects established are the type which can be built into the scientific, economic, and social structure of the country in which they are located. Training programs should be directed to producing a large body of capable personnel for specific responsibilties leading toward the ultimate nationalization of the program in force.

It does not seem desirable or possible that a point may be reached at which abrupt total withdrawal should occur, but rather that this process be gradual and take place over a period of years when it is evident that it is feasible to initiate a withdrawal movement. Even after that has been totally accomplished there may be opportunities to provide special types of support for a period of several years to enable the projects to continue as planned. Subsequently these should be self-propelling, self-expanding, and measurable in terms of increased agricultural production and progress. At this point the cooperating agency will be in a position to know that its efforts have been successful and that a real contribution to the agricultural evolution of the country in question has been made.

With reference to the cooperative program in Mexico, the Foundation is looking ahead toward the time when it will be both possible and constructive to replace gradually its North American staff with equally competent nationals. This in no wise implies lessened opportunities for the North American staff members, who become more valuable to The Rockefeller Foundation each year and more in demand in the field of international agriculture. No date is set for this proceeding, but rather it will take place as qualified personnel become available, are appointed by the Government to appropriate positions of responsibility, and begin to provide the necessary leadership. Simultaneously with this movement The Rockefeller Foundation's emphasis will be shifted to supporting the activities and preparation of the local scientists as an aid to the eventual complete assimilation of the program by local agencies. It is believed that if this can be accomplished, the fundamental aims of technical assistance will have been attained.

International Collaboration in Food Production

From its earliest history Mexico has been essentially an agricultural country, and, as might have been expected, principal effort has been placed on the production of food crops. Among these, corn is by far the most important, and, from time immemorial, it has been the basic item of the Mexican diet. As a result, the corn plant and its products have become an important part of the cultural pattern of the Mexican people, and its influence extends far beyond its role as a food plant.

Over the centuries corn has been joined by many other indigenous and introduced food plants, notably beans, chilies, wheat, potatoes, and assorted truck and vegetable crops. Corn, however, and its two closest companion crops, beans and chilies, still hold major positions in the dietary patterns of the vast majority of the rural Mexican population.

Agriculture in Mexico persisted for many years in a traditional form. Even today, in those areas where communication is not well developed, primitive farming practices are the rule rather than the exception, and all the tradition handed down from generation to generation persists in a relatively unchanged form. But much of Mexican agriculture now has come under modern influences, including improved systems of transportation and communication, extension of electric power, increased use of agricultural machinery, and the application of agricultural science to crop-production problems. Today in Mexico the concept of scientific agriculture is well established, and tremendous strides have been made during the past decade in the development of the most important crop-production areas of the country.

An address presented in Washington, D.C., on October 4, 1954, before the Agricultural Research Institute of the National Academy of Sciences, National Research Council

INDIGENOUS PROBLEMS

In connection with this interest in the application of science to agricultural production, the organization with which I am associated was, in 1942, invited by the President of Mexico and his Minister of Agriculture to collaborate with local scientists in improving local food production. Following a careful study, the invitation was accepted and a start made toward understanding those problems of greatest significance to improved agricultural practices and resultant increased production of food crops and toward establishing projects oriented toward these goals. Corn, wheat, and beans were selected for immediate attention, and it was determined that among the most important problems involved in the production of these three species of food plants were varietal improvement, fertility practices, pest and disease control, cultural practices, and crop rotation.

VARIETAL IMPROVEMENT

The varieties of corn, wheat, and beans grown in Mexico prior to 1945 were essentially unimproved. Most of the corn planted throughout the country was obtained from seed saved from year to year by the farmer, and its quality, good or bad, was largely the combined result of the inherent qualities of the varieties themselves and of the farmer's ability to make visual selection. Generally speaking, the quality was poor and yields were low. A similar situation existed with beans, and an amazing variety of types and quality of beans as well as corn might often be found in a single small field. Wheat is not indigenous in Mexico, and therefore local varieties originally were introduced from other areas including Italy, Spain, various parts of the Mediterranean region, the United States, Canada, and South America. Most of the early introductions now have lost their original identity, and from among these there have been made repeated selections which have resulted in the establishment of the so-called "criollo" or native varieties so widely grown. Most of these are well adapted and yield reasonably well, but they are low in quality and susceptible to rusts and to other diseases which often cause heavy losses.

FERTILITY PRACTICES

The use of chemical fertilizers is just coming into its own in Mexico and cannot yet be considered to be a standard practice. In the early 1940's the amount of nitrogen and phosphorus applied to agricultural soils was negligible in terms of the area planted to crop plants in the country. Most of the fertilizer used at that time was applied to sugar cane, and little or none was utilized in the production of the basic food crops—corn, wheat, and beans. Studies of soils throughout Mexico subsequently have revealed that the fertility level in most of the older crop regions is very low, and tests now have shown that tremendous responses to nitrogen and nitrogen plus phosphorus are often experienced. In fact, it has been found that in certain areas the application of chemical fertilizer with two to three times the standard recommended quantities of nitrogen results in proportionately increased yields, a fact which makes the practice economically sound. Mexican farmers rapidly are becoming convinced of the feasibility and desirability of applying chemical fertilizers to food crops, and it is estimated that the demand in the next several years will far outstrip local supply.

The use of green manure crops to supply nutrient elements and organic material to the soil is uncommon in Mexico. Soils cropped for a considerable period of time all manifest low organic content and respond significantly to the application of organic materials in the form of a legume turned under at the proper stage of development. For a number of reasons the practice of green manuring is growing slowly in Mexico, even though appreciation of this method of soil improvement is becoming widespread.

PEST AND DISEASE CONTROL

As might be expected because of the diverse climate, geography, and farming practices, the crop plants of Mexico are subject to numerous pests and diseases. In the past these have been tolerated rather than controlled, although on occasion they have exceeded any reasonable limit of tolerance. More recently, however, basic studies on the nature of important pests and diseases of crop plants have resulted in the development of techniques for their control, either through cultural practices or through the application of appropriate pesticides. Although still not a general practice, utilization of pesticides and fungicides in the production of such crops as potatoes, tomatoes, small vegetable crops, grapes, fruit, and to some extent beans, has gained in importance. Moreover, weeds now are recognized as a definite menace to agriculture, and weed control is being practiced on a small scale. In the meantime, research is in progress which, it is hoped, will lead to more effective weed control.

The development of disease- and pest-resistant varieties is of great importance, and the most spectacular accomplishments in this area are those effected with wheat. Currently, there are available for all the major wheat-producing areas in Mexico varieties which not only are high-quality, high-yielding varieties but also are resistant to the attack of stem rust—the greatest single limiting factor in wheat production in that country. Similarly, progress has been made in the development of varieties of corn resistant to leaf blight, rust, root rot, and ear rot; beans resistant to rust and root rot; tomatoes with some resistance to virus diseases, blight, and root rot; and potatoes resistant to the late blight disease, which in Mexico is to potato production what rust is to wheat production.

CULTURAL PRACTICES

It was recognized early that one important factor contributing to low yields of food crops in Mexico was poor stands resulting from inadequate seedbed preparation, poor drainage, the use of nonviable or diseased seed, and primitive planting methods. In many parts of Mexico it was found that the average number of corn plants per acre was 10,000, whereas ideally it should be approximately twice this figure. In some areas wheat regularly was planted thinly in the mistaken belief that poor stands protected the crop against attack by rust. Currently, progress is being made toward establishing the philosophy of adequate seedbed preparation, the application of necessary nutrient elements, and a rate of seeding based on the maximum carrying capacity of the soil.

CROP ROTATION

Crop rotation, generally accepted as an important cultural device, is not practiced widely in Mexico. This circumstance is due not so much to lack of understanding or willingness but rather to the fact that, in many instances, landholdings are not large enough to permit rotation of cereals with legumes and at the same time to provide a living for the landowner. Where landholdings are more extensive, however, crop rotation is becoming more widely adopted, and in many areas farm animals are being introduced into this picture with beneficial results.

43

PROGRESS IN MEXICO

These accomplishments in Mexican agriculture have been possible largely as a result of the enlightened leadership provided by the appropriate Mexican officials and of the dedicated and intelligent service of young Mexican agricultural scientists who have carried out the field and laboratory phases of the several projects. Appreciation of the importance of agricultural research and extension has progressed rapidly during the past ten years, and Mexico now supports a considerable body of research scientists working both on food and on complementary crops. These young men are working principally in the field of plant breeding and genetics, plant pathology, entomology, and soil science, and they rapidly are becoming aware of the fundamental agricultural problems of crop production in their country and are making effective progress toward necessary solutions. In addition, Mexico recently established an agricultural extension service, and the individuals directing and participating in that effort are beginning to convey the results of research to individual farmers in an effective fashion and with a minimum loss of time. Agricultural education also has improved markedly in Mexico during the past decade, and each year, as should be the case in a progressive country, better-trained graduates are going from educational institutions into professional activities as agricultural scientists serving crop production, forestry, irrigation, agricultural engineering, and animal husbandry.

CONTRIBUTION OF THE ROCKEFELLER FOUNDATION

The Rockefeller Foundation takes satisfaction in having been able to participate in the modern development of agriculture in Mexico. The pattern of collaboration which has been developed between The Rockefeller Foundation and the Mexican Government, through its Ministry of Agriculture, merits brief description. After the preliminary stages of study, orientation, and selection of projects, a small group of American scientists of proven ability and accomplishment was brought together in Mexico, the several individuals to serve as nuclei for the development of the basic sectors of agricultural science, including soil science, plant breeding, entomology, and plant pathology. By mutual agreement these men initiated interlocking projects aimed at the improvement, both in quantity and quality, of basic food crops through attack on all those factors of greatest importance in limiting yield. Each of these men was surrounded by a group of young Mexican agricultural graduates, who acted as both colleagues and trainees. All the work was carried out on a completely cooperative basis, and the entire operation was organized as a semiofficial office of the local Ministry of Agriculture. The young trainees participated in every phase of the research, from the most elementary to the final step, and these involved land preparation, seed preparation, planting operations, cultivation, application of fertilizers, insecticides and fungicides, breeding operations, note-taking, harvesting, calculation of data, analysis of data, and publication of results.

NEW PROBLEMS

As results began to accrue from this program, it was inevitable that new problems would arise and expansion would take place. This has occurred, and, as a result, the number of young Mexican scientists associated with the program has increased. Many of those with special aptitudes have been granted Rockefeller Foundation scholarships for further training abroad. Others entered directly into some phase of agricultural science and production within the framework of the local Ministry of Agriculture. These were replaced by younger men, and thus the cycle continued. To date about 250 young Mexicans have received training in the office and/or through scholarships and have advanced to positions of greater responsibility where they are utilizing their knowledge and experience in the agricultural development of their own country.

THE ACCRUED BENEFITS

After 11 years of experimentation the Foundation believes that the program of combined research and in-service training has demonstrated its value. This collaboration has, of course, been only a part of the agricultural progress in Mexico, but its influence on the increased production of basic food crops is clearly perceptible. Moreover, there is a growing body of able and dedicated agricultural scientists with competence in teaching and research. These men eventually will be able to do independently many of the things that they now are doing with guidance from personnel of The Rockefeller Foundation. As the number of competent agricultural scientists increases, The Rockefeller Foundation expects gradually to reduce the extent of its participation with the ultimate objective of transferring the entire technical operation to Mexican scientists.

INTERNATIONAL OUTLOOK

As the program in Mexico developed, other countries became interested in this type of collaboration. As a result, The Rockefeller Foundation received numerous invitations to establish similar co-operative relationships in South America. One of these, from Colombia, was accepted in 1950. In collaboration with the Ministry of Agriculture of that country the Foundation set up a cooperative agricultural research program directed toward the improvement of potatoes, corn, wheat, beans, and forage crops. This activity now has grown to substantial proportions, and one of the most gratifying accomplishments has been the demonstration that the improved materials produced through intensive research over a period of years in Mexico may be useful immediately in other areas with similar climatological conditions. Hence, in some areas in Colombia it has been possible to make much more rapid progress because of the background experience gained in Mexico. If other areas should be included in the pattern, it could be expected that the cumulative data from both Mexico and Colombia might be applied rapidly and effectively.

The agricultural program of The Rockefeller Foundation, although concentrated in Colombia and Mexico, now has become truly international in character. Information and improved materials produced within these countries have been distributed widely and exchanged wherever it appeared that they might be useful. The exchange of visits by agricultural scientists representing the several Latin American countries has been encouraged, and important international scientific meetings have been sponsored. Moreover, nearly 60 young scientists from some ten countries of Latin America have received in-service training, principally in Mexico. Upon returning to their own countries these men have proceeded to assume important responsibilities in the further development of agricultural science in response to local needs.

SOME OPERATING PRINCIPLES

It is believed that the international operation herein described thus far has been a useful one, and certainly it has been an educational experience for all concerned. As a result, there are certain principles which, although they may appear to be self-evident, are valid and important.

1. There is no basic obstacle to close international collaboration through science, especially agricultural science with its direct and significant impact on world food supplies.

2. The ultimate success of such operations always is subject to the successful selection of personnel, representing each participant, who are qualified by personality, training, experience, and understanding to join in the collaboration.

3. Progress is necessarily slow during the initial period of organization and adjustment. Real benefits accrue only when there is sufficient stability in the program to see the effort through to its long-range objectives without interruption.

4. Leadership or co-leadership should be provided where and when it is necessary and desired and for the stated purpose of aiding in the development of *local* leadership. As a practical fact, it frequently is necessary to make a frank appraisal of the local situation and to reach mutual agreement prior to the initiation of the program.

5. Objectives should be selected carefully, established by mutual agreement, stated clearly, and limited to those which might be attained with available support. They should, in themselves, produce useful results as well as serve to demonstrate methods for attack on and solution of related problems.

6. Every activity in a cooperative agricultural program should be truly cooperative in that local scientists participate directly in every phase and in that they be given increasing responsibilities as they develop additional skills.

7. Opportunities for additional training and international experience should be provided for selected local personnel of demonstrated ability. The training program should be planned carefully, and the selected individuals should be trained for a specific future responsibility established prior to the training period.

8. Leadership and direction provided from external sources should be transferred gradually to capable, well-trained, and experienced nationals. During this period, the guest group of scientists should concentrate on fundamental research and on the training of investigators and should serve as consultants to the group of local

scientists who are beginning to take over responsibility for the operation.

9. At some point it should become evident that the collaboration has accomplished its purpose and that it therefore is no longer necessary in the original form. Subsequent collaboration might consist of the interchange of information and materials, exchange of visits, and the establishment of regional projects of international importance, with several countries collaborating for mutual benefit.

It is not suggested that the foregoing represents *the* pattern for international collaboration in agricultural science but rather that it represents one pattern seemingly worth further development. Doubtless there are many others and/or variants which may be even more successful.

Food for the Future

When the problem of food for the future is under discussion a standard question concerns the extent to which science can assure that future generations will be able to enjoy an adequate standard of living from the point of view of nutrition. However, this would seem to be only part of the problem, since sufficient food for society is the concern not of the scientist alone but of all mankind. There should thus be two parts to the question: namely, what are the responsibilities of society in assuring an adequate food supply, and how can science be applied most effectively to this end?

Many competent individuals, principally demographers, biologists, and conservationists, are deeply preoccupied by the problem of maintaining a balance between food supplies and a rapidly increasing world population. It is not surprising that their conclusions range from the dismal one, that the world cannot support foreseeable increases in population, to the opposite extreme that a world population of 10 billion or even more could readily be supported from known resources. The pessimists and optimists both contribute importantly to our understanding of the world's problems, and both should be listened to with respect. However, we may be placing too much emphasis on the issues of tomorrow while overlooking the importance of those facing us now. It seems somewhat unrealistic that we should be more concerned about generations as yet unborn than with those living today in substandard conditions. This is a little like worrying about educational opportunities for posterity while keeping one's own children home from school. If we can meet our immediate challenge successfully, we will be better prepared to cope with the still larger populations to come.

Talk given at the Symposium on Natural Resources: Power, Metals, Food at the American Association for the Advancement of Science meeting held in Berkeley, California, on December 27, 1954

Unfortunately, there is a widespread attitude that problems of food production are "agency" responsibilities and are not the concern of all the instrumentalities of our society. Both present and future food requirements involve coordination between those agencies struggling to accomplish concrete results and those responsible for the political, economic, educational, and religious leadership of the world's citizenry. Each discipline and each aspect of human concern inescapably impinge on the others, and unless all these are intelligently linked, divergencies in opinion, objectives, and activities will inevitably result and will seriously impede progress.

We cannot continue to take for granted that increased food production is the exclusive worry of the scientist and that it is his obligation to find ways to satisfy growing needs and to enable mankind blithely to pursue thoughtless and careless practices in the utilization of natural resources. On the contrary, scientists can carry out their part in the total scheme only when they are working as one segment of society in harmony with the others. When each group and each individual accepts responsibilities relative to food for the future, then we can make progress and many of our present fears will disappear. In part, what demographers and scientists mean when they speak pessimistically about future food supplies is that conditions will grow worse if we blindly go on as we are in the face of an alarming population increase. This fear is justified, but need we go on as we are?

It is useless to expect that all the world will soon reach the standard of living enjoyed today by the more favored areas of the world, and we can only hope to have improvements within the limitations of the areas concerned. Some countries can continue to look forward to tremendous agricultural developments and increasing standards of living. Certain others must face the fact that they do not have large reserves of natural resources and will have to hold or improve their positions in the world community largely through the production of goods and services. Isolated material gifts to the less fortunate countries offer no permanent solution to their food problems, but types of aid that will enable them to join the other nations on a proportionately equal basis have great promise.

One of the surest ways to get at those difficulties involved in feeding present and future generations is through education. An uneducated public cannot readily understand problems that are not of visible, immediate, and local impact. Such people may be led in devious directions because of their inability to reach independent judgments and to appreciate the real consequences of their acts. Thus, food production is severely handicapped in areas where the farmers have not enjoyed the benefits of education. It is not to be expected that we can have anything approaching full agricultural production until those who till the soil are capable of making intelligent use of the improvements that modern agriculture brings. The basic approach to "food for the future" is not through the distribution of more plows but rather through the wider dissemination of knowledge. One may argue that if we follow the long route of general education, delays are inevitable and progress will be slow. Such delays, however, are insignificant in terms of "world time." The fact that educational benefits have thus far reached only small segments of society makes it all the more imperative that they be extended as rapidly as possible. Interim advances in crop production can be expected, but these will be small compared with the total benefits that can accrue when sound mass education becomes the rule.

Real progress in mass education will lay the groundwork for other significant developments. For example, one of the greatest existing social problems is to be found in the limitations of rural life and particularly in the role of women in farm communities. The influence of rural women is vital to community progress, but as long as many millions of women are relegated to the role of farm laborers (as is tragically true in many parts of the globe) much of what they have to contribute to family life and to the training of children is lost to society. Instead, society receives only the meager product of unskilled labor. If the future is to be better, this situation will have to be changed so that coming generations will benefit from social values learned in the home, from mothers with at least basic education. At present there is an understandable monotonous similarity, from generation to generation, throughout underdeveloped areas where tradition, rather than initiative, rules.

The economics of food production and distribution is still largely in the theoretical stage, and the great benefits to be gained from the general application of sound economic theories lie ahead. In many parts of the world landholding and tenure systems are economically unsound, and these are most difficult to change. Under the system of latifundia, vast acreages lie uncultivated; whereas, by contrast, there are other regions in which the cultivation of tiny plots has become so intensive as to approach "flower pot" farming. These extremes may be the natural results of local patterns derived from varying degrees of population pressure, and we can never hope to approach maximum potential production until education and economics combine in support of scientific agriculture. Stable currencies and price policies, adequate agricultural credit, and proper marketing all are of vital importance to a successful pattern of crop production, distribution, and utilization. When this is generally understood and accepted by society, there can be hope that all the people will be adequately fed and that the fruits of their labors will provide them with greater comforts and opportunities.

Another influence that profoundly affects food production is applied political science. Since political leaders publicly accept responsibilities for guiding the temporal thinking of the peoples of the world, their moral burdens are heavy. If we are to have food for all, political leaders will necessarily become increasingly aware of the importance of a balance between enlightened nationalism and internationalism. Otherwise, inequalities in one area may become explosive and create disturbances that may eventually become worldwide. Here again, the education and judgment of society are the most significant factors, especially since in many parts of the world democratic procedures prevail and we select our own leaders for better or for worse. Able political leadership is usually available and will continue to be, but we must exercise our franchise with skill and perception if we are to provide ourselves with leadership of the quality necessary to meet the basic human problems.

The role of religious leadership in the solution of the problem of food for the future cannot be overestimated. Lack of understanding among religious leaders and reluctance to broaden the interpretation of their theologies in the light of increasing knowledge could be a serious obstacle to attaining a balance between populations and food production. It would seem, therefore, that the leaders of all faiths have the opportunity and obligation without sacrificing spiritual values to guide their adherents toward the understanding that, regardless of creed, human rights are equal and that they must be jealously protected. And human rights are not merely the right to a minimum of food, clothing, and shelter but rather to all of these on a reasonable scale plus opportunity in the form of education and the chance to participate in social progress.

Before the public demands greatly expanded production from agriculture it should take a hard look at its own responsibilities with regard to conservation of natural resources. In underdeveloped areas essentially all of the limited agricultural products are utilized because of the demand for food by an underfed population, but losses to production through failure to take maximum advantage of available potentials are a serious permanent source of waste. Examples are the use of low-yielding varieties; poor cultural practices; inadequate control of pests, diseases, and weeds; and failure to use fertilizers where they are needed for increased yields. Agricultural scientists could correct essentially all of these conditions in underdeveloped areas, but to be effective their activities would have to be preceded or paralleled by improvements in public health, education, and other social developments.

In areas where agricultural practice is most advanced there is also the greatest waste of food. This may in part be an effect of economic situations that produce unused surpluses, but it is also the result of domestic habits that lead to waste. Perhaps our own country presents the most glaring example of this pattern, and it has been estimated that each year we throw away enough food to support 10 to 15 per cent of our present population. Since the vast bulk of household food wastes is dumped or burned rather than recovered for agricultural or industrial purposes, their loss is total. The same situation prevails with reference to human wastes, which should be used advantageously in completing the food cycle. It seems incongruous to put heavy pressure on scientists, farmers, and resources to increase food production without requiring of society a commensurate sense of responsibility for the conservation of these products so that they will make maximum contributions to human nutrition. Similarly, we cannot complain of mounting costs and failing supplies of food and at the same time use them wastefully and continue to destroy forests, erode tremendous acreages of arable land, pollute rivers and lakes, and throw away large quantities of fossil fuels.

Many persons believe that we can meet the future with assurance, insofar as the technical aspects are concerned. Abundances of agricultural products can be obtained that would far exceed present expectations, if scientists are given a wide opportunity by society to apply their knowledge and ingenuity. There are two requisites: first, public support of pure science that will permit continuous and increased fundamental investigation of the laws of nature so that man's intellectual horizons may be constantly broadened; second, an opportunity for scientists to transmute basic knowledge into applied science, and this must be provided rapidly and be made widely available without restriction. Through the intelligent application of technical advances, an educated public can undertake to feed itself without the wanton destruction of the limited natural resources that are needed also to serve the generations to come.

If we assume that society in general will eventually meet its responsibilities relative to food for the future (and this is a major assumption), then we should carefully examine the responsibilities of science. First, the scientist must gain the confidence of nonscientists so that these two sectors of society will not be separated by barriers of fear or misunderstanding. Real progress is being made in this direction, and certainly the medical, agricultural, and other biological sciences are generally viewed as powerful social assets rather than as liabilities. A long and thoughtful view similarly convinces one that the chemical and physical sciences are equally beneficial, although the public may at times be appalled at the temporary use to which certain advances are put. It is an essential element of the scientific faith that, on a long-range basis, such developments always redound to the benefit of mankind.

We must certainly look to the physical sciences for our future supplies of energy, and nuclear energy may one day prove to be a general source of power. Progress is most rapid when vast amounts of energy are consumed, and the present hope is that power from nuclear fission will eventually replace that from other sources and make fossil fuels unimportant. Up to the present, however, mankind has derived essentially all his useful energy either directly or indirectly from the sun. Fortunately, green plants were busy storing solar energy on the earth for many eons before man came along, and our great heritage of fossil fuels, in conjunction with the radiant energy that the earth receives every day, is materially responsible for human progress. Thoughtful persons are alarmed at the rate at which we are exhausting our fossil-fuel reserves, and the most optimistic estimates give the world less than 200 years during which it may draw necessary power from coal and petroleum. If we are to

54

continue to develop agriculture and industry, we must have sustained sources of energy on an increasing scale, and unless these are forthcoming, other questions become academic.

Significant progress has been made in learning to control nuclear reactions for the release of usable energy. There are many technologic and economic factors that must be overcome before any transition from conventional sources of energy to nuclear sources is accomplished on a large scale. There may be very much more or much less fissionable material than is currently estimated or there may be other conversion methods that may be brought into use. It has been suggested that we may eventually learn how to duplicate the sun's feat of converting hydrogen to helium with a resultant tremendous energy release in the form of gamma radiation. Any such speculation seems fantastic at the present time, even though the necessary raw materials are available in unlimited quantities. However, most major scientific developments seemed fantastic and remote before they became realities.

For many years man has dreamed of harnessing free sources of energy, including the sun, wind, tides, volcanoes, and thermal gradients of the sea. Many ingenious solar engines, heat pumps, heat exchangers, wind converters, and tide turbines have been designed and used with varying degrees of success. All these mechanisms merit further investigation, but only the sun holds promise of providing mankind with quantities of energy of the magnitude we must have in order to continue our progress. We may have been lulled to a false sense of security by our knowledge of the present reserves of oil, coal, and fissionable materials and have failed to place proper emphasis on research leading to the quantitative conversion of solar energy to forms usable in industry and agriculture. All the known reserves of coal, petroleum, and wood barely equal the total solar energy that reaches the earth every 48 hours, and conversion of relatively minute quantities to usable forms would solve our future energy problems indefinitely. The sooner we learn to use this resource, initially as a supplement, the better will be our position when at last it becomes our only major free source. It seems doubtful that the most effective way of trapping and storing solar energy is through vegetation, since photosynthesis itself is an inefficient process. Surely we can devise more efficient methods, and ultimately it should be possible to convert immense quantities of solar energy to forms that can be used immediately or stored for future power demands.

Regardless of technologic advances in other fields, we are going to be practicing agriculture for a long time, and we should learn to practice it more efficiently, if we expect to meet growing food requirements. Even though conventional agriculture as we now know it can solve present and proximate food demands, it can be further improved to the end that the possibility of a diminishing food supply can be pushed back in time. This will be accomplished as the result of continuous fundamental investigation of natural phenomena, with respect to both the physiology and biochemistry of living cells and the interrelationships between living forms and their environment. We have made extraordinary progress in agriculture by taking advantage of knowledge gained through basic research, but past applications will seem crude in comparison with refinements that may be expected in the future.

Conventional agriculture as it exists today is a far cry from the pattern of 50 or even 25 years ago. Among the most spectacular developments have been the mechanical aids. It is possible in a single operation to prepare a seedbed from unplowed land; plant, fertilize, and cultivate growing crops with the same piece of equipment; and dig root crops, pick corn, cotton, and hops or harvest beans, cereals, and peas with mechanical devices. Harvested crops may then be washed, cleaned, frozen or dried, and packed by other machines. These and other engineering advances have made it possible to produce uniform crops, to harvest them at exactly the right moment, and to handle huge quantities of products with minimum labor. Each year new and improved appliances are developed which enable the individual farmer to produce larger quantities of food more efficiently and at significantly lower cost. And a sound pattern of agricultural production always stimulates and supports industrial developments that absorb surplus farm labor.

The application of chemistry to agriculture has revolutionized farming. Chemical control of diseases and pests has reduced the annual crop losses significantly, and it is now possible to eliminate many weed species in cultivated crops without damaging the economic species. We can defoliate plants with one group of chemicals, hold fruit longer with others, and induce the production of seedless varieties of fruits with still others. There is also promising evidence that minute quantities of chemicals may function as protective agents within plant cells to destroy viruses and to resist attacks by fungi and insects. It is also possible that systemic chemicals may stimulate plants to produce larger quantities of stored food or valuable medicinal or industrial compounds. Similarly, it should be possible to improve both the quantity and quality of milk, meat, and eggs through the use of chemicals.

The science of genetics has proved tremendously useful in plant and animal improvement, and varieties of corn, vegetables, fruit, small grains, poultry, swine, and cattle are far superior as a result. The modern geneticist is a sort of biologic tailor who fits varieties to a specific environment, using such techniques as induced polyploidy, multiple topcrossing, and backcrossing to obtain and fix desirable characteristics and produce blended progenies. In recent years the phenomenon of hybrid vigor has been advantageously employed to increase yields, and the most spectacular example of heterosis is to be found in hybrid corn production. As the science of genetics becomes better understood, new benefits may be expected, such as increased quantities of usable products per plant, higher amino acid content, the development of dwarf varieties with increased production efficiency, as well as plants and animals endowed with greater tolerance to drought, temperature fluctuations, and parasites.

The soil problems involved in crop production are better understood than ever before. This is true not only with regard to the role of soil biology, which has long been an almost complete mystery. New fertilizer techniques promise still greater average yields, and it is expected that progress in understanding the interaction of soil microflora and fauna will be proportionately greater during the next several decades. Another promising approach is the direct application of nutrients to foliage as an effective and economical way of feeding crop plants. Nutrient elements may be injected into the moist soil or incorporated into irrigation water with economic benefits, and chelating agents and soil conditioners are being widely tested in the hope that they may contribute toward increased average yields. And finally, soil substitutes in combination with nutrient solutions have demonstrated that under certain conditions hydroponics offer important opportunities for supplementing food production. Whether or not multistoried hydroponics gardens will, as has been suggested, be commonplace in the future will depend largely upon economic factors.

Certain of the techniques of modern atomic physics offer fascinating possibilities for penetrating more deeply into the mysteries of cellular metabolism. The thus far limited use of the radioactive isotopes in tracer studies will in the future permit the further pinpointing of specific cellular activities and help us to understand them as parts of the metabolic process. The use of labeled elements singly and in combination permits the simultaneous study of chemical reactions within the cell. From investigations such as these we shall gain information that may help us to direct the potentialities of the cell toward the conversion of simple substances into more complex compounds of value to man. Furthermore, when crop plants are subjected to irradiations from atomic sources, spectacular changes may occur in metabolic processes. The fact that irradiation may speed up the process of mutation immediately suggests this as a method to induce cellular changes that may be of benefit. Evidence from preliminary trials indicates that dwarfing, increased productivity, and greater resistance to certain diseases may result from irradiation. Present methods are necessarily of the shotgun type, but as this tool becomes more refined it may be possible to use it more precisely and actually apply it for specific results. If, for example, such basic food crops as corn, wheat, and rice could become symbiotic nitrogen fixers, enormous increases in annual world yields would occur, with equally important reductions in costs of production. The phenomenon of symbiotic nitrogen fixation is peculiar to members of the legume family and a few other species; and why this should be true is a tantalizing mystery. There are great possibilities that induced genetic changes in conventional crop plants might increase both the quantity and quality of food production.

The use of microorganisms for the production of substantial quantities of food substances merits careful investigation. This might involve a direct approach through the use of chlorophyllous microorganisms that are relatively efficient producers of proteins and fats and the employment of methods to stimulate the activities of those species that aid in the fixation of nitrogen and other nutrient elements in soil. There is already sufficient evidence to suggest that microorganisms offer promise both as direct and indirect food sources and in the economic conversion of human wastes to usable products. The gap between the costs of the production of fuel or food energy from microorganisms and from conventional sources is still great. But as improved techniques increase production, and price levels rise, this gap will tend to narrow. It seems doubtful that algae will soon be a highly competitive source of direct food in most parts of the earth, but they may be sources of proteins and fat concentrates that would be of great value in the enrichment of foods and feeds.

There is much current interest in the sea, not only as a great potential source of irrigation water, but also as a gigantic and relatively untapped food resource. Covering more than three-fifths of our planet, the oceans contain a wealth of foodstuffs, such as proteins which are needed for the human diet. At the moment, the amount of research going into marine biology is infinitesimal in terms of the food potentialities of the sea. But as we become more convinced of the importance of the sea as a usable resource and understand its complexities, many techniques will be evolved that will enable us to harvest vastly more food from it than we do today. Land is the medium of the land-dweller, and consequently the sea seems foreign and difficult. However, as our knowledge of the sea increases, ultimately it will be possible to solve many of its secrets and to "farm" it more intensively for the greater benefit of mankind.

Similarly, it is generally accepted that climate is capricious and uncontrollable. There is insufficient evidence, however, on which to base such a final conclusion, and there are at least possibilities that man can affect climatic trends in such ways as perhaps to improve both the quantities and distribution of rainfall. Any success in this area resulting from studies of cloud physics in relationship to air movements, temperature gradients, and natural barriers could have an appreciable beneficial effect on agricultural production. Rain water and ground water are at present our only sources of agricultural water and are insufficient for our demands. Effort must be made to conserve fresh waters, reclaim waste water from industry, and begin to convert sea water to semifresh water. At the moment, the costs of partial desalting and transportation make this latter practice uneconomic for agricultural purposes. There is little doubt, however, that we shall eventually learn to process sea water efficiently, and when that time comes there will be an unlimited source of agricultural water available wherever such water can be economically distributed.

SUMMARY

There is ample justification for concern about adequate food supplies for future generations of mankind, but this concern should be broadened to include the immediate problem of an adequate standard of living for the world's present population. The successful solution of the immediate problems would furnish the best background of experience for meeting those that will arise in the future. First steps include the acceptance by society of responsibilities for the extension of the benefits of education throughout the world and provisions for the type of scientific, economic, social, political, and religious leadership necessary to assure food for all on a continuing basis.

Striking improvements in the food supply can be readily made through the application of present knowledge, if the foregoing conditions are met. The rapid pace of modern science, both pure and applied, gives promise that future benefits may be much greater than those thus far experienced. Current advances do not signal the end of a technical road but rather that the great scientific developments still lie ahead. If we have the intelligence and wisdom to recognize human responsibilities and to make constructive use of our natural and human resources, we can look forward to a better world in the future and improved standards of living for all.

Fertilizer and Pesticide Use in Mexico

Traditionally, Mexico has not relied heavily on agricultural chemicals as aids to crop production. In the past this has been caused by such factors as unfavorable trade balances, inadequate transportation systems, limited power facilities, restricted agricultural credit and lack of mechanization. During the last decade, however, this earlier picture has changed radically. Throughout the country, areas once remote are now accessible by road, air, and to a lesser extent rail; rural electrification is becoming available in hitherto out-of-the-way areas; and agricultural credit is becoming more plentiful, with increased use of agricultural machinery and chemicals.

During the same period other important innovations have occurred, including developments in agricultural education, research, and extension directed toward modernization of methods and materials for maximum production. And it is upon these three phases of agricultural science that Mexico must depend for sustained achievements in improving both the quantity and the quality of its plant and animal production. Progress has necessarily been deliberate, and much remains to be accomplished in the years ahead. However, there is a growing body of essential information, an increasing supply of prime agricultural materials, and an enlarging corps of well trained agricultural scientists in Mexico. These give promise of accelerated future progress.

Mexico is most often thought of as primarily a producer of corn, although actually it has a highly diversified agricultural industry. Major crops in addition to corn include wheat, barley, beans, chilies, sugar cane, coconuts, coffee, citrus, cotton, grapes, and bananas. Also

Article appearing in the February 1955 issue of *Agricultural Chemicals* important are cucurbits, potatoes, vegetables, sorghum, tree fruits, pineapple, and forage crops. Agricultural production long has been concentrated on the central plateau, which is the principal population center, but there has been notable geographic extension during the past several years. Sonora in the northwest, the Laguna area in the northcentral section, and the Matamoros region in the northeast just south of the Rio Grande all have become important centers of agricultural production. There has also been increased emphasis on tropical agriculture, principally along the Gulf of Mexico, with a major development in the Papaloapan River Valley. As a result, there has been a marked increase in the demand for modern aids to production, and among these agricultural chemicals are of primary importance.

CHEMICAL FERTILIZERS

Studies of the fertility levels of the soils in the most important food-producing areas in Mexico make it clear that the greatest single chemical need in support of agricultural production is fertilizer, and as might be expected, the element which is deficient most often is nitrogen. Years ago many of these soils were relatively rich in nitrogen, but continuous monoculture has reduced the level of fertility in some areas to a minimum. Coincidentally, local crop varieties have been selected for conditions of rusticity and low fertility, and these are characterized by low yields.

Presumably, the general application of chemical fertilizers would result in great increases in these average yields, but while it is true that the majority of the soils respond to applications of fertilizers containing nitrogen, results have often been both disappointing and uneconomic. In some instances, this fact has led to doubts concerning the value of chemical fertilizer, and in 1940 Mexico was using only a few thousand tons of chemical fertilizer, most of which went into the production of sugar cane and cotton.

The reason for the disappointing results with chemical fertilizers was largely their use in relation to traditional methods of soil management and with unimproved varieties of crop plants. Inadequate seedbed preparation, poor stands, and inefficient rates of fertilizer application and placement with reference to available water all contributed, and it was not until methods and materials were improved that the use of fertilizer became more attractive.

During the 1940's research efforts began to accrue in the form of improved varieties of food plants, notably corn, wheat, and beans. At the same time, Mexican soils were being studied to ascertain their fertility levels. As a result of hundreds of widely separated experiments, it was found that approximately three-quarters of all the soils investigated responded to applications of nitrogen, approximately 35 per cent to phosphorus, and approximately two per cent to potash. Lime usually is not needed.

Response on the part of the native or so-called "criollo" varieties usually was only fair, but when the new improved varieties and hybrids were tested, the responses were striking. Laird *et al.* found that the average increase in corn yield per hectare when nitrogen was applied at the rates of 20, 40, 60, and 80 kilos was .71, 1.04, 1.39, and 1.41 long tons per hectare respectively. In at least one area (Jalisco), responses to nitrogen with phosphorus have been striking in that the application of a 40-40-0 formula increased the yield of improved wheat varieties by one ton, an 80-80-0 formula by two tons, and a 120-80-0 formula by three tons.

Today in Mexico there are sound bases for application of chemical fertilizers for increased crop yields. The various soil types are recognized, their fertility levels are known, and their probable response to fertilizer application can be predicted. Time, rate, and placement data are available, as are data concerning planting rates, optimum stands, and the use of chemical fertilizers on irrigated and non-irrigated fields. In consequence, demand for commercial fertilizers has been increasing each year, and it is believed that the critical factor in increasing yields of crop plants during the next several years will be the availability of fertilizers containing nitrogen and phosphorus. This, of course, presupposes their proper use in terms of rate and time of application, available water, and the use of improved varieties. Gross consumption in 1954 has been calculated at less than 300,000 tons, but unofficial estimates of the probable demand for 1955 approach 800,000 tons.

Although by-products of Mexican oil fields offer possibilities for greatly expanded production of ammonium sulfate, at the present there is only a single plant in operation, with a rated capacity of between 200 and 250 tons per day. At least three other plants are contemplated, with an estimated total production capacity of 600,000 tons annually. Chilean nitrate and ammonium sulfate from the United States are the principal sources of Mexico's chemical fertilizer imports, but these have not been large in terms of total needs even though their value has reached a maximum figure of $12 million in a single year. Currently, there is a growing interest in northern Mexico in the use of imported anhydrous ammonia. Phosphate is usually available in the form of superphosphate largely derived from imported phosphate rock treated locally.

From the foregoing it will be seen that chemical fertilizers are just beginning to play their proper role in crop production in Mexico. As additional research results accrue, and as these are conveyed to farmers by extension agents, demand will increase steadily and this will eventually have to be met by making available to farmers adequate quantities of chemical fertilizers at prices which will permit their general use where needed.

PESTICIDES

The use of pesticides is rapidly becoming more common in Mexico, although great gains in this area are yet to come. Initially, insecticides were used principally for protection of cotton and bananas, but today numerous other crops such as citrus, potatoes, grapes, and beans are beginning to receive chemical treatment for pest control. Total quantities of pesticides used are small, but these are increasing each year. As a result, a greater variety of compounds is becoming available locally, and a number of small mixing plants have been established. The willingness of the producers of insecticides and fungicides to produce experimental quantities of their products has been a great stimulus to this development.

The following selected list includes the more important crops grown in Mexico, the principal pests and diseases attacking them, and chemical control measures:

Bananas—The most important disease of this crop is the Sigatoka or Chamusco disease caused by a species of the fungus *Cercospora*. The pathogen is destructive and, unless controlled, may destroy the banana industry in infested areas. Fortunately, sprays containing copper are quite effective, and their use on an appropriate schedule will keep the disease in check. Spraying with copper fungicides is regularly practiced in commercial banana plantations.

Cotton—Principal parasites are the pink bollworm, the stem borer, seedling blight, Texas root rot, and wilt. Dusting with benzene hexachloride is regularly practiced to control the insect pests, and seed treatment with organic mercury compounds has been found helpful in the control of seedling blights.

Potatoes—Late blight, caused by the fungus *Phytophthora infestans,* and virus diseases are the principal causes of losses in potato production, and when potatoes are grown during the rainy season a regular spray schedule must be established. Bordeaux mixture or similar sprays containing copper are still used most widely, but other compounds such as Manzate, Dithane Z78, and Parzate have also been used with success. The virus diseases are spread through potato fields by insect vectors, and mixtures containing DDT frequently are used to control them.

Beans—This important crop is regularly subject to attack of the bean pod borer, the Mexican bean beetle, viruses, anthracnose, bacteriosis, and root rot. The insect pests can only be controlled through application of insecticides such as parathion and DDT, and fungicides containing copper are useful in reducing losses from pathogenic fungi. The use of pesticides for increased bean production is gaining popularity in such important bean-producing states as Puebla, Aguascalientes, Zacatecas, and Durango.

OTHER AGRICULTURAL ADVANCES

Vegetable production in Mexico is slowly becoming more widespread and less limited to urban areas and to commercial plantings for export. In response to this development, pest and disease problems of vegetable production are being studied, and it is clear that pesticides are important to this effort. Benzene hexachloride and parathion are being used effectively for control of certain vegetable pests, and Systox has been found of value in connection with vegetable plantings for seed production.

Seedling blights of crop plants are common, and many of these can be controlled by seed treatment. Although the practice is by no means universal, seed treatment for the control of seedling blights of cotton, vegetables, corn, wheat, and beans has been found to be effective under certain conditions and in specified areas. It is expected that the use of seed disinfectants will increase.

As agricultural production increases, the problem of storage grows in importance. Insect pests and molds of stored grains and diseases of plant parts such as bulbs, corms, and tubers all require chemical control, and there is growing use of seed disinfectants, insecticides, and fumigants for this purpose. Organic mercury compounds, methyl bromide, DDT, and carbon disulfide all have been used with satisfactory results.

Although nematodes are recognized as important in limiting crop production in Mexico, relatively little attention has as yet been given to them or to their control. As additional information becomes available with regard to the role of nematodes in reducing the production of potatoes, tomatoes, and other crops, it is expected that the necessity for the use of larvacides or nematocides to combat them will become evident.

Mosquito control is widespread largely as a result of successful activities over a period of years involving DDT to control malarial mosquitoes. This, along with other products, is now being widely used in rural communities for control of mosquitoes, flies, and other pests.

Stable flies are real pests in Mexico, especially in connection with milk production. The milkshed area in the vicinity of Mexico City presents a serious fly problem, and it has been shown that fly nuisance may reduce milk production by as much as one liter per day per animal. Recently, careful experiments have shown that three sprays a year, in conjunction with reasonable sanitary practices, keep flies at a minimum throughout the year and increase milk production. Various formulations containing chlordane, toxaphene, dieldrin, lindane, methoxychlor, and DDT all have proved effective.

An interesting recent report from Mexico states that experiments for control of the Guerro scorpion *Centruroides limpidus limpidus Karsch* have been carried out with a number of compounds, with chlordane and isodrin proving most effective.

Herbicides have come into use in Mexico within the past five years. Presently formulations of 2, 4-D are most common, and their use has been principally for the control of weeds in summer wheat plantings. Some 70,000 to 100,000 hectares of wheat are treated annually. On a smaller scale herbicides have been applied for control of weeds in corn, sugar cane, and rice, and experiments are in progress on weed control in alfalfa, clover, potatoes, and sorghum. In view of the importance of weed control and success with herbicides to date, there is little doubt that there is a great future for these chemicals in crop production in Mexico.

SUMMARY

Mexico is currently in a new phase of its agricultural development. This is caused by the leadership provided by government officials, research scientists, extension agents, and agricultural producers, which has now resulted in improved facilities such as roads, rural electrification, better methods and materials, and improved farming practices. These have encouraged increased mechanization of agriculture and the expanded use of agricultural chemicals in crop production. Total investment still is small in terms of potential, but it is expected that it will increase steadily during the years to come.

Greatest single benefit from agricultural chemicals will be from the increased use of fertilizers containing nitrogen and phosphorus. Supplementing these will be the chemical protectants externally applied, as well as systemic fungicides, insecticides, and herbicides. Eventually, it is expected that the use of agricultural chemicals will be an accepted part of production patterns throughout Mexico, with resultant economic benefits.

Technical Aid and Agricultural Chemistry

A number of international agencies are engaged in technical assistance projects throughout the world. Included are United Nations organizations, the U.S. Foreign Operations Administration, the Colombo Plan, philanthropic foundations, and religious and educational groups. Many of these efforts involve agriculture and are stimulating the scientific approach to food production in hitherto underdeveloped areas. At the same time, modern agricultural aids, including machinery and fertilizers and other chemicals, are becoming more readily available. And the extension of these benefits on an increasing scale throughout the Western Hemisphere is producing significant improvements in agricultural production. As technical assistance programs increase in number and gain from experience, their efforts should result in still greater opportunities for agricultural development and growing demands for agricultural machinery and chemicals.

An examination of agriculture in Latin America suggests that only a small fraction of the total potential production is harvested each year. This may be attributable in certain areas to underpopulation, but more importantly to the limitations of existing agricultural practices, systems of communication, power supplies, landholding patterns, and credit facilities. Gains are being made in many sectors of the Americas south of the Rio Grande; and Mexico, Venezuela, Argentina, Brazil, and Colombia are typical of those countries making rapid strides in the improvement of highways and airways systems, the extension of rural electrification, and the development of power resources.

Article appearing in *Agricultural and Food Chemistry,* issue of May, 1955

At least several Latin American countries are studying their own systems of landholding and management in the belief that modifications are needed for increased production. All recognize that the need for credit applies to every aspect of production, from the purchase and improvement of land to loans for seed, fertilizer, and machinery; and agricultural credit is being more widely extended. As a result, interest rates are falling, and there is prospect that major benefits to production and farm income will be obtained. All of these advances are reflected in the extension of cultivation, increased agricultural production, and more efficient marketing.

SOIL FERTILITY IS GREATEST LIMITING FACTOR

Perhaps the greatest single limiting factor in food production in the world today is the level of soil fertility. In many of the so-called underdeveloped areas cropping has been practiced so intensively for so many years that their soils have been essentially exhausted, with pitifully low average yields. If these could be supplied with adequate amounts of the essential elements, principally nitrogen, appreciable increases in yield could be expected. This need for fertilizers is becoming recognized.

In Mexico, for example, it is estimated that the fertilizer demand (principally for N and P) will have grown from less than 50,000 tons in 1940 to approximately 800,000 tons in 1955. And this is only the beginning since Mexico can and undoubtedly will absorb several times this amount in the years to come. Much of this will have to come initially from external sources since local production cannot be expected to supply the growing demand. However, in January, 1955, the Mexican government announced plans for the construction of three new ammonium sulfate plants, which, in addition to the one already in operation, are expected to have a total capacity of from one-half to three-quarters of a million tons annually.

In South America, Chile has been exporting the bulk of its nitrate production, but recognizes that increased quantities must be used locally. Peru is expanding its production of corn, wheat, cotton, sugar cane, and potatoes, with the result that increased quantities of fertilizers are required each year, and these are being imported to the limit which local economy permits. Colombia's agricultural production is increasing markedly, especially cereals, potatoes, cotton, and coffee. This is due in considerable measure to research on these crops, which has resulted in improved methods and materials for higher yields and has created a demand for increasing quantities of inorganic fertilizers. Similarly, agricultural developments in many parts of Brazil have moved ahead rapidly, and programs involving the production of wheat, corn, rice, cotton, coffee, sugar cane, *etc.,* are expanding in response to need.

Although nitrogen is the primary nutrient element most needed in support of agricultural production throughout Latin America, response to phosphorus is reported in most of the soils which are deficient in nitrogen. Therefore, inorganic fertilizers containing both nitrogen and phosphorus are of great importance in support of increased agricultural production, and in some regions potassium or lime or both are also required. Relatively little is known about trace element deficiencies in much of Latin America, but deficiency symptoms have been reported in connection with the production of cotton, citrus, beans, and sugar cane.

Diseases and pests of crop plants are major limiting factors to agricultural production in many areas of Latin America. Traditionally, control of diseases and pests has largely been one of efforts to escape heavy damage through cultural practices. For instance, the underplanting of cereals has frequently been practiced in the belief that thin stands suffer less from rust and smuts than do heavy stands. Whether or not this is a demonstrable fact the result is the same, since underplanting results in underproduction. Similarly, the potato, which is host to numerous pests and diseases, has tended to migrate upward on mountain slopes and into high mountain valleys in an effort to escape these. Experience has taught that under such conditions there may be less insect damage and a lower incidence of virus diseases. It is quite true that it is often possible to grow potatoes at altitudes at which major insect pests and vectors cannot exist, but here again this practice is penalized by reduced production. Modern methods are bringing potatoes down the mountain sides to broad level plains or valleys where the benefits of mechanization in conjunction with the chemical control of disease and pests result in dramatic increases in yield.

The introduction of new crops into Latin America has posed additional disease problems requiring modern agricultural techniques for their solution. For example:

The vast increase in cotton production has brought about the wider distribution of cotton pests and diseases and the need for large quantities of insecticides and fungicides in Mexico, Peru, Brazil, and Colombia.

The Sigatoka leaf spot disease on the banana throughout the commercial banana areas has stimulated the regular use of copper fungicides without which the crop cannot be successfully grown. In Central America, Colombia, and Ecuador spraying bananas for disease control has become standard practice in commercial plantation.

The bean, which is the basic protein source for much of Latin America, is the prey of a variety of pests and diseases, and recent research through technical assistance programs has demonstrated that in many areas yields can readily be doubled or even trebled through the control of such pests and diseases as the bean pod weevil, the bean beetle, anthracnose, root rot, leaf spots, and virus diseases.

Similar examples might be cited in connection with the production of most of the important food and other basic crops grown. Among those which are receiving most attention and which are yielding to the use of modern pesticides are late blight of potatoes and tomatoes; virus diseases of potatoes, tomatoes, beans, and truck crops; nematodes attacking vegetable crops; seedling blights of cotton; and diseases of the vine.

PESTICIDE IMPORTS NOW CONSIDERABLE

The use of pesticides and fungicides throughout Latin America has now reached a point at which the quantity of materials imported by the several countries has reached considerable proportions. Initially, these were almost all in the form of a finished product, but in recent years an increasing number of mixing plants have been established, permitting the importation of basic compounds for subsequent elaboration and packaging. At the same time, there has been marked increase in the importation of equipment for the application of sprays, dusts, and mists, since relatively little is manufactured locally.

The list of those compounds which have been tested or used in the control of plant pests and diseases is an extensive one. Perhaps dusts and sprays containing copper have been or are still of greatest importance, although sulfur in various forms and zinc preparations are also well known. Numerous fumigants including methyl bromide, formaldehyde, and carbon disulfide have been widely used, as have a series of seed protectants including Ceresan, Semesan, Spergon, Granosan, copper carbonate, Cuprocide, Fermate, Arasan, Parzate, and Zerlate. For the control of insect pests the commonly used compounds include DDT, lindane, chlordane, Toxaphene, parathion, aldrin, BHC, and nicotine sulfate. These lists are not complete but demonstrate that the newer insecticides and fungicides are being widely tested throughout the region and utilized where proved valuable.

The possibility that systematic fungicides or insecticides may one day come into general use is of growing interest. These would be of special benefit in those areas which must import large quantities of agricultural chemicals and machinery, with the accompanying heavy additional expenses involved in transportation costs, local taxes, and middlemen. Systemic chemicals would be a great boon to the agriculture of underdeveloped areas because of their ease of application, the reduced frequency with which they would have to be applied, and the smaller quantities of materials involved. Studies of systemic fungicides and insecticides are still in the experimental stage, but there is some evidence that certain synthetic, organic compounds, as well as antibiotic substances from microorganisms, may be both effective and economical. Specifically, experiments on the control of wheat rust with systemic chemicals have been in progress in Mexico for several years in a technical cooperation program.

WEED PROBLEM COMPOUNDED

One interesting development in Latin America is the greatly expanded use of herbicides in crop production. The fact that so much of the area lies in the tropics and subtropics permits year-round cultivation and, at the same time, compounds the problem of weed competition in agricultural production. Moreover, where mechanical aids to cultivation are limited, and regular sanitary practices for weed control are little known, weeds take tremendous annual tolls. Improvements are being made in cultural practices to control weeds, including deep plowing, disking, and frequent cultivation; and flooding has also been used successfully where water is available for this purpose. Weed control in connection with tree crops has been accomplished through the planting of cover crops and the use of hand flame throwers.

In recent years physical methods for the control of weeds have

72

been joined by chemical control measures. Various chemical substances have been used in the past for the control of weeds along railroad rights of way, irrigation ditches, and roadsides, but only during the last decade has the use of herbicides in connection with cultivated crops become widespread. The most spectacular application of herbicides to crop production is in connection with small grains, and thousands of acres of wheat are successfully treated each year in Latin America. This has stimulated research on weed control in other economic crops, and progress has been made with the control of weeds of corn, cotton, rice, vegetables, bananas, citrus, and beans. As might be expected, the compound most commonly used is 2,4-D in some form. A number of newer herbicides are presently being tested for probable future use and include such products as 2,4,5-T, DN-PE (ammonium salt of dinitro-o-sec-butylphenol), PCP (pentachlorophenol), DN-GENS (amyl analog of DN-PE), trialkyl amine salt of 2,4-D, and sodium salt of 2,4-D ethyl sulfate. Without doubt, as new methods and materials become available these will be applied rapidly and generally throughout much of Latin America, with resultant benefits to production.

As average crop yields improve, it is to be expected that much of the resultant additional income will be invested in modern mechanical aids to the practice of farming. In many instances these may be at first, and for some time to come, simple devices which can be made available to the small operator. However, as land tenure and management methods improve, there will be a growing demand for agricultural machinery designed to fit local needs. Undoubtedly, Latin America will depend chiefly on the United States to provide the tools necessary for an expanding agricultural industry, and the degree to which this country responds and the understanding with which it attempts to fulfill these needs will have profound influence on the future economy of all concerned. In the past there have been some instances in which salesmanship has been substituted for service to agricultural needs, with the result that benefits to production and good will were both lost, at least temporarily. Here again, technical assistance programs can be helpful in underlining the specific needs of a given area in terms of both kind and quantity.

From present evidence it would seem that the future of agriculture in Latin America is bright and that the great gains still lie ahead. Truly promising is the growing awareness of the importance of using improved varieties under appropriate soil management techniques and in conjunction with mechanical and chemical aids to production. Coincidentally, the extension of systems of communication, improvements in rural electrification, and increasing sources of agricultural credit will all catalyze and complement the other factors involved in the progress of agriculture. It can be anticipated that there will be dramatic future accomplishments in agriculture and industry in all of Latin America and that technical aid will continue to play an important role in these developments. The knowledge and skills provided to underdeveloped areas through sister relationships between American and foreign agricultural colleges and the activities of FAO field parties and those of philanthropic foundations and other agencies with similar objectives will contribute measurably to the rapidity and quality of the progress made. And it is to be expected that commercial organizations will respond by producing mechanical and chemical aids to agriculture in such forms and at costs which will make them generally available, with resultant benefits to human welfare.

Practical Suggestions to Carry Out a Well-Considered Program

Since I have no direct association with either ICA or any of the universities holding contracts with ICA, any suggestions which I may be able to offer will necessarily be based on my own observations and experience. These have been gained through travel, study, and direct participation in technical assistance programs carried on cooperatively by The Rockefeller Foundation and certain foreign governments.

It has been my privilege to have seen many of the university contract programs in various parts of the world since these were first established. I think I would agree that some of the initial efforts were neither of exceptional quality nor highly successful. On the other hand, there are logical reasons why the beginnings of this now far-flung activity might have been less successful than everyone hoped. Available information was inadequate, experienced personnel were few in number, and there were numerous conflicts in the philosophies and objectives of technical assistance operations overseas.

With respect to ICA and its predecessors, the restrictions under which any democracy must function in the establishment of new operations produce delays in recruitment and procurement and in the maintenance of active supply lines. In this instance there has been considerable confusion in the establishment of a *modus operandi* geared to fit the needs and objectives of the programs which have been established in increasing numbers. Changes in policy-making personnel and disagreements as to long-range plans and ob-

Paper presented in November, 1955, at East Lansing, Michigan; the 17th conference convened by the Committee on Institutional Projects Abroad of the American Council on Education

jectives have resulted at times in lost motion and personal dissatisfaction. Pressures to start operations sometimes prevented adequate preliminary surveys and planning. In consequence, it must be granted that there have been many legitimate complaints and that these merit careful consideration by those responsible for improving present operations and planning future ones. Any program which involves diverse activities in many countries and large numbers of technical personnel must, of necessity, have both strengths and weaknesses. In the face of pressure to expand and get more programs and projects under way rapidly the weaknesses are often overemphasized. In one sense this can be a useful development, if constructive measures are then taken to rectify undesirable situations.

It is my judgment that definite improvements are already visible on the ICA side. There seems to be a little more stability with regard to personnel, and modifications in programming have been made, which are improvements on previous practices. It also appears that more of the policy makers are getting into the field in an effort to learn the local problems at first-hand and that greater latitude is being given to staff in the field, which is a most desirable development. Although there are still many problems to be solved, I think we can expect continuing improvements with increased experience and that the long-range outlook for the success of technical assistance programs through university contracts is visibly brighter.

On the university side it seems to me that there have been errors, which, compounded with those of ICA, have contributed to those aspects of the technical assistance programs which have been undesirable. In some instances, at least, the universities have sought contracts but have failed to accept in the fullest sense all of the responsibilities which these entail. Occasionally, universities have used questionable criteria in the selection of individuals sent abroad under university contracts, and have placed availability ahead of competence for such assignments. This has contributed to the unsatisfactory progress reported from some areas and the resultant criticism of the entire program. Some of the recruits have been poorly selected with respect to personality, and, although a certain amount of difficulty in this area must always be expected in a large operation, perhaps the percentage was too high in the early years of foreign technical aid programs. I think, however, this situation has been or is being rapidly rectified and that more and more of the specialists who are being sent to foreign countries are qualified for this work and are motivated by appropriate ideals.

Most of those countries in which technical assistance is in progress through United States agencies have well-defined cultural and agricultural patterns which for definitive local reasons have become established over long periods of time. It is unwise to attempt to revolutionize local customs and procedures through mass attack or by the rapid substitution of American ideas and practices for local ones. Rather, experience has taught us that careful preliminary and long-range planning based on a sound understanding of local conditions is requisite to embarking on specific projects. The most important next step is to obtain acceptance of the program on the part of nationals of the country involved. This can only be accomplished through a definite effort on the part of foreign guests to understand the philosophies and mores of the citizens of the country in question, and to convince them of their desire to be friendly and helpful through social and scientific actions which demonstrate this to be a fact. Especially important is an effort to learn the language of the host country to whatever degree this may be practicable under individual circumstances.

Once this first phase of a technical assistance program is well begun, it is possible to establish projects of obvious significance to the host country. Probably these should be initially modest and neither overstaffed nor overinstrumented or equipped. As progress is made, the need for greater effort, broader geographic expansion, and increased support in the form of personnel, budget, and equipment will become manifest to all concerned. At this point the demand for increased assistance will be indigenous, which is infinitely more sound than expansion that is the result of outside pressures.

Perhaps the most critical phase of any foreign technical assistance program relates to dealings with local officials, scientific personnel, and nontechnical employees. Pride is an important and useful human trait which, when properly oriented, stimulates individuals to their best efforts. The invasion of large numbers of self-styled "experts," who on occasion may try too hard to live up to this appellation, not infrequently creates a very difficult climate within which to establish sound working relationships. Vocal and unconsidered criticisms of local situations and individuals result in misunderstanding, hurt pride, and even active resentment which may eventually stalemate the entire operation. On the other hand, genuine partnership—not necessarily based on counterpart designations, but rather on mutual respect and the contribution by each party of his maximum abilities to the problems at hand—permits progress and at the same time creates an atmosphere within which the ideal of transference can ultimately be accomplished.

I think that, by and large, Americans are liked and respected by the peoples of other countries. I am sure that often we are too prone to accept the generic evaluation that some of our more vocal critics apply to Americans abroad, assuring us that we are envied and disliked. Certainly this is true in individual cases just as it is true of certain nationals of other countries, but from my own experience I am convinced that by far the greatest number of American citizens who travel or live and work abroad are, by their actions, sound interpreters of our ideals and philosophies to our friends and associates in other lands. We must, however, continue to keep this important facet of foreign relations foremost in our thinking, so that each individual, who is now or who may in the future participate in a foreign technical aid program, will contribute the best of his own philosophy and good will, as well as his technical competence, to the effort.

Without doubt, the training aspects of technical assistance are among those most vital to the ultimate success of the entire program. I think there is no ideal way in which the training of foreign scientists may be accomplished, but rather that different techniques are required in response to special circumstances. I am inclined to think that in the past there have been instances in which mass action has been substituted for selective action based on sound judgment. There is doubt in my mind that the appointment of large numbers of fellows or scholars for short-term experiences in the United States accomplishes much. In the long run, our friends in other countries are going to accept major responsibility for the education of their own scientists, and it is both impracticable and undesirable for us to attempt to find any substitute arrangement which might delay the realization of this fact.

Probably the best type of training for young nationals associated with a sound technical assistance program is in-service training by which they participate directly in projects which are designed to, and actually are, aiding in the solution of local problems of national significance. Quite large numbers of individuals can be handled by this technique, and during the course of the process it is possible to select especially qualified persons who should be given advanced training abroad because of their demonstrated potential for future responsibilities in research and scientific leadership. Careful selection of these individuals, as well as of their training program in this country, should make it possible to build local projects around them after their return and thus set the stage for a gradual transfer of responsibility to qualified nationals. As this transfer is slowly accomplished, it will be possible for the guest scientists to deepen their scientific activities at the same time that an increasing body of well-trained young nationals are broadening the entire program. Ultimately, carefully selected nationals might receive a second period of foreign training for future positions of leadership at the policy-making level or in institutions dedicated to research and education.

I should like to say a little about the whole matter of training as it refers to technical assistance programs. It seems to me that both government and the universities have an obligation to work together to assure that two types of training activities are carried out as effectively as possible. One of these deals with foreign students who come to this country. Their problems are special ones and their needs are not always identical to those of our own students. It is recognized that universities cannot readily set up a special school within the university system dedicated to the training of foreign students, and probably no single school could accomplish this purpose. On the other hand, effort can be made to try to guide each foreign student in such a way that he will be able to take maximum advantage of his visit to this country and that he will receive the special training and experience which will be most useful to him after his return.

This may require greater flexibility than now exists in some institutions and greater attention to foreign students as individuals who have both academic and cultural problems to face. Probably there should be less emphasis on degrees for foreign students and greater emphasis on a well-rounded training program which might result in university certification of accomplishment in lieu of a degree. If properly planned and worked out, such certification might well carry prestige which would make it equally sought after as evidence of significant accomplishment within the purposes of the training experiences. There are, of course, numerous individuals who come to this country for training who are well qualified to carry on studies leading to an advanced degree, and in such cases there is no reason why this plan should not be followed.

The second type of training which I should like to mention has to do with the training of United States citizens who expect to enter the field of foreign technical assistance. We now know that we were woefully understaffed in this area at the time the university contracts program with Point Four was undertaken. However, a considerable body of competent scientists have now had foreign experience and a number of university administrators have spent longer or shorter periods of time in the field familiarizing themselves with areas and programs. This should make it possible to consider ways by which we can begin to train a core of men who would be available for foreign assignments in the future. Other things being equal, we shall probably be involved in such programs for some time to come and, if they are successful, they will in themselves create other types of opportunities for foreign service by United States citizens.

Probably it would be impracticable for a considerable number of universities to attempt to set up training programs in foreign technical aid for United States nationals, but all concerned might give some attention to the problem and agree on one or a few centers at which there will be concentration on this type of training. In such a case it would be possible for agricultural or other scientists to carry out their professional studies at the university of their choice and, during or after their graduate careers, spend a period of time specializing in the foreign service aspects of their particular science. This would provide a pool of trained individuals from which ICA, FOA, foundations, and other interested agencies could draw properly qualified persons for assignment to foreign posts. It should also provide a core of qualified individuals for staff positions in various governmental agencies dealing with foreign service activities. Ultimately, it may be that we shall realize the necessity for adding to our university faculties and to various federal departments more staff members who are experienced in foreign technical assistance projects and who will serve both in action programs and in the instruction of national and foreign students for increased mutual understanding and cooperation.

Although at least several of the following may be redundant, I should like to list a few suggestions which may have some practical value in foreign technical assistance programs involving ICA and land-grant universities:

1. Every new program should be established only after there is evidence that there is a real opportunity for service to the host country and that there is genuine local enthusiasm for this aid based on the conviction that the projects contemplated have been carefully selected in terms of the needs of the country and the opportunities for sound progress.

2. The recruitment of personnel should always be accepted as a deciding factor in the success or failure of a technical assistance program abroad. Thus, individual scientists and their families should be selected with great care to assure not only that they have the technical and personal qualifications necessary, but that the post to which they are assigned is the one which best fits these.

3. Programs and projects should not be initiated unless and until there is assurance that support in the form of necessary personnel and equipment are or will be available when needed. A failure of this prerequisite inevitably leads to discouragement and dissatisfaction on the part of the staff, which will be reflected in their attitudes and accomplishments to the detriment of the effort.

4. Effort should be made to avoid the establishment of classes of United States citizens abroad, and perquisites and privileges of technical assistance staff members should be comparable to those of other United States governmental agencies located in the area.

5. Emphasis should always be placed on the training of local nationals by precept, example, and direct action, and each staff member should be made to realize that his individual accomplishments must eventually be measured by his success in this direction rather than by physical accomplishments as a plant breeder, forester, engineer, *etc.*

6. It is dangerous to attempt to develop a single pattern for all technical assistance programs, and it is necessary that enough imagination and flexibility be applied to each situation to assure that the design applied to a given area will be best for that area. In one program emphasis should perhaps be on research, and in another it might perhaps be on education or extension or on various combinations of these and other important aspects of agricultural science.

7. Finally, the objective of transfer should always be kept before all concerned in the program. This does not imply excessively rapid growth, expansion, and retirement from the scene. Rather, the normal evolution of a program should involve useful accomplishments and the demonstration of future potentialities through the efforts of both nationals and foreign scientists. As the program grows in accomplishment and expands geographically and produces larger numbers of trained individuals, it is then possible slowly to effect transfer of responsibility, which will ultimately lead to nationalization of the entire effort.

In conclusion, I should like to repeat my conviction that in spite of the difficulties which have been incurred in the past, as well as those which still confront us, the general movement of technical assistance programs under ICA-university contracts is forward. I do think we should not be discouraged by past failure or disappointment, but rather that we should be greatly encouraged by the progress which has been made. I think the work which is being carried on in many parts of the world by university people through ICA is becoming increasingly appreciated and is gaining us friends and colleagues as well as better mutual understanding.

Food and Agriculture and Man's Health

The health of mankind is clearly dependent on adequate quantities of suitable foodstuffs to sustain life. In global terms this means that today the 2.4 billion acres of land under cultivation should provide nearly 3,000 calories daily for a world population of approximately 2.6 billion individuals. And population increases of from one to two per cent per year must be balanced by comparable increases in agricultural production, if minimal health requirements are to be maintained. It has been estimated that land now under cultivation could support two to four times the present world population, if available knowledge could be generally applied. Therefore, if these favorable estimates are even approximately accurate, an adequate dietary standard for all the world in the foreseeable future depends on scientific advances and social progress.

The invention of agriculture was the basic factor in permitting the establishment of stable populations, which, in turn, enabled society to develop local patterns of education, art, science, and industry leading to the present day political and cultural organization of the world community. Since the development of modern agricultural science coincides with a greatly accelerated population increase, primary emphasis has necessarily been on the quantitative aspects of food production. This increase in the numbers of individuals, human and plant and animal, has intensified the problems of public health and created, at the same time, serious "public health problems" of crop plants and domestic animals. Urbanization and the mechanical crowding of society, which contribute so importantly to the development of communicable disease, have dramatic parallels

From an address delivered at Massachusetts Institute of Technology on June 11, 1956

in crop production. When 3,500,000 nearly identical individual wheat plants are planted on a single acre the possibilities for epiphytotic outbreaks of plant disease are extremely favorable.

The world has accepted approximately a dozen of the 200,000 described species of plants as principal sources of bulk and protective food. Of these, the grass family provides the largest share of the world's food calories in the form of rice, corn, wheat, sorghum, sugar cane, barley, millet, and forage grasses. Other major crops are the potato, sweet potato, banana, coconut, bean, and cassava. Most of the remainder of the world's food supply is derived from cucurbits, crucifers, tree and small fruits, and miscellaneous vegetables. Although they, too, are dependent upon plants, livestock, poultry, and fish provide from 10 to 15 per cent of the approximately 900 million metric tons of foodstuffs currently required by society each year.

Over the years tremendous progress has been made in improving the yield of agricultural products. During the past 50 years alone, potato production has climbed from an average of 19.8 bushels per acre to 253.4, with a record of 1,180 bushels (California); corn from 26.6 to 42.5 with a record of 304.8 (Mississippi); wheat 14 to 19.5 with a record of 125 (England); and rice from 28 to 60.6 with a record of 400 (Australia). It is both striking and comforting to note that although average yields of crop plants have increased from 50 to 200 per cent during the past 50 years, potential increases of several hundred per cent of present averages can be obtained under optimum conditions. On the animal side, average yields of eggs and milk have increased. Milk production is 45 per cent greater than 40 years ago and egg production is 50 per cent greater than it was 10 years ago. Modern meat animals dress out 20 to 50 per cent higher than 50 years ago, and these added quantities of human foods are produced in less time and with less expense than formerly. Moreover, improvements have been made in the quality of essentially all of the basic food crops and animals so that they supply greater quantities of the key elements for human nutrition than their prototypes.

AGRICULTURAL ADVANCES IN SUPPORT OF HEALTH

Current advances in agriculture are the product of the combined efforts of agricultural scientists, engineers, chemists, and biologists. Other notable results will certainly come about from: (1) proper land management, (2) developments in farm machinery, (3) control of disease, pests, and weeds, (4) genetic improvements of food crops and animals, and (5) increased use of agricultural chemicals.

LAND MANAGEMENT

Modern advances in soil and crop management include ingenious systems of rotation, irrigation, fertilization, and cultivation which greatly enhance the average productivity of various classes of agricultural soils. Efforts to obtain the optimum balance between crop and available water and nutrients have been increasingly successful and have led to the aforementioned record yields. In the future, deeper understanding of soils as living media essential to the support of plant and animal life should permit dramatic increases in production. Soil conditioners offer possibilities for improvement in soil texture and structure, and compounds which influence the activity of soil microflora and fauna will take advantage of this enormous biotic resource for greater food production.

Like industry, modern farm practice requires such diverse knowledge, skills, and equipment that, for reasons of efficiency, farms must become larger or highly specialized in the future. In the latter case, increased knowledge and improved aids to agricultural practice may well convert the present system of crop diversification and rotation into one of balanced monoculture. Moreover, the future trend in the management of livestock and poultry will be more toward a production-line system under which conditions are carefully controlled. The use of increasingly valuable crop land by relatively small numbers of animals will probably decrease in the face of the growing demand for food, with the result that methods of *in situ* production of food animals may become commonplace.

Inevitably, some increase will occur in the total area of land under cultivation as a response to growing population pressures. Some land can be recovered from saline and eroded areas and the drainage of inundated regions. Progress can certainly be made in the conversion of semi-arid and arid lands to agricultural production and in the extension of agriculture more widely into the humid tropics where lateritic soils predominate, as well as in the cool humid regions typified by podsols. This will depend to a large extent on the conservation and efficient utilization of available water, the degree to which natural rainfall can be influenced, the conversion of salt water to sweet or semisweet water to supplement irrigation requirements (which are 88 billion gallons daily in the United States), and the increased use of solar and nuclear energy in agriculture. The most optimistic estimates indicate that something less than one billion acres of additional land might be brought under cultivation. These estimates do not, however, take into consideration the losses of present land under cultivation through mismanagement, flooding, and increased urbanization.

There is considerable evidence that approximately one per cent of the world's food which now comes from the sea will be increased several fold through new methods of harvesting existing marine forms and the improvement of species through hybridization.

DEVELOPMENTS IN FARM MACHINERY

A host of new types of machines has become available in response to the growing needs of agricultural producers. These include both tractor-drawn and self-propelled equipment for soil manipulation, planting, cultivating, spraying and dusting, and harvesting, as well as airborne equipment for seeding, weed control, and disease and pest control. One of the great bottlenecks in the past has been insufficient labor at harvest time, but this situation is being met with such machines as cotton, corn and hops pickers, cane harvesters, and modern combines.

The percentage of the United States' labor force devoted to agriculture during the past 150 years has dropped from 75 to 10, and today each farmer feeds 18 other people rather than seven as in 1925. Future progress can be expected in the development of machines for harvesting tree crops and other products not readily handled by presently available equipment. And it may also be that one or more stages in the processing of crops may be carried out in the field at the time of harvest, with corresponding improvement in quality and reduction of losses which may occur between the field and the factory.

DISEASE, PEST, AND WEED CONTROL

The traditional practice of applying excessive quantities of fungicides and pesticides to crops is both crude and wasteful. Modern spray materials and dusts are more effective and more economical than those used in the past and are applied in smaller quantities.

However, we still make external applications to compounds containing phosphorus, zinc, copper, mercury, sulfur, and other elements for the control of fungi, bacteria, and insects attacking crop plants. Ultimately, more precise methods should replace most of the current practices, and there is already evidence that certain organic compounds can function as systemic protectants against certain pests and diseases. Eventually, it should be possible to introduce systemic chemicals into plants through normal absorption and translocation pathways or through epidermal tissues and external openings. This could be accomplished in connection with the standard practices of soil preparation, or the compounds might be placed on seed before planting in the form of chemical dusts or slurries.

Naturally occurring antibiotic compounds offer great promise as systemic protectants. Probably many commonly occur in the soil and have important roles in controlling the numbers and distribution of soil-borne microorganisms, both pathogenic and nonpathogenic. As these and other antibiotic products of metabolism and microorganisms are better understood, they may well provide materials for the more effective control of many of the pests and pathogens responsible for much of the more than five billion dollar loss of agricultural products which now occurs each year.

GENETIC IMPROVEMENT OF FOOD CROPS AND ANIMALS

Modern advances in genetics have resulted in the use of techniques of pure line selection, inbreeding, backcrossing, and recombinations resulting in hybrid vigor. This phenomenon has provided record yields of cereals, poultry, and other foods, and has opened new avenues of investigation directed toward the greater utilization of combinations of germ plasm for increased production. We can anticipate that chemical and physical aids will induce combinations of genes presently considered to be impossible. This would permit the blending of widely divergent characters with commensurate improvements in production. Although induced genetic aberrations such as polyploidy have resulted in larger and more productive plants, it is probable that in years to come crop plants may be largely efficient perennial dwarf hybrids producing maximum quantities of fruits, seeds, tubers, and so forth, per foliage unit. Similarly, domestic animals can be expected to undergo further improvement in ratios of milk, eggs, and meat production to nonedible by-products.

AGRICULTURAL CHEMICALS

Considerable progress has already been made, not only in the use of chemical fertilizers, protectants, and herbicides, but also in the synthesis of compounds which advantageously affect growth rhythms of domestic plants and animals. It is now possible to influence certain growth phenomena such as abscission, rooting, and sprouting, with natural and synthetic compounds such as 3-indole acetic acid and related indoles, ethylene, acetylene, propylene, phenylacetic acid, beta-naphthoxyacetic acid, and 2,4-Dichloro-phenoxyacetic acid. Research in this area is being intensified, and in the future spectacular new benefits may be expected. Such growth phenomena as photoperiodism, senescence, and dormancy can probably be affected in ways to improve production and to induce plants to grow over a wider range. It may also be possible to increase the quantity of desired storage products to a degree presently impossible through conventional methods. Thus, in the future the combined efforts of plant breeders and agricultural chemists will be toward the tailoring of plant types to fit human needs and to control growth phenomena for improved yield.

FARM CHEMURGY

The role of farm chemurgy is an important one in assuring the most efficient utilization of large quantities of agricultural products and by-products. Each year new developments in this science result in bringing about greater use of plant and animal materials with economic benefit. At the same time the list of valuable chemical by-products which can be extracted from agricultural residues is growing.

There are four to six times as many tons of plant materials produced annually on noncultivated land as through conventional agricultural practices. If marine forms are considered, these figures must be raised to the third power. Added to these resources are some 300 million tons of farm residues from plants and animals, of which only a small fraction is utilized by industry. It should be feasible in the future to convert larger quantities of these potential food resources into forms useful in human diet as well as for the nutrition of ruminants and other animal forms. It is a well-known fact that rumen microorganisms can synthesize most of the vitamins in addition to carbohydrates, fats, and proteins, and that ammonium salts and urea can supply a significant fraction of the protein required for animal growth. This permits greater use in feeds of herbaceous matter, sea plants, and farm residues such as corn cobs and beet pulp, citrus pulp, bagasse, and even wood pulp when economical. Essentially, this system is the ingenious utilization of the ability of bacteria and fungi to act upon nondigestible compounds with the production of usable quantities of usable protein substances. Efforts toward making multipurpose use of domestic plants and animals for the health and comfort of society are being rewarded to the extent that we can expect residues which are now wasted to become valuable agricultural assets.

FOOD TECHNOLOGY

Complementing advances in agricultural science and practice are those in food technology, which has now grown to a multibillion dollar business. The transportation, storage, and processing of foodstuffs linking production to consumption has become a vast and far-flung industry which has produced enormous improvements in modern diet. These might be illustrated by comparing the American diet of 30 years ago with that of today, which, on the average, contains 15 per cent more calcium, 10 per cent more protein, 30 per cent more thiamine, niacin, and riboflavin, and 30 per cent more iron. Typical accomplishments in food technology include: (1) control of disease in transport and storage, (2) modern methods of food preservation, (3) sanitation and quality control, and (4) food and feed enrichment.

Natural cycles of agricultural production require that minimum quantities of foodstuffs be moved long distances during a relatively short harvest season. In the past, millions of dollars have been lost annually as a result of pests and pathogens attacking food products in transport or in storage. Modern methods of handling and the control of temperature and moisture, along with fumigation and chemical treatments, have markedly reduced the quantitative losses of stored foodstuffs as well as physiologic breakdown with resultant reduction in quality.

Modern methods of food preservation are now being applied to enormous quantities of food, much of which might otherwise be lost due to spoilage. These include the application of heat or cold; dehydration; physical action such as irradiation, distillation, com-

89

minution, vacuumization, and concentration; chemical treatments; and fermentation. These techniques permit rapid and wide distribution of products which would otherwise have to be in storage for long periods, and in effect, transfer much of the storage problem to the individual home, which can readily accept a much larger share of this burden. An added advantage is the fact that treated foods retain their original quality for an indefinite period of time and essentially eliminate seasonal diets.

Progress is being made in sanitation and quality control. Present-day foods are purer, more nutritious, and freer from parasites and pathogens than ever before. This has been accomplished by the establishment of rigorous standards of purity and cleanliness and their general application to public food supplies.

Food and feed have been enriched. As the requirements for animal nutrition have become better understood, great improvements have been made in the nutrient quality of foodstuffs and in the preparation of balanced rations supplemented with minor elements, hormones, antibiotics, vitamins, and antiparasitic agents. This has made it possible to increase both production and quality of meat, eggs, and milk with economies in both time and money.

The enrichment of human foods has become commonplace in modern food technology. Riboflavin, niacin, thiamine, vitamin D, iron, calcium, and phosphorous are regularly added to cereal products and other foods. It is expected that a much wider range of nutrient elements or compounds can be economically introduced into the average diet through the enrichment of foods without affecting flavor. Obviously this technique is most appealing in areas of the world where the variety of available foods is limited.

OBSTACLES TO AN ADEQUATE WORLD FOOD SUPPLY

On the foregoing pages attempt is made to present evidence that there are available resources and knowledge which, if universally applied, would make it possible to feed a world population several times greater than the present one. By extrapolation it can be expected that future progress in agricultural and related sciences will make available those quantities of quality foodstuffs necessary to maintain adequate levels of public health. And yet, nearly two-thirds of the people in the world today receive less than the minimum essential elements of diet considered necessary for normal health and vigor. This great gap between demonstrated agricultural potentials and actual production reflects the degree to which modern technology has outstripped the capacity of society to apply its benefits generally. Until this situation is remedied, even though estimates as to the potential world food production may be reasonably accurate, they cannot be realistic.

The vast differences in social development that exist between the more advanced countries of the world and those considered to be underdeveloped are in part the result of the unequal distribution of natural resources, climatic extremes and irregular topography. These and other factors have affected the distribution of populations and the development of agriculture and industry, and in consequence, local standards of living. Until recently the status of underdeveloped areas was only vaguely understood by society in general, but modern advances in communication and transportation have brought the situation into sharp focus. The growing fear that population pressures threaten world peace and the future well-being of mankind has resulted in public insistence that remedial action be taken.

During something more than a decade there has been a growing preoccupation with technical assistance programs designed by nations or groups of nations to extend the benefits of science and industry into areas where the need is great. Many of these efforts have been soundly planned and well executed and have had important and useful impact on the rate at which local social and technical evolution occur. This is particularly true when such efforts take advantage of indigenous materials and customs so that progress made will be in terms of the economic, educational, and other capacities of the countries concerned. Violent permanent changes are rarely possible and usually undesirable. It is more realistic to recognize that changes in habits, traditions, and ideas are necessarily deliberate, and that these can only come after it is demonstrated that they are sound. Even when assistance programs are highly successful, there will still be a considerable lag before the less developed nations can assume positions in the world community commensurate with the potentials of their human and natural resources.

Perhaps the greatest single need in the world today is for educational opportunities for those people who have been barred from avenues of communication and understanding by illiteracy. Education brings understanding, and with understanding come ideas and ideals without which real progress is impossible. Although tremendous contributions have been made toward alleviating the ills of the world through the application of medical, agricultural, and engineering science, progress in mass education has been relatively meager. It might be worth considering whether the major emphasis of assistance programs should not be on education and training rather than on more practical physical needs of underdeveloped nations. In the long run, each country will have to take primary responsibility for its own destiny, and, therefore, the great urgency is to develop understanding and responsible leadership as rapidly as possible. It would seem that all nations have the obligation to assure that their citizens are learning as well as living, and that friendly efforts to help should be heavily accented on the development of indigenous human resources.

CONCLUSIONS

From available evidence it can be postulated that if the physical and biological sciences are adequately supported, most of the factors adversely affecting the nutrition and health of mankind can be gradually overcome. This postulate is unsound, however, unless parallel developments in the social sciences and humanities are implicit in it. Otherwise, there will continue to be a serious lag in time between scientific discoveries and their general application for the benefit of society. This gap will tend to grow larger in the future unless rapid strides are made in mass education and unless society faces the necessity of stabilizing populations. With these accomplishments, science and society can be more rapidly brought into phase and the future will hold commensurate improvements in living standards and health for an ever-increasing fraction of mankind.

Food, Science, and People

INTRODUCTION

The growing body of literature on the balance between world population and food supplies reflects the increasing pressure that mankind is placing upon science and technology with each succeeding generation. A study of this material reveals that individuals representing a wide variety of disciplines in the physical, chemical, biological, and social sciences, as well as those interested in the humanities, are becoming acutely aware of the implications of explosive increases in population with which the world is presently faced. When it is realized that mankind has increased from approximately 500 million in 1700 to 1.25 billion in 1900 and 2.5 billion in 1950, the demographic problem resulting from pure increases in numbers becomes startlingly apparent. Extrapolated into the future the problem becomes frightening. At some stage society will find it necessary to cast up the balances between expanding human requirements and the capacity of the world to satisfy them in the immediate and more distant future. The remarks that follow represent an attempt to examine certain aspects of the population and food problem and raise questions that must be resolved by society as a whole if mankind is to attain adequate standards of living and human dignity during at least the next century.

The scholars concerned with the balance between procreation and production tend to divide themselves generally into two categories. One group seems convinced that man's mismanagement of the world's natural resources, coupled with the uncontrolled increase in human population, essentially guarantees ultimate chaos through

Lecture given before the New York Academy of Sciences, New York City, December 9, 1957 the sheer weight of numbers. The other school of thought holds that, with adequate economic support, human imagination and ingenuity will enable science and technology to improve in all of their aspects and to break through some of the existing barriers to greatly increased production. Presumably this would result in enormous gains in available energy and an agricultural and industrial productivity so much greater than is presently possible that current estimates would be nullified. This group believes that these developments will occur within the foreseeable future and that the world can then comfortably accommodate two and three times its present population, and perhaps even more.

Obviously, there are many variations on these two themes, and it would be inaccurate to suggest that all observers or students subscribe fully to one or the other philosophy. It is my personal belief that there are basic truths in each point of view that in themselves tend to modify each conclusion. I should say, however, that in spite of my deep faith in the capacity of all fields of science to combine to achieve technological heights as yet not envisioned, I am definitely perturbed by my growing conviction that science and technology could lose the battle to unlimited procreation. I believe that, unless there is a determined and organized effort on the part of all sectors of society to balance population increases with social and scientific advances, grave problems lie ahead. The question is not just one concerned with sufficient food for millions and even billions of additional hungry mouths, but rather one involving, in addition to an adequate dietary standard, opportunities for education and employment and the development of social standards of living compatible with human dignity. There is perhaps too great a tendency to seek an arithmetic solution to human problems whereas, in truth, the total answer can be given only in humanistic terms. The sections that follow attempt to delineate certain current and future problems, suggest ways in which science may contribute to their solution, and indicate the necessity for comparable social adjustment.

PRESENT WORLD FOOD SUPPLIES

The most sobering fact encountered in the study of ways and means to feed future generations is that the world of today is completely unsuccessful in providing satisfactory diets and standards of living for even one half of its citizens. We are thus forced to discuss possibilities of future success in providing for billions more people than are now in existence, although our past record has been one of substantial failure. As currently estimated, the world's population approximates 2.6 billion. In support of this number of individuals world food production is in excess of 900 million tons annually. This quantity is totally inadequate to provide the ideal of approximately 3,000 calories per capita. In fact, it supplies only 25 per cent of the population with more than 2,750 calories daily, 20 per cent with 2,250 to 2,750 and 55 per cent with less than 2,200 calories daily. Since two-thirds of the world's labor force is engaged in agricultural pursuits, these figures emphasize the fact that a disproportionate fraction of the population of the earth is chained to inefficient agricultural practices with comparable losses to industry, business, education, and the arts.

Obviously, production capacity in terms of human effort varies enormously throughout the world. Individual human output is critically affected by health, education, and economic resources. In certain areas favored by geography, human and natural resources have been combined to develop the highest standards of living that thus far have been obtained, and have produced agricultural surpluses that are piling up at an alarming rate. In contrast are those less favored regions with natural barriers to efficient crop production, public health problems, inadequate natural resources, and restricted educational opportunities. In these areas yields of domestic crop plants and animals are among the lowest in the world, labor requirements are excessive, and standards of living are inadequate. For example, completely mechanized rice culture in the best areas in the United States requires two to four man-days to produce rice at the rate of 3,500 lbs. per acre, whereas in certain of the more primitive rice-growing areas in the world 400 man-days of labor are necessary to produce 700 lbs. or less of rice per acre. In terms of calories the United States, with six per cent of the world's population, produces 15 per cent of the total world food supplies and has an average per capita caloric intake of 3,100 calories daily. India, with more than twice the population of the United States, produces only about seven per cent of the world's food supply and has an average caloric intake of 1,640 per capita daily. Moreover, the United States uses only eight to nine per cent of its total labor force in achieving its current position of overproduction with respect to agricultural commodities, whereas India underproduces local demands even though utilizing 70 per cent of its labor force for agriculture.

Many reasons are given for these extremes in agricultural efficiency. These are frequently colored by the particular interest or philosophy of the individual concerned, but together they add up to a formidable series of problems that require solution before the world can hope to rectify current inequalities, not to mention provision for increased future demands. Among the more important barriers to efficient agricultural production the following may be cited as critical:

Soil—Man is his own greatest enemy in the matter of contributing to the destruction of arable soils that has now reached the point at which millions upon millions of acres have been partially or totally ruined for agricultural purposes. As the most optimistic estimates indicate that the world can never expect to have more than approximately four billion acres in crop production, the prevention or control of erosion quickly becomes of critical consideration. Opinions vary as to whether badly eroded areas can ever be restored to productivity, but with time and intelligent management, some could be brought back to a level of productivity at which they could contribute to needed food supplies. Unfortunately, time is the least available commodity, and only when pressures become irresistible do political and economic measures come into play, and then only very slowly. Meanwhile, urbanization, industry, flood control, and other public works continue to encroach upon valuable agricultural soils, with the result that possibilities for increasing food supplies by bringing new land into production are now essentially being nullified by the rate at which land is being taken out of agriculture.

Much of the world's land surface is barred to the practice of agriculture by climate, as in the Arctic and, to a degree, the sub-Arctic regions. Also, while the humid tropics represent our greatest potential resource in terms of solar energy and humidity, many tropical soils are low in productivity. Moreover, heavy economic investments are required to make life in the tropics attractive to entrepreneurs who might successfully develop local agricultural potentials. The tropics of Africa, Asia, and much of South America have thus far failed to contribute their share to world food supplies, and they represent the greatest remaining land resources that could be brought under cultivation in response to human need. Here again, however, the time factor is critical; there are many obstacles to rapid progress so that it cannot be expected that this resource will become fully developed in the early future.

Water—Water is all too often the limiting factor in crop production. Modern agriculture demands that man manipulate domestic plants and animals for his benefit; in doing so, he must give first consideration to soil and water requirements. In certain instances water may be in excess, but unfortunately in the vast majority of cases inadequate water supplies constitute the major barrier to optimum yields. The conventional practice of putting crops in the ground at that time of the year when it is hoped that subsequent rainfall will be of sufficient quantity and distribution to support normal plant growth is risky. The conventional farmer is always at the mercy of the elements and can never be completely sure that during any given year he will have normal production rather than crop failure due to drought or other causes. Although there are many reasons for crop failure, the most important is lack of sufficient quantities of water during critical periods in the growth cycle of crop plants. Man has learned to compensate for the vagaries of nature through techniques of irrigation in those areas where natural bodies of water, artificial impoundments, or adequate subsoil pools are readily available. He has found that irrigation provides insurance against undesirable variations in rainfall patterns and offers the additional advantage of permitting the application of adequate quantities of water during the time when moisture is of greatest significance in supporting growth and reproduction. Many otherwise potentially productive areas are condemned to desert status because of the unavailability of water for agricultural purposes.

Pests and diseases—To add to the many other ills of agriculture, the world is populated by an amazing array of microorganisms that annually extort tolls of agricultural products sometimes reaching 15 per cent of gross production. Estimates vary, but there is little doubt that at least 100 million tons of food are destroyed each year through the activities of insects, fungi, bacteria, viruses, nematodes, and weeds, which parasitize crop plants and domestic animals. In an effort to prevent this total from becoming very much greater, agriculturists are forced to make heavy investments in insecticides, fungicides, and herbicides and the machinery for their application. These represent economic sanctions imposed upon agriculture by pests and diseases. In many areas economic resources are inadequate to permit the regular application of protective compounds to prevent disease epidemics. The result may be heavy annual losses or forced change to cropping patterns that are less economic in terms of supply and demand.

Mineral resources—A major factor in the inequalities that exist in standards of living in various sectors of the world is the distribution of mineral resources. Deposits of base and precious metals, radioactive substances, nitrates, phosphates, sulfur, and potash are all critical in the rational development of agriculture. The successful utilization of mineral resources inevitably demands large quantities of cheap energy. These can be satisfied only where there are readily available sources of coal, petroleum, water power, and, more recently, fissionable materials. Since power demands are increasing enormously each year, it is quite evident that energy quickly will become the limiting factor to future agricultural and industrial production unless additional resources can be tapped or developed.

Human resources—As previously suggested, the human factor is of paramount importance in the problem of world food production and living standards. It is obvious that healthy, well-nourished individuals are most productive, and they, of course, require an adequate diet to support their output of energy. Of at least equal importance is the understanding and competence that can be applied to the art of agriculture by individual growers. Among the most serious barriers to the production of food crops and domestic animals are ignorance and tradition, which lead not only to low yields but to wasteful use of land and other resources, as well. To the unlettered citizens of many lands the benefits of modern agriculture are mysterious and out of reach; until education becomes an integral part of the experience of essentially every individual, there is little hope that science and technology can correct the present unsatisfactory ratio between numbers of individuals and human nutrition. It would seem, therefore, that society will have to invest vastly increased funds to make the benefits of education generally available and to utilize resultant improved manpower most effectively.

ROLE OF SCIENCE IN FOOD PRODUCTION

Those who insist that adequate food supplies and comfortable levels of existence for all of the people are the responsibility of sci-

98

ence and technology produce a wide variety of statistics to support their contention. They point out that the potential world food supply is limited only by the capacity of the globe to produce carbon compounds. They cite the fact that total crop production on cultivated land alone approximates four billion tons, which in theory could support nearly 30 billion people. Actually, however, half of this amount is eaten by animals that convert only three to five per cent of the total into food for mankind. Of the other half that occurs in the form of crop plants, only about 20 per cent is currently usable as food. If, then, there were no losses to contend with, present agricultural production could be expected to support a maximum world population of 3.5 billion. However, storms, floods, pests, diseases, and waste reduce this total to the point where currently available world food supplies, even if properly distributed, could support only 2.3 billion people at recommended rates of caloric intake. This number is less than the actual population, and inequalities in purchasing power and the distribution of commodities result in extremes in agricultural surpluses and deficits and per capita caloric intake in various parts of the world.

The sea and noncultivated land together produce more than 150 billion tons annually of carbon compounds; if a relatively small percentage of this total could be economically transformed into food and feedstuffs, world food supplies would increase proportionately. Science is not defeated in this matter, and there are already dramatic demonstrations of the effects of the scientific method on average yields of crop plants and animal products. Yields of certain plant and animal products from the practice of agriculture have doubled, trebled, and even quadrupled during the past fifty years, and the more complete utilization of domestic animals and cultivated plants as food substances has contributed significantly to human nutrition. Nevertheless, all of these advances have resulted in average annual increases in food production that, according to most optimistic estimates, do not reach two per cent per year. At this rate the world level of human nutrition cannot gain on population and, with the addition of nearly 100,000 new citizens each day, production may well lag even further behind the need. If, however, society is willing to provide greater support to science and technology, there is little doubt that dramatic improvements can be made in the production and conversion of nonfood carbon compounds into forms that can be readily assimilated by man. These improvements alone will not in any sense resolve the critical problem of balance between food and people that lies ahead, but could be a major contribution toward its solution. Several specific possibilities are described in the following paragraphs.

Plant improvement—Of the approximately 300,000 plant species that have been described, less than 3,000 have ever been used for food; only 300 are now widely grown, and a mere dozen provide the world with over 90 per cent of its annual food supplies. Thus, there still exists a rich resource from which it is certainly reasonable to expect that plant species of great natural value in terms of ratio between consumable foods and by-products may be selected, domesticated, and brought into production on a wide scale. Plants already domesticated can be further improved through conventional breeding techniques and nonconventional methods leading to the establishment of wide crosses that will blend the desired characteristics of two or more types that are not necessarily intimately related phylogenetically. The science of genetics is progressing with great rapidity and, as we understand more fully the function of the nucleus and cytoplasmic inclusions in relation to ontogeny and metabolism, we may be able to develop plant types several times more efficient as food producers than those conventional forms currently in use. Physical and chemical methods of modifying cellular behavior are already available and will doubtless be of major importance in making it possible to increase productivity further. Sooner or later we should be able to improve substantially the quantity and quality of food species harvested from the sea.

Soil improvement—Science is making tremendous progress in understanding the soil as a living medium upon which food and other plants depend for major quantities of water and mineral nutrients. We are learning to alter or modify the physical, chemical, and biological properties of the soil for improved production. Ecologists and agronomists have studied the roles of soil and climate in relation to crop production and have developed ingenious systems of combining applications of water and nutrient elements at critical times with predetermined cropping patterns for maximum production. The roles of micronutrients in crop production are becoming better understood, and modern soil management has resulted in increasing the carrying capacity of agricultural soils to levels once believed impossible. Where there are no soils we have learned how to create artificial hydroponic systems that are invaluable for special purposes; that is, the production of noncontaminated vegetables for military personnel abroad, high-quality cash crops for winter markets, and the production of vegetables in areas without arable soils where necessity makes this practice economically feasible.

Soil microbiology is a most complex science, but it has gradually begun to reveal some of its secrets to investigators. Progress is being made in learning to influence populations of soil microorganisms in order to increase the rate of decomposition of crop residues, to augment the quantities of available nitrogen and phosphorus in the soil, to change soil pH, and to create antibiotic barriers to soil-borne pests and pathogens. Doubtless, as our understanding of the biology of soil types throughout the world improves, many modifications can be brought about with resultant benefit to economic crop production.

Protection—In the past we have depended principally upon exclusion and external treatment to protect domestic plants and animals against pests and parasites. Many quarantines have been effective in excluding insects and pathogens, and modern sprays, dusts, and slurries are of great value in the protection of seeds, plant parts, and animals from those pests and pathogens that would otherwise take a much heavier annual toll of food production. Many of the great sweeping epidemics of plant and animal diseases that were long feared as regular occurrences have been gradually brought under control and in some instances essentially eliminated. Nevertheless, 15 per cent or more of the world's food supply is destroyed each year by parasitic or pathogenic microorganisms.

Great strides are being made in plant and animal protection as the result of fundamental studies of hosts and parasites and their metabolic relationships. The conventional systems of plant protection are gradually giving way to new methods in which the use of synthetic systemic compounds, antibiotics, and naturally occurring protective substances may well provide greatly improved protection at a lower cost. In combination with the use of resistant varieties, mechanization, and modern management techniques these methods offer increasing hope that we may more nearly close the gap between potential maximum production and the actual figures that reflect heavy economic losses from the attack of pests and pathogens.

Mechanization—The increasing use of modern machinery in those areas where such investments are possible has resulted in greater yields and lower costs for many of the major crops and domestic animals. Land preparation has become more rapid and more efficient and less costly. Planting, fertilizer placement, and cultivating are handled more simply and quickly than ever before, as are applications of herbicides, insecticides, and fungicides. Once a crop is mature, machines again assume control in the harvesting operation and continue to play important roles in such postharvest processes as packing, shipping, freezing, drying, and canning. With the help of modern devices, quality is maintained, spoilage is avoided, and losses in processing are minimized, with resultant benefits to human nutrition. With adequate supplies of raw materials and cheap power sources, the use of mechanical devices in agriculture would undoubtedly increase many fold and make dramatic new contributions to production. In the first instance, this would reduce still further the number of individuals required in the practice of agriculture; in the second, fruits, vegetables, cereals, meat, and milk products of improved quality would be produced in significantly increasing quantities. Eventually, much of animal husbandry may yield to techniques of the production line for greater efficiency.

Agricultural chemistry—Modern chemistry is making what are perhaps the most dramatic modern contributions to agriculture. The use of chemical fertilizers and protectants has already been mentioned, and the traditional materials have now been joined by a host of new compounds that are gradually enabling man to dominate domesticated plants and animals more completely and precisely for his benefit. Through basic studies of plant and animal metabolism chemical methods are being found that influence physiological processes to bring about a host of desired modifications in plant and animal behavior. Many modern plants are both visibly and invisibly different in structure and function from their ancestors. Through chemical and other techniques we have learned to produce dwarf varieties with improved ratios between waste and desired food products; to alter the growth habits of plants and animals so that larger quantities of desired food products are produced in shorter periods of time. We can induce or delay flowering, prevent fruit drop, delay senescence, modify disease resistance, and control numbers of offspring. Thus are we learning to tailor our plant and animal servants to our own requirements and by so doing make it possible to increase further the proportions of usable end products to waste materials. Moreover, many of the so-called waste materials of the past have now become economic assets through chemical transformations. Some transformations may result in nonfood industrial products, but others have contributed directly to world food supplies by changing relatively indigestible materials into substances that can be utilized as food or feedstuffs.

If there is to be any major breakthrough in the rate of annual production of food supplies, it will undoubtedly occur in part because of important developments in the fields of basic and applied biology and chemistry. Many substances are already in use and new possibilities for further improvements are becoming increasingly apparent every day. Examples are gibberellin, the antibiotics, hormones, synthesized organic compounds, and a wide range of as yet unidentified extracts from plant and animal organs. Each year there are new discoveries that help in the better understanding of cellular metabolism and suggest ways in which life processes can be further modified for the greater production of desired commodities. Biochemical studies of the nucleus and of cytoplasmic inclusions, enzyme systems, and the process of photosynthesis provide an accumulating body of data that may ultimately offer keys to methods by which plants and animals can be more precisely influenced and manipulated for the benefit of mankind. If it were possible to increase significantly the rate at which photosynthesis takes place, to increase the efficiency of water utilization in plant cells, to control growth rhythms more precisely, to induce symbiotic nitrogen fixation in cereal and other nonleguminous crops, or to control the balance between vegetable growth and fruit or seed production, the annual rate of increase in food production in the world might easily be three, four, or even five per cent instead of the present rate of less than two per cent.

In spite of man's long association with plants and animals and his absolute dependence upon them, we are still groping at the threshold of understanding with respect to their metabolic processes. If society is willing to provide very much greater support to the chemical as well as other approaches to basic biology, chemistry doubtless will return the investment many fold.

Energy—In any discussion of increased world food supplies and improved standards of living, energy must have a major role. Although reserves of conventional sources of energy, that is, petroleum and coal, have increased during the past 50 years, it is not clear that newly proved reserves will be found at similar rates in the years to come. In any event, these resources are not inexhaustible, and it behooves us now to think about coal and petroleum in terms of what we shall do as our reserves begin to dwindle. Further developments in water power are still possible, but these represent an insignificant fraction of total future power demands.

Solar energy presents a tantalizing subject for speculation, because every day the world receives energy from the sun at a rate of approximately 2,000 times the amount of energy that man presently contrives to use. Physical methods for the utilization of this energy are well known, but thus far they have been unable to compete to any significant degree with conventional sources of power. Solar cookers, space heaters, pumps, and engines have been developed experimentally and have had at least a limited utility under rather special circumstances. If and when free solar energy can be economically captured in vast quantities and used for the comfort and well-being of mankind, the resultant benefits will be enormous. Electrical and photochemical conversion processes for the transformation of solar energy into power have been investigated to some extent for many years and have now become the object of more intensive study in the hope that they will lead to economic supplements to present power resources.

Nuclear energy is a subject about which accurate long-range forecasting is difficult. However, rapid progress is being made in the technology, and all the evidence suggests that the energy product of atomic fission will provide enormous power supplements to industry, agriculture, and urban development. Large reserves of uranium are available, and, sooner or later, nuclear fuel stations will probably assume major importance as energy sources. Fission batteries and reactor heaters are also potentially important, and, if it should become possible to master the fusion reaction on an economic basis, then power would become the least of our worries for an indefinite period in the future. Although nuclear fission has long been a subject of pure speculation, recent developments have stimulated scientists to the conviction that it can be mastered and ultimately harnessed for the benefit of society.

It is unrealistic to assume that because of need the energy question will be resolved promptly and effectively by science and technology. Certainly, one potential breakthrough has already occurred, that is, nuclear power development; others may occur that would put many presently unavailable resources at the service of society. With great quantities of relatively cheap power the conversion of sea water to fresh water for irrigation purposes might well become practicable, as would the extraction of salts and minerals from sea water and the mass culture of useful microorganisms for use in agriculture and industry. The transformation of proteins from noncultivated plants into foods and foodstuffs would be facilitated and a whole host of new possibilities for adding to world food supplies would become apparent.

Examination of past and present scientific progress and future possibilities rather clearly suggests that science and technology, under favorable circumstances, can make immense contributions to vitally needed food supplies for future generations. The possibilities are many and exciting; without doubt the accomplishments of the next several decades will be as dramatically superior to those of today as the latter are in comparison with those of the early 1900's. Important and encouraging as these expected developments may be, they do not ensure that population growth will not continue to outstrip their total capacity for production. It would seem axiomatic that ultimately the requirements of unrestricted population increases will exhaust man's ingenuity and the supplies of natural resources.

PEOPLE

In the preceding sections I have attempted to outline what appear to me to be certain of the more important considerations involved in the role of science in meeting present and future demands for human food. To me these add up to the conclusion that society, as of the present moment, is unsuccessful in providing reasonable standards of living for all of its citizens and that there is no evidence that this situation will soon be rectified. While there is encouraging evidence that science can make significantly greater contributions to world food supplies during the years to come, it does not appear that conventional methods, even as they improve, can result in production levels that will balance to any reasonable degree the numbers of people who may be expected to populate the earth a hundred or more years hence. If new advances in science occur that permit power and production increases at different orders of magnitude than are presently possible, immediate worries fade into the distant future. However, it is unrealistic to assume that future technological progress will provide for any number of citizens that society cares to impose upon the already heavy burden of human nutrition.

In the last analysis the true standard of living of any country is that enjoyed—if this is the word—by the great majority of its citizens. Actual levels in a given area are the product of human potential times natural resources. When one factor is lacking to any significant degree, living standards necessarily suffer. There are areas in the world in which per capita income is relatively high because of some special resource, such as petroleum, but the standards of living of the masses are pitifully low. Only when the benefits of education, training, and opportunity are extended to the bulk of the individuals populating a specified country can that nation expect to improve its economic position through the development of its own resources, both natural and human, and the exchange of goods and services with other countries.

In the literature on world food problems and standards of living there may be too much emphasis on the role of energy, food, and the improved utilization of natural resources and scientific developments in contrast to the emphasis on the population side of the problem. Society in general seems blandly to accept as fact its right to multiply itself in a completely unrestricted fashion without considering either the additional burden that this places upon natural resources and technology or the fact that, because of the lag between population increases and advances in technology, millions of the world's present and future citizens may be condemned to ignorance, poverty, disease, and famine. Living things are born, grow to maturity, reproduce, and die to the degree that these life functions are possible under existing conditions at a given time and place. An examination of natural phenomena will produce a multitude of examples demonstrating that any biological community may reach the point of saturation in terms of the carrying capacity of its surroundings. When this point is reached, new individuals can come into being and prosper only at the rate that other individuals disappear from the community. Under such circumstances the community reaches a state of dynamic stability.

The human community is in no wise free of the basic laws of nature. Because of man's intelligence he is better able than any other biological form to modify his surroundings to his own taste and mitigate many of those forces that tend to destroy him. However, there is no evidence that this process can continue indefinitely and that the population of the globe can increase unchecked for an indefinite period in the future without catastrophic results. A simple illustration is the fact that the 2.6 billion human individuals occupying the world today, at the current rate of increase, will reach a total of seven billion by the year 2050. When these figures are extrapolated into the future, the obvious result is chaos induced by the sheer weight of numbers.

The radical increase in the population of the world is, of course, a simple function of geometric progression. It has been brought about by a variety of sociological and other factors, no one of which can be pointed to as the basic cause. These include various sorts of taboos, ignorance, and in the more sophisticated areas, a lack of understanding of ultimate consequences. Efforts by students of demography to delineate the problem and suggest remedial action are often met with opposition from groups that disagree with the conclusions reached or believe that their own philosophies more correctly apply. A hopeful sign is the fact that there are areas in the world where the problem has become so acute that local leadership has been forced to recognize it and to begin to consider and experiment with ways for achieving the stabilization of populations before complete social breakdown occurs.

It is futile to belabor continuously the roles of science and technology in response to human need and to ignore completely the social implications involved. This becomes perfectly clear when one realizes that nearly two thirds of the world's citizens of today have substandard living conditions. While this situation is often viewed with alarm and with compassion, rarely is thought given to the fact that if we could suddenly bring the entire world up to the standard of living enjoyed by the most economically advanced nations we would immediately drain our natural resources at a rate approaching 100 times the current one. We should then have to expand this rate of consumption to care for further increases in population, with the certainty that we should rapidly exhaust most or all of the major natural resources upon which society now depends. It would be naive to assume that science would immediately find available substitutes in adequate quantities to fill the already rapidly widening gaps in critical quantities of petroleum, minerals, agricultural products, and all the other elements basic to what we consider an adequate level for normal existence.

The ingenuity of mankind will be put to the acid test during the coming generations. At best we are going to have to learn to cope with multitudes of new citizens, to feed, clothe, house, and educate them, and to teach them to live together under increasingly crowded conditions and decreasing standards of living. Those who now enjoy the highest standards may well find themselves in a situation in which many of the luxuries they took for granted in the 1940's and 1950's will be nostalgic memories. Also, unfortunately, this decrease in living standards in many advanced areas of the world will not necessarily be compensated for by commensurate improvements in the underdeveloped countries. On the contrary, it may probably simply represent a contribution to the increasing numbers of human beings in the world. The rich will get poorer and the poor will get still poorer as mankind continues to pour into society enormous numbers of individuals without provision for their adequate support. This suggests that an ever-increasing number of persons will be condemned to short lives of poverty and misery which, in turn, will adversely affect the lives and well-being of those individuals who by reason of their own industry and more fortunate geographical location have managed to develop relatively advanced standards of existence.

Although this paper is not to be considered a treatise on demography, my subject cannot properly be discussed if the population problem is entirely ignored. The success of every effort to improve food production and technology hinges in the last analysis upon whether society, through its myriad social, religious, political, and academic organizations, is prepared to understand and to face this its greatest single problem. If so, the logical first step is to apply the intellect to the establishment of principles and practices by which society can begin to balance at the earliest possible moment the demands of mankind against nature's ability to respond. Failure to make such an effort may mean a continuing and even an increasing series of wars, famines, epidemics, and other ills that plague mankind.

CONCLUSION

If I have been able to make one point by this discussion, I hope it is that the problems of providing the most basic needs for society affect us all and that, unless there is concerted and successful effort, the outlook for the future is not an attractive one. To a reasonable degree modern science and technology have provided, through agriculture and a wide variety of industries, enormous contributions to the well-being of mankind. Also, these have been fantastically successful by any comparison with previous years or decades. This is true even though the distribution of commodities has been inequitable and despite the fact that vast extremes exist between the so-called developed and underdeveloped areas of the world. There is, of course, no single solution, and no one sector of society has more responsibility than any other for working toward the rational solution of this fundamental problem that affects all of mankind.

It is suggested that there are several ways in which we can forestall or at least delay some of the developments that presently seem imminent. We can see to it, for example, that science and technology are properly supported with funds and understanding so that, insofar as possible, new developments will keep pace with growing needs. We can attempt in logical and responsible ways to help less fortunate nations to develop their own natural and human resources so that they may more nearly approach standards of living that are essential and desirable. We can concentrate enormously greater emphasis on improvements in education so that vastly increased numbers of the world's citizens will have opportunities without which they can never hope to progress. We can see to it that educational patterns do not become static, but remain flexible, dynamic, and become increasingly better. Subsequent improvements would accrue to all of the areas of science, to the social sciences, and to the humanities. Finally, it would seem that it is time now for society to make an objective examination of the world's population problem, to face the implications of increases that in many areas exceed three per cent per year. We must soon decide whether we are prepared to fall behind in each succeeding generation until there is no longer room to move and insufficient bread and opportunity for all, or whether we shall recognize and interpret the laws of nature in logical fashion and take appropriate measures not to violate them at the expense of our descendants.

Agricultural Horizons

The quirk of phylogenetic fate that resulted in the emergence of *homo sapiens* is the most significant single event in the history of the earth. All the stages of biologic evolution which occurred before man appeared become relatively insignificant when compared with the violent changes he has caused during his short span of existence. Although physically man is no match for many other forms of life, his powers of reason have enabled him gradually to improve his competitive position among biologic species. Today he is the master of every form of life but his own, has at times wantonly destroyed other types that were here before him, and has converted still others to forms best suited to his personal convenience.

The invention of agriculture signaled the end of a biologic system based primarily upon physical competition and the survival of the fittest. When man learned to cultivate plants and to domesticate animals he also made possible the organization of society with division of labor and the opportunity to plan for the future. This doomed other forms of life to secondary roles and to restrictions imposed by man. Simultaneously the stage was set for man to multiply himself and his communities until today he is to be found essentially everywhere. For many years there has been an understandable tendency to think of increasing populations as symbols of prosperity, in the philosophy that the results would be a greater labor force and more people to participate in education, the sciences, and the arts for public benefit. Now, however, we are forced to realize that the population of the earth is at least doubling each half century, and at

Invitational address, the 51st Annual Meeting of the American Society of Agronomy, Purdue University, August 5, 1958 this rate the point of saturation will one day be reached. In the past we thought that there were new worlds to conquer and were comfortable in this knowledge. Today there are few geographical frontiers on the earth. Tomorrow there will be none, and the 2.6 billion people that now occupy the globe will apparently be more than seven billion in less than 100 years. After that, what?

In the long run, the decisions affecting social organizations and development are made by society in general. Although he can help, no scientific, educational, political, or other leader is individually competent to make the major decisions that affect all of society. Though there are multitudes of groups with diverse points of view and strong convictions, ultimate judgments must be reached by common consent. Thus, society itself will have to decide whether its future lies with unrestricted increases in its members or whether logic and the laws of nature dictate stabilization of populations before people become so numerous as to compete seriously for space and survival.

The decision as to the need for increased agricultural production has already been made by society. Although certain countries, our own among them, can take great satisfaction in their technological accomplishments and established standards of living, this situation is by no means uniform among the nations of the world. In fact, more than half of the present world population lives in substandard conditions.

The world demand for energy is increasing by leaps and bounds, and energy is the critical factor in the continuing forward progress of civilization. Fortunately, advances in nuclear physics and related fields give us hope that the world may soon be in much better position than ever before relative to power supplies. This will mean commensurate advances in technology and opportunities for the development of processes and practices which are currently uneconomic in terms of their energy demands. Moreover, in addition to the expected increase in available power from nuclear fission, fusion, and other reactions, we still have the enormous but essentially untapped solar resources. Progress on this front is being made, and we can surely expect that in the years to come greater utilization of the solar resource will be economically possible.

If man can learn to coexist in an atmosphere of mutual trust and respect, the currently astronomical investments in power, machines, and men for military purposes could be diverted with enormous benefit to standards of living everywhere.

TECHNOLOGY

In response to the demand for increased production, the technologies of agriculture are expanding and improving daily. Most spectacular perhaps is the development of machines which every year do the work of a larger number of men. The manipulation of soil, seed, chemicals, and crops has become highly mechanized as have the various steps involved in processing and preserving the final product. The science of agricultural chemurgy has made rapid strides in the conversion of what were once by-products or wastes into materials which have significant economic values. As a result, the farmer is able to multiply his services to society, and each year his efforts supply a larger number of individuals with essential foods.

Paralleling the modern developments of agricultural engineering have been those in the techniques of soil management, fertilizer practices, irrigation systems, and plant and animal protection. Today crop plants and domestic animals are handled with a preciseness and attention to detail which was inconceivable only a generation ago, with the result that crop losses are minimized, and maximum yields are assured under normal circumstances. The health of domestic plants and animals is likewise taken into consideration through carefully designed management practices and the application of synthetic compounds with specific qualities for the control of air-borne, soil-borne, or seed-borne pathogens capable of causing epidemic diseases. Various degrees of systemic protection have been added to the traditional practice of external protection, with significant benefits.

When the science of genetics joins forces with other agricultural disciplines the total effect becomes dramatic. The manipulation of the genic potentials of crop plants and animals by hybridization and induced mutation has resulted in varieties of domestic plants and animals which in terms of their usefulness to man are more successful than any ever encountered in nature. Size, shape, quality, color, yield, and disease resistance are only a few of the factors which can be selected or blended to achieve desired end products. Within relatively few years commercial crop varieties will no doubt differ as greatly from their present form as these do from ancestral types.

The field of chemistry necessarily extends into every branch of agricultural science. As already indicated, chemistry comes into play in the preparation, preservation, and enrichment of agricultural products, in fertility studies, and in plant protection. However, these are only a few of the multiple aspects of the value of the chemical approach to crop and animal production. Currently, we are learning to take advantage of naturally occurring and synthetic organic substances to affect growth types and rates and to control fruit and flower production, abscission, and many of the other phenomena involved in growth cycles. Results to date suggest many additional possibilities for artificially influencing the behavior of plants and animals in such ways as to economically increase their proportional yields of desired products in minimum periods.

Modern technologies offer appealing opportunities for nonconventional methods for increasing the world's food supplies. One of these is the possibility of using organic material which thus far has not been available. Several billion tons of leaf protein are produced every year by the so-called noneconomic plants growing wild in fields and forests and especially in the humid tropics where conventional protein sources are limited. There is little doubt that the recovery of large quantities of usable protein from this free source involves only the costs of collection, extraction, and preparation. Presumably the proteins recovered would in the first instance be used in animal feeds, since we may soon find that we can no longer dedicate vast acreages of agricultural land to pasture crops. Rather, we may probably have to urbanize animal communities and import their foods just as we do our own. Eventually, significant quantities of protein supplements for human foods may be derived from leaf extracts.

We have not yet learned to take full advantage of available marine resources. Doubtless, future population pressures will force us to give increasing attention to the sea as a potential source of foods and feeds. By definition, perhaps the sea does not fall within the domain of conventional agriculture. From the realistic point of view, however, agriculture is going to have to go very much beyond the conventional if we expect to feed future generations of citizens, and it would behoove us to think of the sea as a great untapped food resource and one that we should study with the same scrupulous care we apply to soil science and related fields of conventional agriculture. Such a study would be tremendously rewarding in terms of advancement of knowledge and the development of techniques of management and production resulting in a vastly greater volume of marine plants and animals for human consumption. Scientists working in the fields of oceanography and marine biology have made significant progress, and agriculture should participate in the broad field of marine growth in an effort to take ever-increasing advantage of this important resource.

The current revolution in technologies has already resulted in enormous gains in the production of goods and services needed by society. Future developments will necessarily have to be many times greater than all those that have gone before, and in this regard agriculture is no exception. Presumably, farming as a way of life will give way to agricultural production as a strictly business enterprise, with significant increases in landholdings and comparable decreases in the number of individual landowners and the size of the farm labor force. Only when the business of farming assumes a financial and corporate structure similar to that practiced in industry can it become truly competitive. This will bring the science of engineering directly to the land and make push-button farming a reality with all of the mechanical, electrical, and electronic devices that have been so effectively applied in industry. These developments will first come to the more advanced areas of the world but will later have to be applied generally. Coincidentally, progress in developing non-conventional sources of food production will be expanded and intensified, and one day these will be of major significance in meeting the future demand for food and other agricultural commodities.

RESEARCH

The success of agriculture in our own country has been dependent upon the degree to which we have been able to exercise control over the behavior of domestic species. In the short span of a few thousand years man has changed from a position of complete dependence upon the natural bounty of plants and animals to one in which he exercises precise control over cultivated species that are essentially his dependents. The degree to which we can extend and increase our control over our living food resources will be the measure of our success in augmenting world food supplies in the future.

All of the real gains in the management of plant and animal species for human consumption have been based on an infinite number

114

of research efforts. Results to date reflect the degree to which research has been supported, and axiomatically, future progress will depend upon recognition of this fact by society. Probably in the foreseeable future we will reach the point of diminishing returns if we limit our research efforts to improvements along well established patterns. Rather, we are going to have to break through the production barriers imposed by genetic limitations, destructive pests and pathogens, and fertility levels. We are going to have to transcend the limits of quantitative and qualitative genetics and learn to control genes and to tailor plant and animal species to our own requirements. These will be types with immunities to destructive pests and pathogens and with productive capacities greatly in excess of anything now in existence. Ultimately, it may be possible to synthesize protoplasmic units for specific purposes. Without detracting in the slightest from previous dramatic developments in agricultural science, the really great innovations still lie ahead. The speed with which these come about will depend upon the support received by science for the purpose of training selected individuals and providing opportunities for them to push forward the frontiers of knowledge.

EDUCATION

The radical new developments that must occur in agriculture can take place only as a result of progress in education. In the past, agricultural education has been heavily oriented toward crop and animal production and the training of what might be called the practitioners of agriculture. These are the producers, regulatory personnel, extension specialists, and those carrying on the conventional practices of plant breeding, agronomy, farm management, plant protection, and allied functions. Certainly these individuals can take great satisfaction in the knowledge that theirs has been a major role in past progress. In the future we are going to need even larger numbers of practitioners with still better training. But high priority must now be given to the training of scientists dedicated to fundamental research, who will provide the increased knowledge to promote and support advancing technologies.

In response to population increase and growing demands for goods and services, agricultural curricula and educational patterns will have to be flexible and progressive. The practitioners of agricul-

115

ture will need training at a level considerably above that which has been offered in the past, and research scientists will require more fundamental training than ever before. The agricultural scientist will have to be thoroughly grounded in basic biology, chemistry, mathematics, and physics. He will have to be familiar with the instruments of modern science and their usefulness in fundamental research. He will also have to be educated in the broadest sense and cognizant of human as well as scientific values.

A number of questions are being raised concerning current philosophies of agricultural education and established curricula. For example, are we offering too much of what is essentially vocational training at the university level? Must we not strengthen the agricultural training by including substantial amounts of chemistry, physics, mathematics, and biology within the curriculum? If so, would this not have the dual advantage of selecting the best qualified students and producing a much better trained body of scientists? Is it not apparent that in the field of agriculture we will have to search for and attract students of outstanding ability, train them to a high degree of research competence, and offer them career opportunities which are competitively attractive in comparison with other fields of endeavor?

It has been estimated that under appropriate circumstances it would be possible to double the annual output of crops and domestic animals within a few years. But this is a theoretical conclusion and there are many obstacles to its early attainment. Moreover, even if this goal were achieved, we would by that time be still in short supply of those basic foods required for an adequate diet on a world-wide basis.

In view of the current situation and the foreseeable future, two conclusions appear to be clear. The first is that the more highly developed nations of the world are going to have to make tremendous improvements during the next several generations to be able to maintain or improve their own standards of living and contribute to those areas in which standards are still much too low. In the second place, the so-called underdeveloped countries seeking to improve their positions will themselves have to work intensively and extensively toward this objective with such help as can be obtained from outside sources. Each future generation must be better educated and more productive than its predecessor, with the aim of

116

ultimately achieving at least acceptable levels of human subsistence in the countries concerned.

RESOURCES

It is clear that future agricultural scientists and producers will have to unite to provide the enormously greater quantities of agricultural commodities desired by society. Our ability to do so will depend to a great extent on available resources, the way in which they are used, and the development of substitute methods and materials. The major resources with which we have to work are land, water, and minerals, in addition to human resources expressed in terms of education, research, and technology.

Land—Our greatest single resource for the conventional practice of agriculture is, of course, land, and the situation in this regard is quite variable throughout the world. Although there are still large land areas which conceivably could be brought into agricultural production, there are many obstacles to this goal. Some are climatic as a result of extremes of temperature and moisture. Others are physiographic. Some are due to population imbalances, and still others result from unrealistic landholding patterns.

Although agriculture has gradually been extended into subarctic regions, the low temperature barrier prohibits crop production on large expanses of otherwise arable land. Conversely, the humid and dry tropics present serious obstacles to intensive cultivation. These affect not only the crops and domestic animals concerned but also the lives of human inhabitants, and we will one day have to learn that it is just as necessary to provide creature comforts, including air conditioning, to the dwellers of the tropics as it is to consider central heating and other amenities as essential to northern latitudes. As long as the still underdeveloped areas are treated as outposts of civilization, they cannot be brought into a properly productive state.

A variety of landholding patterns adversely affect agricultural production. These range from the minifundia, in which landholdings are totally uneconomic because of their smallness, to the latifundia in which the landholdings are uneconomic because they are too large. In the latter situation enormous areas are permitted to remain uncultivated and represent only the patrimony of future generations of the families of the landowners. These problems are, of course, the responsibilities of the sovereign states concerned and

117

some have already taken steps to improve land tenure patterns. In the future further improvements may be expected since population pressures will tend to eliminate those patterns which are clearly uneconomic or even destructive of this major natural resource.

Another undesirable situation exists in connection with those agricultural areas which annually fail to produce yields commensurate with their potentials. Millions upon millions of acres in many parts of the world are cultivated each year but return to the cultivator only pitifully small yields. This may be due to a variety of climatic, economic, educational, political, or other causes which prevent the optimum utilization of these resources. Obviously, significant improvements must one day be made in the management and productivity of these huge acreages, with commensurate gains in food production for society.

In the more highly developed countries available agricultural land is almost totally in production, and their problem is to increase yields while maintaining fertility. In our own country, although we have in the past 50 years doubled and trebled the yield of many major economic crops, we are now seeking fractional improvements through the use of improved varieties, better soil management, and more efficient plant protection. Here we also find ourselves in the anomalous situation of overproduction and accumulating surpluses, with the result that economic losses accrue from waste and the spoilage of undistributed commodities.

If we are to take maximum advantage of our land resources, we will have to work toward the optimum utilization of agricultural lands throughout the world. This means more efficient production everywhere, modifications of landholding patterns where these limit the rational utilization of extensive acreages, and improvement in living conditions where these now deter the progress of agriculture. Implicit in this situation is the need for commensurate improvements in the exchange of agricultural commodities on a sound economic basis so that all the nations concerned will prosper in accord with their efforts.

Water—Man has conquered many of his natural enemies but he has never conquered drought in those areas in which crops are dependent upon the quantity and distribution of rainfall. We cannot continue to afford tremendous crop losses each year as a result of droughts that occur in some areas of the world. We will have to approach this problem through the development of drought-tolerant crop plants, the more efficient utilization of rain and irrigation water, and the use of desalted sea water for irrigation when this becomes economically available. It will be necessary also to gain a deeper understanding of the phenomenon of rainfall in order to affect distribution patterns not so much for the purpose of supplying additional water directly to crops as for maintaining supplies of ground and impounded water for critical applications to growing crops.

There are vast areas of the world where drought is a permanent condition. These are the arid lands and they constitute a most tantalizing agricultural resource. Some have been or are being gradually invaded by irrigation systems and have become among our most productive areas. Others are used to a limited extent for the production of certain drought-tolerant crops and still others remain deserts. The great expanse of arid land found in many countries represents an agricultural potential which one day must be utilized to a much greater degree. This will require heavy investments of funds and human ingenuity and will involve a combination of water impoundment, the use of treated sea water, the artificial variation of rainfall patterns, and advances in plant ecology and genetics.

Mineral Resources and Energy—Each year we expand the rate at which we are using our mineral resources and petrochemicals. Hopefully, we will continue to find new mineral resources, and surely we will have the ingenuity to develop substitute materials as the supply of critical minerals becomes short.

CONCLUSIONS

There would seem to be general agreement that the number of individuals who will people the earth one or two centuries hence will be five or ten times greater than the number today. The actual figure will of course depend upon the decisions taken by society with reference to social catastrophes such as total war, and the adoption of policies toward the stabilization of its numbers. In any event, the increase will be great, with inevitable growth in the demand for food, goods, and services and the other elements which go toward the maintenance of adequate standards of living. The several branches of science and economics will have to share the brunt of providing and distributing the materials demanded by society, and among them agriculture is paramount because of the role of food

119

production in permitting society to continue to exist on the globe. Conventional agriculture must respond to population pressures and evolve with great rapidity toward levels of efficiency and productivity not heretofore visualized. These developments can occur only if education becomes the rule everywhere and higher education and research are the subject of increased concern and support. Agriculture has a significant role in the development of future leadership toward a world with a relatively stable population and with standards of living compatible with human dignity.

New Scientific Developments
in the Area of Food

The subject of food production is one of vital concern to all of us. On a world-wide basis society has been spectacularly unsuccessful in providing an adequate dietary for everyone. Today less than one-half of the world's population receives each day an adequate number of calories for normal health and activity. When we look ahead this problem becomes alarming since, at the current rates of growth, the present world population of 2.6 billion will essentially double during the next 50 years and double again in each succeeding half century. Without dwelling on the other social implications, the astronomic increases in food which will be required to feed future generations will continue to present an immense challenge to scientists, economists, technologists, and producers.

In our own country we tend to be lulled into a false sense of security by the surpluses which we have accumulated and the perplexing problems which they present. However, in most of the rest of the world this situation of abundance does not occur. Rather, the reverse is true, which emphasizes the tremendous inequalities which exist between demand and supply of agricultural commodities. Regardless of future decisions made by society with reference to the stabilization of populations, there will be an explosively increasing demand for food throughout most of the world during the foreseeable future. To satisfy this demand to any reasonable degree will require advances in fundamental research and technology far beyond those presently available or perhaps even contemplated. We shall have to reach new levels of technical competence and to improve economic

An address made at a forum sponsored by the Joint Council on Economic Education and held at Sarah Lawrence College, August, 1958

and social planning to permit more people everywhere to apply current knowledge to the problems of food production. Only in this way can we hope to provide the enormous increases in food production and the other goods and services necessary to a progressive society.

In examining this matter of new scientific developments in the area of food it would seem logical to discuss first those which affect conventional practices of agriculture as we know them and, secondly, those which admittedly are, at the moment, speculative but which must be given increasing consideration if we are to meet the problems of the future.

CONVENTIONAL AGRICULTURE

In conventional agriculture the components are land, water, minerals, domesticated plants and animals, power, machinery, and people. When properly coordinated, these elements together comprise the art of agriculture. Its objective is to combine well-managed soils, productive varieties of domestic plants and livestock, appropriate quantities of water and nutrient elements, and fungicides, insecticides, and herbicides in such ways as to obtain maximum yields of wanted commodities most economically. These are then harvested and marketed or processed and packaged prior to eventual shipment to national or foreign markets through which they reach the consumer.

During the past 50 years, tremendous strides have been made in improving conventional agriculture, with the result that yields and quality of essentially all food crops and animals have improved markedly. In some instances average yields of basic food crops have been doubled or even trebled. Ingenious combinations of men, machinery, land, and materials have increased the output of individual producers until today the average American farmer is able to provide agricultural products for himself and approximately 20 other individuals. This development has had an important impact upon the structure of our society and has permitted a level of industrial production never before attained. It has freed other citizens for non-agricultural and industrial pursuits, with the resultant strengthening of our educational system, professions, social sciences, and the humanities.

The principal developments which have made possible the extraordinary production figures which reflect the United States' agricultural effort may be listed as follows:

Machinery—Modern agriculture is very much unlike that of only a generation ago. Today multi-purpose machines accomplish in a single operation land preparation that used to require many hours or days of toil with simple horse-drawn or tractor-drawn implements. Other highly efficient machines plant, fertilize, cultivate, irrigate, and apply protective dusts and sprays. Still others are designed for the special requirements of harvesting a wide variety of crop plants. The harvest is then processed by a series of mechanical devices to obtain the desired end product. In a parallel fashion, machinery has simplified the process of animal production in the form of equipment to handle forage and feed crops and to mix and mill feed for poultry and livestock. Others come into play in milking parlors, slaughter houses, pasteurizing plants, poultry units, and wherever meat, milk, and eggs are in production.

Present trends toward automation on the farm suggest that in the future the number of farms in the United States is going to become smaller and the number of individual units larger. As new machines are invented and as modern electronics enters the field, much of the present agricultural labor force can be replaced by a series of automatic devices. It can be expected that with rapid advances in technology our arable lands will become more productive than ever before and that our farm operators will be able to feed increasingly large numbers of individuals.

Water—Water is the single most important limiting factor in agricultural production throughout the world. Vast areas of potentially agricultural land must be designated as arid or semi-arid, owing to the unavailability of sufficient water for agricultural development. Other areas in which agriculture is now practiced are subject to intermittent drought, with the result that production is uncertain and often uneconomic. Even in our own country water is a limiting factor to agricultural production. This is true not only in the more arid parts of the United States but also in many of those areas that have in the past been considered as adequate for agricultural production.

The unstable distribution pattern of rainfall from year to year keeps agriculture forever at the mercy of the elements, and each year drought adversely affects agricultural productions somewhere. It has become clear that as a component of agricultural practice it is as necessary to have adequate quantities of water available at appropriate times as it is to have fertilizers, crop protectants, and machinery. Great increases of production could be expected if the benefits of irrigation or partial irrigation could be extended into many of those areas now completely dependent upon natural rainfall. The highest yields of crop plants have been recorded where irrigation has been regularly practiced, and if we are to be able to satisfy growing population pressures for food, one requirement will be vastly increased supplies of water for irrigation purposes.

We can accomplish a good deal through better soil and water management, but sooner or later we are going to have to have additional supplies of water available at a reasonable cost. Progress is being made in the study of cloud physics, and we may one day be able to influence rainfall patterns in such ways as to protect and even improve our ground water supplies and to increase those in artificial impoundments. In another direction rapid advances have been made in the technology of desalting sea water, and one day this almost unlimited water resource may become economically available over extensive land areas.

Soils—In the past we have been comforted by the knowledge that there were vast areas of virgin soils which could be brought into a productive state in response to social need. These are fast disappearing, and in a relatively short period of time they will cease to exist. Soon we will have to learn to manage agricultural soils to permit sustained productivity indefinitely. We have already learned that under cropping patterns the soil functions primarily as a medium in which crop plants may be grown continuously when other circumstances permit. As a result, the science of soil management has become highly developed, and now involves proper seed bed preparation, rotation patterns, and the application of water and nutrient elements in ways and times shown to be most effective in supporting normal plant growth. The introduction of artificial methods for the maintenance of soil fertility has resulted in average yields that were previously considered impossible. Thus, under modern management our soils are many times more productive, but our success in this direction has created other problems which must be resolved.

Plant protection—The increased carrying capacity of our agri-

124

cultural soil means that we have made it possible to grow greater numbers of uniform, highly productive crop plants per unit area. This crowding of millions of individual plants, such as wheat, into a single acre has produced critical problems of "plant public health." As a consequence, it has become necessary to devise improved methods and materials for the protection of domestic plants from the destructive effects of virulent pathogens and devastating pests.

In a similar fashion the development of uniform, high quality, and productive livestock and poultry has required careful attention to their nutrition and health problems. It is axiomatic that the modern technique of handling very large numbers of domestic animals, such as poultry, in limited areas is a type of directed urbanization which will inevitably intensify disease problems.

Thus, many of the most important modern developments in agriculture have been in the control of the pests and diseases which attack crop plants and domestic animals. Synthetic organic compounds, antibiotics, and a series of biological products have played major roles in maintaining plant and animal health and thereby protecting the world's food supplies. Great as these successes have been, it is estimated that between 15 and 20 per cent of the total annual agricultural product is destroyed each year by pathogenic microorganisms and insect pests. These percentages must be reduced as a factor in increasing world food supplies for future generations of mankind.

Agricultural chemistry—Agricultural chemistry is playing an increasingly important role in food production. In addition to the conventional practices of fertilization and the chemical control of pests and diseases, we are learning many new applications of chemistry which are beneficial to agriculture.

A most interesting development has been the discovery of a series of compounds that affect plant and animal physiology and growth phenomena. Their use has permitted increasing and more precise control over the behavior of crop plants and domestic plants. Among plants we can now stimulate or inhibit flowering, fruit formation and abscission, induce root formation, and in some instances change their form and size. Similarly, we have been able to manipulate the forms and qualities of livestock and to a considerable degree tailor them to our own requirements. The combined effect of modern genetics and chemistry has been the development of plant and animal types with a high degree of efficiency in relative productivity.

The application of chemistry and chemical engineering (chemurgy) to the problems presented by agricultural by-products and wastes has been most effective in increasing our food supplies. Each year we are obtaining a greater percentage of economic product in relation to the total output of plant and animal materials. In the future these combined technologies can be expected to make other major contributions to improving the ratio between agricultural input and output.

NON-CONVENTIONAL AGRICULTURE

It is quite apparent that the future demands of society for food are going to force agricultural science and related disciplines to reach levels of efficiency never hitherto attained. Admittedly, we can, through the more general application of conventional technologies, greatly increase and perhaps even double present world production figures. However, even if we are successful to this extent, it is quite clear that we shall still fall behind the requirements of a growing population.

If we are to hope for any reasonable degree of success, we are going to have to enter into what might be called non-conventional methods of food production. This means we will have to be increasingly imaginative and ingenious and seek to use every possible method of increasing available quantities of agricultural commodities.

One requirement for the agriculture of the future will be increasing quantities of cheap energy. Fortunately, modern developments in nuclear physics promise vast expansion in power resources, and these should make possible the mechanization of farming and related industries to a degree not hitherto contemplated. Moreover, we still have the tantalizing problem of how to convert economically the enormous free solar energy resources to the daily needs of mankind. Although it would appear that our energy resources are almost limitless, our ingenuity will be heavily taxed to bring all of these into economic application.

We are conditioned to thinking of our food as being the product of conventional agricultural practice. In consequence, we rarely contemplate the fact that there are a number of billions of tons of plant materials which are produced each year by those plants not grown under cultivation. Although not necessarily highly specialized for the production of conventional foods, these living plants produce, in total, enormous quantities of protein and other substances which are not now utilized to the advantage of society. Here then is an abundant resource, much of which is available for the cost of collection, extraction, and preparation into usable form.

In the humid tropics where protein deficiencies are common, quantities of leaf protein are especially great and suggest an appealing opportunity for the improvement of local diets. Presumably, proteins thus obtained might, in the first instance, be utilized in the feeding of domestic animals, but it is expected that they could also be converted into forms acceptable as human food. The study of the possibility of the utilization of this food resource, which is many times greater than conventional food production of the world, is one which could readily have great significance to the problem of supplementing our regular food supplies.

We are all aware that the sea, which covers more than three-fifths of the globe, is a tremendous but relatively undeveloped food resource. Of the total plant and animal material produced by the sea, only a minute fraction is currently available to man. Presently, we are more or less confined to harvesting from the sea those foods which we can gather blindly or by chance, occasionally with the help of certain modern instruments.

Man has not yet really begun to pit his imagination and ingenuity against the problems posed by the sea as a vast area from which millions upon millions of tons of foodstuffs could be obtained. This situation will have to change as we are forced to seek proteins for our human diet on an ever-increasing scale. The sea is rich in both plant and animal species which are potential sources of bulk foods, minerals, and vitamins, and vastly increased quantities could be obtained with improved technology. Current research in oceanography and marine biology is contributing to our knowledge of the sea and its contents, and as these disciplines are joined by investigations of methods for increasing productivity and exercising greater control over the behavior of marine species, the annual harvest may be multiplied many fold.

Synthetic foods have long been discussed as a future possibility. These certainly cannot be ruled out as the science of chemistry continues to progress and to permit molecular transformations which have hitherto been impossible. Although opinions vary, there seems little likelihood that substantial quantities of bulk foods can be produced synthetically in the foreseeable future. However, we can expect that critical nutrient substances which are necessary in small amounts in the human diet, will be synthesized in larger quantities at lower cost with resultant benefits to nutrition and public health.

The progress of modern conventional agriculture reflects the degree to which man has been able to control biologic species. In the earliest stages of man's evolution, he was dependent completely upon the bounty of the wild plants and animals which he was able to collect through his own ingenuity or agility. Today the situation is reversed so that modern crop plants are dependent for their continued existence upon the skill with which man manages and protects them. This has reached a high state of perfection, but we have still been unable to break through the barriers which limit us to the conventional practices of agriculture.

Today we utilize the techniques of hybridization and induce mutation and genetic recombination to improve crop plants and domestic animals in terms of their productivity. Tomorrow we may be able to design the types of plants and animals we would like to have and ultimately synthesize protoplasmic units. We should also be able to create plants with very much increased photosynthetic efficiency and ultimately to carry on this same process *in vitro*. This breakthrough will be one method of enabling us to take advantage of free solar energy and the production of almost unlimited tonnages of basic food materials.

Another approach is through the development of immunity in plants and animals to devastating pests and pathogens with resultant reduction in annual losses. If we learn the secrets of nitrogen fixation, we shall have another technique for significantly increasing agricultural production at reduced cost. These are, of course, only a few of the ways in which we must seek to extract from the earth those elements which are essential to the perpetuation of mankind.

CONCLUSION

It is the judgment of many that scientific innovations of the future will be of a greater order of magnitude than those of the present and recent past. They will, of course, depend upon continuing increases in the support of science by society and the utilization of the results of research through modern technology.

However, it is an oversimplification to believe that the problem of society today and tomorrow is primarily one of nutrition. Certainly food is basic to life, but unless all of the other elements which go to make up social organization and human welfare are in phase, there is little profit in progress in a single direction.

Scientists believe that they can meet the future challenge in their fields of endeavor and that the other sectors of society can do likewise. If so, we can hope to look forward to a future in which stable, well-fed populations are peacefully and gainfully employed in making the world a better place in which to live from every point of view.

Principles and Problems of Increasing Food Crops in Low-Production Areas

Although society continually faces grave problems, those related to human nutrition are among the most pressing. These often lead to a variety of social disturbances which, in turn, are detrimental to human progress. It is frequently difficult to realize the extent to which dietary deficiencies exist in essentially all the "underdeveloped" areas of the world. The contrast is so great between them and the Western nations that one must see the situation at first-hand to become truly aware of its implications.

Essentially, all interested groups agree that progress toward peace and the well-being of mankind is, in general, dependent upon the availability of sufficient quantities of appropriate foodstuffs to provide an adequate diet for the world's population. As a consequence, many efforts have been made to introduce into the diets of rural and urban populations in food-deficient areas increased quantities of critical foodstuffs. Usually the first effort is directed toward the diets of infants and young children with the introduction of milk and meat or their products, plant proteins, and vitamins, in order to supplement or enrich diets which are excessively high in carbohydrates. In combination, these efforts have been useful and effective, and their continuance and intensification should result in still greater benefits to the peoples concerned.

It is generally recognized that it would be uneconomic to attempt to resolve the dietary problems of the world solely through the con-

From a speech delivered at the Conference on Nutrition,
Arden House, Harriman, New York, December 15, 1958

tribution of protein and other foods from the surplus-producing countries of the world. The only permanent solution is the development of ways and means by which the people concerned can be helped to increase and diversify their own agricultural products, and when necessary, modify local food habits toward a more balanced diet. This is neither a simple nor a quick process, but it is fundamental to the human and economic development of the nations concerned.

In response to an official invitation The Rockefeller Foundation in 1941 agreed to collaborate with the Government of Mexico in an effort to increase the quantity and quality of the basic food crops available to the Mexican people. This program got under way early in 1943 and has continued until the present time. It was a new venture for The Rockefeller Foundation, and the field staff in agriculture, which has been created in response, has had to learn a great deal in order to be able to function effectively. The first requirements were to learn the local language and to become completely familiar with agricultural and economic situations. A study then had to be made of government and private organizations dealing with agriculture and the capacity and potential of agricultural institutions and available manpower resources. There then had to be agreement as to the most important areas of investigation, priorities with respect to crops to be improved, initiation of projects, and arrangements for program support on a cooperative basis.

During the past 14 years the program in Mexico has produced a number of definitive results. Among these has been the increase in average yields of corn and wheat to the point at which the country is self-sustaining with respect to these two basic foods. This development has made it possible to expand into projects on the improvement of potatoes, vegetables, forage crops, poultry, and livestock. At the same time, opportunities have been afforded for the training of increased numbers of young nationals in the several specialized fields within the agricultural sciences. These young men, who are now occupying important government and institutional positions, are fully aware of local dietary problems and are deliberately and effectively moving toward their solution.

As a result of the demonstration in Mexico, other countries have requested similar cooperative programs, and three additional operating centers have been established in Colombia, Chile, and India,

131

respectively. These have been used for the training of young scientists from still other countries who, upon their return to their own institutions, have been encouraged and supported in efforts to initiate programs for the improvement of the quantity and quality of local food crops.

As a result of the experience in Mexico and subsequently in a number of other countries, it has been learned that at least a considerable number of the underdeveloped countries could, within a reasonable period of time, begin to satisfy their basic food requirements if given an opportunity to do so. This opportunity involves not only financial assistance such as loans or improvement of transportation systems, power plants, communications, water impoundments, *etc.*, but, equally important, the development of sound agricultural programs which can be expected to play a major role in making these and other developments economically feasible. Perhaps too often there has been a tendency to attempt "crash programs" or "breakthroughs" which in some mysterious way might with great rapidity convert the economy of an underdeveloped nation to the level of the highly developed countries of the West. Efforts of this sort almost inevitably fail. The altruistic motives which lead to attempts toward extremely rapid progress are understandable, but the rational examination of local situations inevitably reveals the need for the application of substantial doses of time in order that change will come about through understanding and local enterprise rather than as a result of heavy applications of cash and kind from external sources.

Often it is necessary to proceed indirectly toward an established goal. For example, those countries which are identified as cereal-eating, *e.g.,* corn, rice, and wheat, often find themselves in situations in which there is an inadequate supply of these food grains to satisfy the normal demand. Under such circumstances attempts to rapidly diversify local diets and perhaps introduce exotic foods are viewed with doubt and distrust. If, however, the local problem is recognized and understood, and sound effort is made to resolve it, the response is unhesitating, and the confidence thus engendered can be utilized effectively in the development of projects and programs which, although not dramatically different from accepted practice, are oriented toward improvements in production systems and food habits.

The traditional belief that dietary patterns of many rural peoples cannot be changed because of cultural convictions has been shown on numerous occasions to be a false premise. Farmers in general tend to cling to those materials and habits which have proved most successful in the past, and do not drop them lightly at the suggestion of people whom they neither know nor understand. They depend on the results which they have obtained over a period of years through local systems of farming, and are unwilling to risk crop failure and even famine by abandoning tradition in favor of methods and materials which to them are untried. On the other hand, once they have been shown that there are simpler and better ways to accomplish their own purposes, they are eager imitators, and the community leaders quickly become ripe for innovations. Their neighbors readily follow these leaders, and with skill a chain reaction can be initiated which will gradually extend throughout individual communities and ultimately the country concerned.

As is true everywhere, the older people are the least amenable to rapid change. They will modify their habits and practices only if they have ample opportunity to recognize and understand the benefits of so doing. On the other hand, the younger members of the community are instinctively curious and willing to take chances and to learn, and as they do, they become the greatest single force for progress within the community. In many instances their influence on their elders is the most important leverage which can be employed.

Once confidence has been won and useful results demonstrated, the rapidity with which technical cooperation programs are accepted and extended is frequently startling. At this stage the program is in danger unless long-range plans have been laid to assure that there will be supply in answer to the rapidly growing demand for information, seed stocks, fertilizers, and the other materials essential to production. As these requirements are satisfied, opportunities become available for introduction of further improved methods and materials, the use of more efficient mechanical devices where these are economically feasible, and a gradual diversification of family patterns. One of the most important benefits is the at least partial emancipation of women and children from heavy work in the field, with resultant improvements in family life and educational opportunities.

The entire process of entry into and establishment in a foreign country requires tact and patience, and from the outset, the association of the foreign specialist with local individuals who will one day undertake total responsibility. Training can best begin at whatever level is encountered locally, whether this be elementary, vocational, or relatively advanced. In each instance there must be "learning through doing" and a gradual increase in self-confidence on the part of the individual trainees. As more and more persons become qualified for specialized responsibilities, there will be among them individuals who can be trained to the succeedingly higher levels, until ultimately each of the various educational stages is being properly developed with increasing output of qualified individuals for local tasks. Then leaders can be selected in order to give imagination and stability to the program and to stimulate and train younger groups who will one day have to accept important responsibilities.

Programs such as those described here can be in themselves of significance in the improvement of the level of nutrition of the populations concerned. Ideally, however, they should be built into the local structure and economy and be coordinated with related efforts directed toward economic and social improvement. This results in synergistic effects and more rapid progress toward the goal of an adequate diet for an increasing proportion of the world's population.

An International Approach to the Study and Control of Plant Disease

The basic function of science is to serve society, with the ideal that each generation may progress in terms of standards of living and opportunities for intellectual development. The reasoning powers which set man apart from all other forms of life have enabled him to modify his environment more nearly to suit his own convenience and have resulted in improvements in health, comforts, and opportunities which have made possible the accommodation of increasing numbers of individuals in society. Now the effects of lowered infant mortality and greater longevity are making themselves felt in both an encouraging and an alarming fashion. Gains in health lead to rapid gains in population, and many would find the single most important problem facing society is what to do about people. There are at least 100,000 more of them every day to be fed, clothed, housed, educated, and eventually productively employed. As recently as 50 years ago no one predicted that within a half-century the population of the world would double, but, by extrapolation, we can predict now that by the year 2050 there will be at least seven billion people in the world. These figures alone are frightening, but the implications are even more so.

In the years ahead science and technology will have to reach unprecedented heights of efficiency if we are to preserve any semblance of reasonable standards of living during the next century, let alone elevate those in areas where they are still much too low. The role of plant pathology in this effort is an important one if future generations are to be adequately supplied with food and other agricultural commodities necessary to an enlarging population. It can be prop-

From *Plant Pathology, Problems and Progress, 1908-1958*, University of Wisconsin Press, Madison, Wisconsin, 1959

erly discussed only in this broad context and in relation to the other disciplines of science and sociology. However, all of society will have to face the demographic problem which it has created and decide between positive action toward the stabilization of populations and falling standards of living.

CURRENT STATUS AND PROBLEMS OF PROTECTION

In the more advanced agricultural areas of the world the response of the agricultural sciences to the demands of an explosively increasing world population has been dramatically successful. An intimate alliance of the fields of biology, chemistry, physics, engineering, and economics has resulted in doubled, trebled, and even quadrupled average yields of major crop plants with commensurate improvements in quality. In modern agricultural practice, crops are seeded to vast acreages with the aid of machinery, are watered, fertilized, and protected artificially, harvested mechanically, and rapidly transformed into wanted products which are then transported speedily through national and international trade channels to appropriate market centers. In fact, information and methods are now available which theoretically at least would make it possible for the world to double its current food production if social and economic factors would permit.

Unfortunately, however, there are many areas in the world that are relatively unaffected by modern technology, with the result that in these areas agricultural practices are still primitive, yields are low, a high fraction of the labor force is required for food production, and economic and social progress is retarded.

Each of these two extremes presents a different and perplexing series of obstacles to significant future increases in production.

The most progressive agricultural countries have been extraordinarily successful in terms of production levels. In fact, in certain of these a situation of gross overproduction exists, in the sense that current surpluses of agricultural commodities cannot be economically absorbed by foreign markets; the surpluses continue to accumulate. In these more highly developed areas the destruction of natural ecologic patterns resulting from the intensification of agricultural practices has created a whole series of new problems. These derive from continuing efforts to increase the carrying capacity of arable soils which, although sensationally successful, have enor-

136

mously complicated the problems of soil management and plant protection. For example, because the extensive mechanized type of production is conducive to the industrialization of agriculture, there is a tendency to specialize on growing such crops as corn, wheat, and rice, with resultant extension and concentration of populations of the same kinds of plants. The crowding of more and more individual crop plants into unit areas creates difficulties which, to some degree, parallel those of intensified urbanization, with all of the benefits and ills that accompany this process. In fact, modern stands of crop plants constitute the greatest mass media that plant pathogens have ever encountered. This situation poses a perpetual threat of devastating epidemics that may extend from one country to another.

At the other extreme are the vast sectors of the world in which agricultural practices are in sharp contrast to those of the most advanced nations. In these, limited natural resources, climatic extremes, and inadequate educational opportunities have too often combined to prevent the general application of the benefits of modern technology. One of the consequences is that these regions suffer regularly from epidemics and thus are a continuing threat to economic crop production in other countries as well.

These contrasting situations emphasize the growing international responsibilities of plant pathologists with respect to the study and control of plant disease. Each year it becomes more obvious that we must be increasingly aware of the distribution of virulent pathogens and of the occurrence of epidemics wherever they may be, and must join forces with our colleagues in other countries in organized efforts to meet these threats to food production. An essential preliminary is the extension of the benefits of modern agricultural practice generally, with attendant improvements in production and protection. This would provide the basis for international projects in the study and control of plant diseases, with the object of ascertaining the occurrence and potentialities of pathogenic microorganisms; the development of techniques for their containment and control, with resultant reduction in the number and severity of epidemics and attendant economic losses.

THE PATHOGENS

During the century following the establishment of the phenomenon of parasitism as a scientific fact, we have gradually become

137

aware of the myriad forms of life which to some degree are able to parasitize other species. Although we define the term "disease" broadly to include the ills induced by a wide range of climatic variables as well as those caused by pathogenic organisms, it is the fungi, the bacteria, the nematodes, and the viruses which in never-ending sequence challenge man's intellect and ingenuity in the production of those agricultural commodities which are essential to his continuing existence. Thus, the science of plant pathology is based upon the most intimate organic relationship possible between unrelated species or organisms, namely parasitism. The delicate biologic balance which exists between host and parasite during the process of disease is still only dimly understood, but it is this phenomenon about which we must gain an ever-deepening understanding if we are to be successful in meeting the future and increasing demand for agricultural products.

The origin of parasitism is still a theoretical rather than a finite subject, but there is evidence that, functionally, parasitism is a measure of biochemical compatibility between unlike organisms. Plant pathogens demonstrate a broad spectrum of compatibility reflecting their phylogeny and their heterogeneity. There are those with factors for compatibility which render them essentially omnivorous in their ability to attack a wide variety of plant species; others are limited to a few host species, and still others are compatible with only a single host and are unable to grow and multiply if dissociated from it. Within morphologic species many pathogenic organisms display a bewildering array of races which may vary only in factors for virulence. Studies of these groups point up their extreme genetic variability, their propensities for hybridization, and frequently their extreme mutability.

Regardless of the degree to which plants may be modified by genetic recombinations within species, there seems little likelihood that this will result in anything approaching permanent immunity from their parasites. Modern techniques in conventional chemical and irradiation genetics and plant nutrition all may contribute markedly to increasing the resistance of crop plants to their pathogens at least temporarily, and even though temporary, the resistance phenomenon must be utilized to the utmost in the absence of something better. However, microorganisms are at least as variable and mutable as are their hosts, and the frequency with which hybrids and mutants occur among them is enhanced by their presence in vast numbers. Their often-demonstrated success in adjusting and in adapting themselves to genetic variation among cultivated crop plants affords no reason to expect lesser success in the future. Thus, at least as long as the practice of conventional agriculture continues, we may expect that plant pathogens will take their tolls from society. Biologic entities that have had, and continue to have, such a profound effect on the lives of men merit the most careful and respectful attention from members of society, their ultimate victims.

An examination of modern problems and probable future ones involved in the international study and control of plant diseases suggests that there are three lines of attack which must be continued, intensified, and expanded if we are to expect ultimate success. Specifically, these may be described as follows: (1) the prompt and continuing accumulation and dissemination of information concerning the distribution, activities, and potentialities of plant pathogenic organisms wherever they exist; (2) the application of modern protective and control measures as generally as possible; and (3) greatly intensified research on the fundamental nature of the phenomenon of parasitism through a coordinated approach from the viewpoints of the biological, chemical, and physical sciences.

DISTRIBUTION OF PATHOGENS

The march of microorganisms is relentless, and modern plant pathology must take this fact into consideration in planning its strategy and tactics. It is futile to hope that the prevention of plant diseases through the containment of pathogenic microorganisms within a prescribed area can ever be a practical approach to plant protection. The dubious belief that natural barriers to the movement of microorganisms could long prevent their general distribution was dissipated once and for all with the advent of high-speed surface and air transportation. Although regulatory legal measures have been taken in an attempt to close trade and transportation channels to pathogens, these and all related efforts, at best, can only buy time. Although time thus gained is precious, any illusion that world-wide distribution of many virulent pathogens is not ultimately inevitable is quickly destroyed by a knowledge of the rapidity with which plant pathogens multiply and the astronomical numbers of minute reproductive elements which may be produced in a matter of days or even hours. Many known and perhaps even more unknown virulent pathogens lurk wherever plant species occur. Their size and numbers essentially assure that they will be disseminated continually and invisibly over wide geographic areas by surface air currents, by water, and the movement of insects, animals, and men. They are fellow travelers through all national and international trade channels and public transportation systems, and a goodly number ride the jet streams.

We have already had many costly experiences which illustrate the varying degrees of damage that may result from the uncontrolled migrations of exotic pests and pathogens. Three of the most classic are the introduction of chestnut blight fungus (*Endothia parasitica*) into the United States, with the ultimate destruction of native American chestnut forests; the introduction of the Dutch Elm disease (*Ceratostomella ulmi*) into this country, which fortunately has never reached the severity attained by chestnut blight; and the introduction of blister rust of pines (*Cronartium ribicola*) into the United States, which after many years is still a serious problem. In these cases the pathogens were known elsewhere before the introductions occurred, but we had inadequate legal machinery and insufficient knowledge to prevent the introductions and to realize the threat which each of the pathogens posed to important native tree species, and only learned this lesson after the damage had been done.

Scientists are aware of several other pathogens which, though still restricted geographically, are very destructive and would presumably wreak havoc if introduced into new regions where susceptible varieties are extensively planted. Coffee, which is grown principally in the tropical equatorial belt, is susceptible to the rust disease (*Hemileia vastatrix*) that is widespread throughout essentially all the important coffee-growing countries exclusive of the Western Hemisphere. In contrast, the so-called American leaf spot of coffee (*Omphalia flavida*) has thus far been limited to the New World. If and when one or both of these pathogens should invade coffee countries in which they do not now occur, terrific economic losses could be expected and possibly at least temporary destruction of local coffee industries. Cacao production is in a similar situation. Cacao plantations in the Americas are often seriously damaged by "witches' broom" (*Marasmius perniciosus*), whereas many in Af-

140

rica have been devastated by the virus causing "swollen shoot." Here again, the potential dangers of the introduction of either of these pathogens into a presently free area are obvious.

There are a number of diseases which have long been known and have on occasion caused great losses. However, as yet we have not been able to develop precise methods for their containment or elimination. A classic example is the citrus canker (*Pseudomonas citri*), which is, so to speak, an "old" disease. We are all aware of the history of this trouble following its introduction into Florida and the Gulf States of the United States. Now, many years later, it has reappeared, this time in Brazil, where it is currently becoming widespread and presenting troublesome economic and other problems. Similarly, *Puccinia polysora,* which causes maize rust and has long been known has during recent years invaded Africa and moved from the west coast across the central part of the continent. Although factors for resistance have been known for some time, local varieties proved quite susceptible, with the result that heavy crop losses have occurred. A somewhat more localized case is that of the blister blight of tea (*Exobasidium vexans*), long established in India and recently introduced into Indonesia, Malaya, and Ceylon with serious adverse effects. Finally, the tristeza virus of citrus is an example of a well-known disease of the Old World that was quite destructive when introduced into the New World.

Added to the list of those pathogens, which we do understand to some degree, are many others which are little understood and are potentially serious menaces to agricultural production. A considerable number of these appear to be caused by viruses, an example of which is the *hoja blanca* disease of rice, now well established in Cuba, and recently reported as destructive in Venezuela, Colombia, Panama, and Florida as well. At first it was thought to be entirely new, but there is now some evidence that *hoja blanca* has been a minor disease in Cuba and Colombia for a number of years. Apparently it was never a serious threat to the industry, and little or no effort was made to study its etiology and potential destructiveness. Subsequently, there has been a gradual shift in varieties to those more susceptible to *hoja blanca* in the current outbreaks.

A virus infection of barley, wheat, and oats has recently been reported from Colombia. Unknown until crop improvement programs resulted in the production of new varieties, this virus has demon-

141

strated a high degree of virulence on susceptible hosts. Although still quite localized in the Department of Nariño, here again is a pathogen which presumably could cause serious damage to susceptible varieties of small grains if it were to become established in areas where they are extensively grown.

The stunt disease of corn first described from southern Texas, Mexico, and Guatemala has made its appearance in other countries of Central America, and may possibly be established elsewhere as well. Although it is evidently dangerous, little is known regarding its distribution and potential threat to production in important maize growing regions. In the same category of virus troubles are the *cadang-cadang* disease of coconuts, which has been destructive in the Philippine Islands; the apparently new virus condition of sugar cane reported as witches' broom from Okinawa; sugar cane stunt and the *Moko* disease of bananas. These pathological curiosities of today may well be the calamities of tomorrow.

Fungi, bacteria, and nematodes are similarly continuing to threaten production through the appearance of diseases which are still localized and not generally known or understood. An apparently new and virulent bacterial pathogen of maize has been reported quite recently from India; a hitherto unreported root rot of rice has been the subject of study in Japan, as have nematode troubles associated with the decline of paddy rice in the northern range of rice production in that country. It also appears that nematodes may have a more important role in limiting the production of such crops as bananas, sugar cane, and pineapples when grown during extended periods of years in a single location. These and other reports are appearing with great regularity, but owing to delays in communication and prompt action many pass relatively unnoticed as being localized phenomena. Here again, it is essentially certain that some of what now appear to be minor troubles will one day rise up to plague crop producers unless ways are found to evaluate their destructive potentials and design control measures before the pathogens become widely distributed and reach epidemic proportions.

If it is generally agreed that the geographic diffusion of plant pathogens is inescapable, then current knowledge of the pathogenic stocks of the various regions of the world and of their migrations becomes of utmost importance. Without this knowledge we may expect continuing surprises as the microorganisms mutate, multiply, and migrate with disastrous results. However, the prompt accumulation and dissemination of essential information depend primarily upon the plant pathologists themselves, since they have the moral and scientific responsibilities for standing between society and epidemic outbreaks of plant disease.

In the first instance, it is the obligation of plant pathologists everywhere to recognize that they have roles in both the national and international scene with respect to plant disease control. Their individual and concerted efforts through their institutions and professional organizations should form the foundations of any sound international plant protection program. Unfortunately, the record thus far has not been an outstanding one. This is due not to a single factor, but rather to a combination of heavy local responsibilities, limited travel budgets, and in some instances at least, the conviction that foreign problems belong to foreigners and to government quarantine agencies. It is to be regretted that greater progress has not been made in convincing institutional, state, and federal authorities of the importance of special support for international projects dealing with the study and control of virulent plant pathogens. For this situation plant pathologists and their professional organizations must share the responsibility.

INTERNATIONAL ORGANIZATIONS AND PROGRAMS

Currently we are in a better position than ever before in history to apply generally the benefits of the modern plant disease control methods. This is due in part to the vast amount of information available and in part to the comparative ease of communication and transportation today in contrast to a generation ago. Moreover, we now have a further, and most significant, resource in those individuals who are field staff members of a considerable group of international organizations. Although in the past, government and private institutions on occasion have supported the travel and exchange of individual scientists, now a significant group of scientists representing various disciplines are living and working in countries abroad. Many of the projects concerned deal with some aspect of plant protection, and consequently, the modern methods of disease control are becoming more widespread with obvious benefits.

There are over 200 organizations which, to some degree at least, are concerned with the international aspects of plant protection. In most instances these organizations are concerned with broad international agricultural problems, including those of the study and control of plant diseases. Among the truly international organizations there is one which occupies a unique position with respect to its influence in the field of the international study and control of plant disease. This is the Food and Agriculture Organization of the United Nations, which has ready entree into most of the countries of the world, a staff of bilingual and multilingual scientists, and facilities for travel, and handles the collation, publication, and distribution of pertinent data and information. Although the contributions of FAO to international plant protection have been significant, these could be greatly increased and strengthened through a well-organized and coordinated program dealing with the study and control of plant diseases on an international scale. This would necessarily involve the close cooperation of plant pathologists in many countries and the establishment of projects at local and national levels to enable individual plant pathologists to participate. Specifically, the program should be based upon a continuing international survey of the occurrence of known and new plant pathogens throughout the world, the occurrence of important epidemics in any part of the world, and the results of research leading to effective control measures or the production of resistant varieties. With the continued accumulation of this information it would be possible to plan and coordinate international projects for effective control of many of our most destructive diseases.

It is, of course, recognized that there are numerous important efforts already in progress which would supplement and enhance international projects in plant disease control. Specific examples are the publication of the *Plant Disease Reporter* by the U.S. Department of Agriculture, the *Review of Applied Mycology* by the Commonwealth Bureaux, the international plant protection meetings, and the activities of professional organizations of plant pathologists. However, there is still urgent need for a dynamic central organization which will receive regular reports on a world-wide basis, integrate and interpret them, and make the information generally available using all modern communication media. Only in this way can we hope to keep an up-to-date record of the occurrence, movements, and depredations of pathogenic microorganisms, knowledge and materials essential to their control, and international projects directed to this end for the benefit of all of society.

A striking example of a new national approach to international cooperation in agriculture is that of the International Cooperation Administration of the United States through its own staff and through contracts with a number of American universities. The ICA has stationed pathologists in many foreign countries, and their contributions to local problems have been numerous and useful. American and other plant pathologists can now be found in various sectors of the world working on diseases of rice, sugar cane, coconuts, coffee, cacao, maize, sorghum, and forage crops, to mention only a few. Information which has emanated from these projects and the experiences and friendships gained by these individuals will continue to have multiple benefits. Not the least among these is the fact that upon return to their permanent posts these international plant pathologists will be able to share the results of their foreign experiences with their colleagues and students.

There are in the Western Hemisphere certain international plant protection programs which, although only semiformal, have been extremely effective. One which might serve to illustrate this approach is the International Stem Rust Control Project, which involves informal cooperation among a rather considerable number of agencies. In the first instance, the appropriate government officials of Canada, the United States, Mexico, Colombia, Brazil, Argentina, Chile, Peru, and Ecuador have undertaken voluntarily to carry on the extensive program of testing wheat varieties each year and to make the results of these tests generally available. The World Wheat Collections are included, as are lines or varieties developed within individual breeding programs in the hemisphere and elsewhere. A number of U.S. and Latin American universities have cooperated, as have the Rust Prevention Association and the agricultural programs of The Rockefeller Foundation which maintains operating centers in Mexico, Colombia, and Chile. No general organization or budget is involved in the stem rust control program, but rather it is the sum of voluntary efforts on the part of the individuals and agencies concerned in the recognition of its national and international importance. In view of the regular exchange of rust spores between Canada and the United States, the United States and Mexico, and between the several wheat-breeding countries of Latin America, the economic

145

significance of this effort is manifest, and it has been fully justified by the gains which have already accrued.

Individual scientists from outside the Americas have visited one or more of these projects, and the basis of international exchange of improved rust-resistant materials has been broadened. In addition, they have served as training centers for significant numbers of young scientists who, in many instances, subsequently received fellowships for further training at a foreign center prior to undertaking greater responsibilities in their own countries. Still greater gains may be expected in the future as this program becomes organized in such a way as to take maximum advantage of the important contributions of all cooperating individuals and agencies. Finally, the International Wheat Rust Project has opened the door to many other opportunities for cooperation in the study and control of epidemic plant diseases, an example of which is a program, now in the course of development, directed toward the study and control of late blight and the virus diseases of potatoes in the Americas.

There are numerous other international programs under way that are directed toward the study and control of certain important international diseases. These may involve two or more countries with mutual interests and problems. A few examples are the cooperation in wheat stem and stripe rust control between the United States and certain countries of Western Europe; the work on coffee, cacao, and rubber diseases at the Inter-American Institute of Agricultural Sciences in Turrialba, Costa Rica, in collaboration with the U.S. Department of Agriculture and several of the countries which are the most important producers of these crops; the informal cooperation on virus diseases of citrus, particularly tristeza and psorosis complex of citrus, involving the United States, Brazil, and Argentina; sugar cane smut investigations in which the same three countries are interested; and the study of the sugar beet yellows complex, of concern to Chile, the United States, and the beet-producing countries of Western Europe. Collateral efforts include a project to establish banks of germ plasm for sugar cane in Coimbatore, India; of coffee in Costa Rica; rice in India; maize in the United States, Mexico, Colombia, and Brazil; and bananas in Central America and Trinidad.

From these individual cases it is evident that there is a growing awareness of the importance of the international approach to the study and control of plant diseases. Each of these has had positive accomplishments and each has stimulated and facilitated other projects of international value. As more basic and comprehensive international efforts are undertaken to meet the challenge of plant pathogens everywhere they occur, and to attack them with the knowledge and resources of many areas, significant and more rapid progress in disease control can be expected. Hopefully, we can expect the emergence of strong international organizations which will serve the needs of pathologists everywhere, help to orient them with reference to problems and possibilities, and provide leadership for concerted action.

INTENSIFIED RESEARCH

As has been pointed out, we are today in possession of a vast store of knowledge and a considerable body of plant pathologists who could apply it generally and successfully in the control of plant disease if given the opportunity. This information has been accumulated over a considerable period of time as a result of research undertaken in many countries. Probably, if present knowledge could be applied wherever needed, we could very significantly decrease the incidence of epidemics, with resultant increases in annual tonnages of food and other agricultural products of the world. The striking advances already made have been possible because of the growing awareness that only through continued research can we hope at least to keep abreast of the march of microorganisms. Early empirical methods of plant disease control have gradually been replaced by precise scientific techniques with extraordinary improvements in methods, machinery, and materials. The most recent developments have come as a result of research with systemic protectants and antibiotics, and these, in conjunction with the present array of organic fungicides, offer the greatest opportunities for the control of plant pathogens which have ever existed.

In spite of all of the demonstrable progress that has been made, we are still in the position of carrying out a holding operation, and to date there has never been a major breakthrough by which we could hope to wipe out a virulent plant pathogen. Perhaps we can never expect accomplishments parallel to the control of smallpox, yellow fever, typhoid, and other ills of mankind which have already been essentially eliminated from huge sectors of the world's popu-

147

lation. Admittedly, our medical colleagues have had the advantage of enormous support from society seeking self-preservation, as well as the added benefit of being able to concentrate their energies on a single species. Plant pathologists, on the other hand, have usually had to dilute their efforts in response to the demands of the producers of a wide variety of crop species. Moreover, the financial support for plant pathology has been modest. Nevertheless, the gains already made suggest that we may be able to break through some of the long-standing barriers to the control or cure of major diseases. This hope must necessarily be based on the expectation of increasing support for fundamental research on the phenomenon of parasitism with all that this implies. The fields of plant physiology, biochemistry, biophysics, organic chemistry, genetics, cytology, microbiology, and related disciplines must all be brought into play in a coordinated fashion in order to give us a better understanding of the organic relationships between the host and pathogen, how these come about and develop, and what can be done to prevent or limit this undesirable and destructive symbiosis.

It is not at all suggested that fundamental research in the field of plant pathology is not now in progress. It is suggested, however, that a great deal more is needed and that the agricultural institutions of the world have the responsibility of participating fully in this effort. One of the most useful developments would be increasing emphasis on basic research on the part of agricultural institutions both for the purpose of acquiring additional knowledge of the specific areas of science and as an outstanding mechanism for the training of future scientists. It would appear that the field of plant pathology will in the future include not only practitioners of the art of plant disease control but also a growing body of investigators with extensive training in biology, chemistry, and physics who are familiar with modern instrumentation and the techniques of advanced research. Their efforts will result in methods and materials which can be applied through modern technologies to the more effective control of the devastating pests and pathogens which now destroy more than 100 million tons of food crops each year.

CONCLUSIONS

Regardless of advances in all branches of science, it can be expected that conventional agriculture will be practiced during the foreseeable future with such modifications as are brought about through improving technologies. Efforts will be toward still greater production per unit area and improvements in quality and disease resistance. These latter will be countered by the inevitable evolution of pathogenic microorganisms whose biologic plasticity and propensities for travel will enable them to continue to menace agriculture. It therefore behooves society in self-defense to provide increasing support to the study and control of plant diseases on an international basis so that in the first instance we will be aware of our enemies, and in the second be in position to take effective action against them on the basis of current knowledge. Finally, we should continue to delve into the mysteries of those microorganisms which attack crop species, in the expectation that we can maintain our present position and the hope that we can eventually break through some of the barriers to the goal of immunity.

Cooperation in the Training of Scientists and Engineers

From the point of view of physical development one needs only to visit educational centers throughout Latin America to become aware of the increasing emphasis that has been placed on the construction of modern centers of learning during the past decade. Building costs have been heavy and the investments in time, architectural imagination and creativity, and program planning have been substantial. The University City in Mexico has become an international attraction because of its beauty and boldness of concept. New university cities are under construction in Guatemala and at Quito, Ecuador. The University del Valle and the University de Los Andes in Colombia are making significant progress in plant development, and the College of Engineering and the new Veterinary Faculty at Lima, Peru, are models of their types of institution. Expansion is in progress at the National University, the Catholic University, and the University of Concepción in Chile, and a relatively new university is being developed in the south. Brazil is creating or expanding research and training centers at Pelotas, Pôrto Alegre, Sao Paulo, Rio de Janeiro, Belo Horizonte, and Recife. Other exciting educational experiments are in progress elsewhere. These are all visible testimony to the rapidly growing interest in Latin America in the advancement of education in general and of science and technology in particular. They represent heavy investments in funds and also in the faith that the future education of an increasing proportion of the population is the ideal approach to social and economic growth.

We are prone to think of Latin American universities in super-

From an address delivered at the Plenary Session of the Seventh National Conference of the U.S. National Commission for UNESCO on Science in the Americas, Denver, Colorado, September 29, 1959

ficial terms and to emphasize that they seem to be centers of political agitation in which students have too much influence and authority and that the professors are underpaid, insecure, and most frequently on a part-time basis. Also we tend to feel that institutions and class-rooms in Latin America are overcrowded, standards are low, and teaching and research facilities entirely inadequate.

There are, of course, elements of truth in these concepts. However, we need only to look at our own educational history to realize that evolution in this field is always painful and slow. We have gone through a long period of trial and error and have by no means yet attained a utopian condition. Educational systems and patterns are the products of history, tradition, and the slow evolution which comes with experience, and, unfortunately, although everyone concurs in the importance of universal educational opportunities to the level of individual capacities, too little attention has been given to the public responsibility which this objective demands. The result has been that our centers of learning, which in the last analysis are the cells from which the tissues and organs of society are built, have been inadequately supported from both the financial and social points of view. Both time and substantial economic growth are the essential ingredients in the process of converting education from a limited privilege to a universal practice. During this process the citizenry must provide continuing moral support and accept the principle that taxation is the basis of support to educational systems from the elementary to the postgraduate level.

Contrary to what sometimes appears to be popular belief, there is no single or universal educational pattern that can be adapted to all locations and circumstances. Ideally, educational institutions should be adequate, stable, progressive, and imaginative and should provide intellectual leadership on both the scientific and cultural fronts. Academic freedom is precious and should be protected, but should never be misused or abused. Thus, academic freedom implies intellectual discipline and the determination to represent the highest values in social organization.

Each country of the world is sovereign with respect to its educational pattern. It would be both unwise and undesirable to attempt to impose the system which prevails in one country on another. On the other hand, educators and scientists in all countries should be willing and eager to study patterns which exist elsewhere and to

151

profit from them wherever possible. The results could well be a blend of the best elements of several systems carefully adapted to the local culture and economy.

It should always be remembered that quality in science and engineering, and indeed in all education, is not measured by the level of instrumentation and luxuriousness of educational facilities. Rather, it must be measured by the competence, dedication, and inspiration of the individuals who have the responsibility for guiding the training of young people and in teaching them to think creatively.

Perhaps the greatest single force in the progress of education and research is the hybrid vigor which comes from the interchange of individuals, information, and ideas. In concert, these have a synergistic effect and catalyze intellectual progress on all fronts. Although by no means insignificant, there has been too little intellectual interchange within the Americas. Our friends in Latin America have done much more in terms of their resources than we have. They have done us the honor of learning our language and of sending many of their leading students to institutions in this country. These young men and women have become valued members of the university community, have taken advantage of the intellectual opportunities which the university offers, and have contributed materially to intercultural understanding on the campus and elsewhere. In return, we have tended to take the flow of Latin American students to this country for granted, although in our defense we have made every effort to welcome them and to assure that they have full opportunity to take advantage of the facilities of our educational institutions in the fields of the humanities, social sciences, biology, and technology. However, we have not reciprocated to a satisfactory degree in the promotion of the study of Spanish and Portuguese, in the development of strong centers of Latin American studies, and in the dispatch of substantial numbers of North American students for study at leading centers of science and technology in Latin America. Our record is improving. At the moment, for geographic and linguistic reasons, the largest number of United States students go to Mexico, but more are finding their way farther south. Increasing numbers of educational tours of Latin America are being organized each year by the United States colleges and universities. At the postgraduate and professional levels interchange between the United States and Latin America is undergoing a gratifying increase.

Food in National and International Welfare

Americans today are the best fed people in the world. Thanks to our rich natural resources and their efficient utilization by agriculture and industry, we enjoy an unlimited and continuous variety of appetizing and high-quality domestic and exotic foods. Thus, to many persons it is almost inconceivable that serious limitations on available food supplies are anywhere a major factor in human health and welfare. In the presence of abundance it is difficult to realize that more than one-half of the 2.8 billion inhabitants of the earth are undernourished. As Americans, we are indignant that this is the case and generous with our contributions for aid to our less fortunate neighbors.

Much has been spoken and written on the subject of world food supplies, and numerous action programs have been initiated to help ameliorate human want. While I fully share the concern that many feel at the shocking disparity in standards of living throughout the world, I am equally preoccupied by the necessity for emphasis on the total spectrum of the problems of the less advanced nations.

Although gifts of food and, more particularly, the establishment of sound programs directed toward increased local food supplies are of great value in a variety of ways, it is unrealistic to assume that these efforts alone are a solution to the problems of the food-deficient nations. Certainly, adequate food supplies and happiness are not equated in our society. We all recognize the absolute necessity for an adequate diet as basic to the enjoyment of a healthy, productive, and satisfying existence, but we do not think of food as the

Presented May 5, 1960, at the dedication ceremony of the new food research building at State College of Agriculture, Geneva, New York

goal of humanity. Our own sophistication should make us aware of the fact that the solution of the imbalance in food resources among nations is only one of the many vital considerations which underlie the goal of international peace and prosperity.

We are told that a hungry people is an unhappy people, prone to ill health and limited life expectancy during which they are susceptible to any ideology appearing to offer hope for the improvement of their lot. With this thesis I would agree, but would add that well-fed prisoners are rarely contented whether their fetters be chains of iron or those of hopelessness. When food is the critically limiting factor it is obvious that attention to this need is basic, but unless appropriate measures are taken to provide opportunities for self-improvement, the distribution of food surpluses merely puts a comma in a life sentence.

As a prelude to broader considerations, I should like to comment on agriculture as related to world food supplies. The invention of agriculture was the single accomplishment which permitted man to establish stable communities, create social structures, and bring about division of labor for the common good. Now some 10,000 years after the beginnings of husbandry, there are in the world today substantial numbers of social groups whose food-gathering habits encompass the entire evolutionary history of agricultural practice. There are tribes who still pursue their food and are limited to those aliments that they can gather or catch; some dwell in the nomadic state and others exist in the most primitive forms of agrarian societies. Still others have progressed to the use of hand implements, animal power, and a few elementary machines. In its most advanced state agriculture takes maximum advantage of power-driven equipment for every facet of production, in conjunction with soil amendments and a variety of chemicals essential to the protection of crops and livestock and the processing and preservation of their products.

Agriculture has never been an easy way of life. Primitive farmers, who gradually learned to cultivate indigenous plant species and to domesticate a few forms of wild animal life, found it necessary to put in long, arduous hours of labor in order to produce adequate food supplies for family and community needs. And the heavy physical labor and long hours traditionally associated with the practice of agriculture still persist in much of the world. The concept that food production, especially in the humid tropics, is so facile that

154

farmers in these areas develop habits of indolence is erroneous. Serious public health problems and improper diet have been largely responsible for limiting the physical capabilities of rural populations in the tropics, and this fact, in conjunction with the lack of adequate equipment and facilities, has resulted in excessive manpower requirements and low yields.

In spite of the almost insurmountable difficulties confronting primitive farmers, some have shown great ingenuity in reaching the solution to formidable obstacles. An early technique for the utilization of land too steep to plow was the construction of terraces. These often were carefully engineered and required enormous investments in time, manpower, and skill for their construction and maintenance. Striking examples of this are still apparent in Ceylon, the Philippines, Lebanon, and elsewhere. A still more highly developed form of terracing is apparent today in much of the rice bowl of Asia where paddies are carried up sloping terrain in a beautifully engineered fashion. Certain dwellers in arid or semiarid regions, faced with the choice of migrating, existing as nomads, or developing engineering techniques to collect and utilize efficiently all available moisture, chose the latter. Their success in this endeavor is clearly manifest in the catchment and irrigation systems developed by the early civilizations in the Middle East and by the Mayas and Incas in the Western Hemisphere.

A most interesting and important result of the migrations and agricultural activities of earlier civilizations was the distribution of crop species and domesticated animals from their places of origin throughout the world. Although it might be expected that indigenous crop species would be primarily confined to those areas in which they occur in nature, this is not the case. Over the centuries, society has selected approximately a dozen plants as the sources of two-thirds of all human food. This selection is not based on origin, but rather upon palatability, adaptability, and productivity. Thus, wheat, which has an Afro-Asian origin, is the most widely planted crop in the world wherever it can be grown. Sorghum, another African crop, has become increasingly important in the Western Hemisphere during the past 50 years. Rice, with its origins in Asia, is still grown most intensively in the so-called "rice bowl" of Asia, but it has become widespread in most of those countries in which it can be successfully propagated. Maize, potatoes, and sweet potatoes, all of American origin, are especially important in the Western Hemisphere but have been widely accepted and utilized in a variety of forms in most of the temperate and tropical countries. Finally, the soybean, which has been of such great significance in feeding the Far East, has found a place in many countries of the West with significant benefits. The fact that rice, wheat, corn, sorghum, potatoes, and the pulses are internationally popular makes it somewhat simpler to help those in need through the distribution of surpluses of these foods to areas in which they are known and desired.

It is frequently stated that the general application of Western technology to agricultural production on a world-wide basis would readily result in doubling or even tripling annual food production. There is little doubt that this statement is accurate, but there is no possibility that this goal could be realized within any foreseeable period of time. The evolution of agricultural technology depends in the first instance upon the availability of adequate national resources and their rational utilization. Thus, countries may be barred from attaining satisfactory production levels by size, climate, physiography, and the size and development of indigenous populations. Political boundaries are at best illogical, and the course of history has produced countries of tremendous size and potentialities at one extreme and at the other those that are so minute as to be virtually microscopic communities surrounded by larger nations. Only under exceptional circumstances is it possible for these small nations to provide any substantial fraction of their total food requirements. Countries whose climate is too cold or too dry or whose terrain is unsuited to agriculture or whose natural resources are severely limited do not find it possible to develop a stable agricultural pattern to provide food for the nation and surpluses for trade purposes. Finally, there are areas where the populations are so sparse and scattered that there is an inadequate labor force for agricultural purposes, in contrast to others where population pressures are so intense that it has become the practice to divide and subdivide each job in an effort to give a modicum of employment to as many persons as possible.

It is futile to speculate on the possibilities of any sort of crash effort to convert the less well-developed countries to Western levels of agricultural technology in a short time span. The vital role of adequate natural resources has already been described, but of equal importance is the educational level of the agricultural labor force. In too much of the world little or no education in the Western sense is available to the rural populations. Thus, they would be unable to take full advantage of the technologies of modern agriculture, even if they were to become immediately available to them. In fact, the lack of understanding as to the necessity of maintaining a balance between natural resources and production is bringing about the gradual destruction of important resources. Shifting patterns of cultivation, the indiscriminate use of fire, overgrazing, monoculture, and other practices which lead to the exhaustion of soil fertility, erosion, stream pollution, and the destruction of forests and pastures have proceeded apace in many areas.

Educational deficiencies manifest themselves in every facet of social organization. Public administration for the planning of national development and the use of mineral and other resources, the establishment of school systems, communication, transportation, and the encouragement of agriculture and industry must depend upon sufficient numbers of well-trained leaders. Public health measures cannot be successfully instituted without trained professionals and a public educated to accept these benefits. Today, progress in many areas is severely limited by the destructive effects of many diseases that have been brought under control elsewhere. Smallpox, yellow fever, tuberculosis, bilharziasis, and malaria, as well as numerous parasites, are responsible for the death of untold thousands and the ill health of millions more. Serious as are the diseases themselves, they are made more so by the fact that their victims are usually undernourished and thus without the natural defenses of healthy bodies. When this condition prevails from childhood, morbidity figures are high and life expectancy figures are low. One of the saddest direct products of malnutrition is the number of children whose symptoms of Kwashiorkor and other deficiency diseases signal the melancholy future.

Against this background, the more fortunate nations cannot hope to feed the rest of the world even for a short period of time. Neither can they expect to fill quickly the void in the education and understanding of millions of the underprivileged. Whether we like it or not, millions are doomed to live and die much as did their forebears. However, help can and is being provided in many ways. Gifts of food and other supplies are helpful as emergency measures and loans are extremely useful in support of economic development. More important still are efforts directed to the training of nationals to serve their country's needs. This requires maximum effort and the support of indigenous programs for the education and training of personnel and collateral programs to provide training abroad for selected individuals who will become teachers, lawyers, economists, physicians, engineers, and others during the years to come.

Special circumstances have thrown upon the United States a heavy and disproportionate burden in foreign aid since World War II. We cannot be expected to bear this same proportion of the needs of the decades ahead. Other countries are in a position to make a larger effort to meet the technical and capital requirements of the less developed areas. Certainly, United Nations organizations are important instruments of foreign aid and should be further strengthened, but there is need for many more bilateral and multilateral programs, as well as for others under the auspices of private organizations. Effort must be made to bring more emphasis to bear on all forms of technical aid to assure that these are catalytic individually and synergistic in concert. It is not necessary for each underdeveloped nation to repeat all of the stages of development which lie between its present state and modern standards, but the rate of progress will inevitably be conditioned by the speed at which educational progress toward stable and organized social patterns occurs.

Thus far, I have not discussed the more distant future, but rather have confined my thoughts to the present and immediate future. I do so in the belief that if the world cannot learn to resolve the fundamental problems which face it now, worry about the future may be a fruitless exercise. Many are greatly preoccupied about explosive increases in population and available future food supplies. I think we should be equally worried about the present. The world is not now feeding its present population properly, so that future calculations must be extrapolated from failure.

I have complete faith that continuing research and its applications will result in technological advances even more dramatic than those of the past 40 years. I believe also that many countries will, during the next several decades, make tremendous advances toward a reasonable degree of self-sufficiency. Thus, while there will still be hardship and misery for millions during the years to come, I believe that if we can avoid war or economic exhaustion from massive armament efforts, we will gradually approach a better balance between the nations of the world with benefit to all.

On the other hand, the arithmetic of population increase is incontrovertible. As standards of health and comfort improve, life span increases and infant mortality decreases. I think no one denies that this means a growing population. I find neither profit nor comfort in the discussion of the issues as currently drawn. To me the issue is not sectarian, but simply human. Since biological laws are immutable, in the absence of catastrophe population will increase rapidly. This increase will continue to place greater and greater pressure on available food supplies and dwellings, on technology for the production of goods and full employment, on transportation, and on the land itself. I think that for many years to come we can at least maintain and perhaps even improve our present position. Eventually, however, society must decide on the sort of world it wishes to live in. Our great cities have already created more human problems than they have resolved. Our conquest of physical disease is apparently being neutralized by the increase of mental ills, and we have not learned to live at peace with our neighbors. Vastly increased numbers of persons will inevitably further complicate and compound our problems. Ultimately, we must decide to stabilize world populations at a level compatible with human dignity and prosperity or suffer the chaotic consequences which will surely follow.

The Influence of Current Social and Economic Trends on International Health

Sixty years ago Americans considered that disease was the prime deterrent to human comfort and prosperity. Now, after engaging in two world conflicts, limited war under United Nations auspices in Korea, and a more or less continuous cold war, our ideas of the dimensions of the threats to human existence have undergone radical evolution. In spite of the intrusion of these major military considerations into social patterns, tremendous advances have been made in medical science with commensurable benefits to public health in the Western world. Nonetheless, serious and widespread health problems still present a major challenge to world society.

Prior to World War II we had little knowledge or interest in the affairs of most of the nations of Asia and Africa or even of Latin America, our closest neighbors. We occupied a position of unprecedented power, were at peace, and were moving toward a high level of prosperity. Our own standards of public health had improved dramatically, thanks to the efforts of the group of professionals responsible for the protection of food and water supplies and immunization and preventive medicine campaigns. These reduced the incidence of many of the most dreaded communicable diseases and of the epidemics which were once frequent occurrences. In fact, the very success of the practice of public health in this country led to the gradual relegation of this vital sector of medical science to a position of secondary eminence in the total discipline. Public health officers still have critically important federal, state, community, and industrial functions, but the great thrust to overcome or control the mass killers of all society has been attenuated in proportion to accomplishment in our own.

From a talk given in Boston on July 20,1960, at the Fourth Conference of the Industrial Council for Tropical Health, Harvard School of Public Health

In the early forties we began to discover much of the rest of the world previously little known to us, and to take greater cognizance of the needs of large groups of less fortunate peoples and their claims to the right to live healthy lives and enjoy decent standards of living. One of the most forceful ways in which the situation was brought to our attention came as the result of sending hundreds of thousands of our own young people overseas to the tropics during World War II. Subsequent events made us increasingly aware of our international responsibilities for the economic development of the less fortunate nations, and the necessity to examine both needs and opportunities for assistance. It quickly became clear that areas of distress were all too numerous and that less than half of the world's population enjoy minimum acceptable standards of health and nutrition. This is particularly true in substantial sectors of the Near East, India, Pakistan, Southeast Asia, Sub-Sahara Africa, and parts of Latin America. The social and economic imbalance between these areas and the more highly developed nations has become of increasing concern and the object of intensive and extensive attempts to bring about improvements.

We have long known in a vague way that large sectors of the world's population are underprivileged by any acceptable standard. Among the pioneers who first recognized this situation and attempted to take some remedial action were missionaries representing various church organizations. For more than a century these groups have been contributing to the well-being of a modest segment of the underprivileged overseas through projects in the fields of medicine and public health, agriculture, and education. A second important force in the field of international welfare has been philanthropic organizations, including the foundations and volunteer agencies. A third has been private American enterprise with investments abroad. Each, whatever its failings, has made significant contributions to the well-being of the peoples concerned.

FOREIGN AID PROGRAMS

There are numerous social and economic trends which influence international health. Among the most important of these are the social changes which have been occurring rapidly in many of the underdeveloped sectors of the world as the result of efforts to obtain political independence. These have drastically changed systems of government and at the same time have disrupted established economic patterns. Independence has brought about insertion of nationals into all levels of government, business, and education, frequently before there was adequate preparation for such responsibilities. The emerging nations are now demanding higher standards of living for their people, which will require in the first instance increasing emphasis on improvements in the nutrition of urban and rural populations through the application of modern techniques of public health and agricultural production.

Most of the emerging nations simply do not have either the manpower or the economic resources to satisfy the requirements of a new state. They must, therefore, make *pro tem* arrangements to maintain and improve their social and economic levels until such time as they can function independently. This means the continued use of expatriate technicians, scientists and administrators, substantial loan funds, and foreign aid programs. Ultimately, it would be expected that well-trained nationals would provide the necessary leadership so that it would be possible to withdraw gradually emergency and temporary assistance.

On the other side, the immense needs of the emerging nations have definite social and economic impact on those nations which extend foreign aid. The amounts of money which have already been channeled to the assistance of underdeveloped countries are enormous, and it is expected that still larger sums will be required during the years to come. This, of course, means that a significant fraction of the gross national product of countries heavily engaged in foreign aid is utilized in this enterprise which, although largely nonproductive in the commercial sense, can be expected to have both social and economic benefits over the long range.

Foreign aid programs necessarily involve large numbers of people who participate directly or indirectly in them. For the first time in our own history we maintain large numbers of technical and other personnel overseas as members of technical assistance missions of one sort or another. At the same time, increasing numbers of foreign students are reaching this country from abroad. The small stream of postdoctoral fellows coming to the United States for advanced study has now become a flood of individuals, principally from underdeveloped areas, whose early training has been limited or inadequate. Unless this great group is handled with skill and judgment,

162

there may well be adverse effects on our own educational patterns. On the other hand, there may also be substantial benefits derived from the communication and exchange of ideas between the youth of our own country and that of many other nations.

The number of agencies engaged in some form of foreign aid has steadily increased during the past two decades. Their programs embrace the fields of education, agriculture, health, transportation, communication, industry, and many others. As might be expected, the largest and most widely extended efforts are those carried on by government, either in the form of bilateral programs, as typified by the International Cooperation Administration, or multilateral programs, especially those under the United Nations Organization through its specialized agencies such as the World Health Organization, the Food and Agriculture Organization, and the United Nations Educational, Scientific and Cultural Organization. Results to date range from spectacularly successful to unsatisfactory; doubtless these extremes were inevitable, since a sense of urgency has often led to decisions based on too little information and understanding. Moreover, foreign aid personnel frequently were inexperienced and had to go through a period of orientation and adjustment before becoming effective.

Ideally, foreign aid programs are directed toward the social and economic improvement of the areas of concern. They may be in part motivated by political, social, economic, or other forces, but underlying all of these is the unselfish desire that substantial human benefits will result on an increasing scale. There is a wide divergence of opinion as to what constitutes the ideal type of foreign aid, but there probably is no ideal pattern; rather, the goal can best be reached through many efforts directed to the critical needs of the countries involved. These should consist of projects of readily demonstrable benefit which can be completed or ultimately transferred to national agencies. The degree to which the several projects are in phase with each other is a prime factor in determining the rate and ultimate level of achievement. Most basic of all considerations is the extent to which each project serves as a training facility for nationals of the countries concerned. Only by emphasizing the training aspect is it possible to develop permanent roots and to achieve continuity and multiple benefits from an enlarging force of competent personnel able to serve national needs.

There are three basic elements in any sound foreign aid program to an underdeveloped area. These are education, agriculture, and public health, which conjointly must provide the foundation for all future accomplishment. It is still true that most of the world's citizens are engaged in some form of agriculture and that most of the world's real wealth is derived from agricultural commodities. All the rest of society depends upon the practitioners of agriculture for an adequate dietary to sustain the health and vigor which is essential to a productive existence. It is axiomatic that nutrition and public health are inseparable, and any effort to improve agricultural production must of necessity be carried out in parallel with the identification of major public health problems and the establishment of action programs designed to resolve them. Simultaneously, every effort must be made to improve educational opportunities in those areas where these are still totally inadequate. Only when these three basic facets of human existence are given adequate attention is it possible to build a sound pattern of social organization and economic development for national progress.

Although education, health, and nutrition are inseparable elements in the compound of human existence, real progress is made only when efforts in health and nutrition are functions of the educational pattern. Invariably, the most critical national deficit in underdeveloped countries is in educational resources. This fact places immediate and severe limitations on the structure and effective function of foreign aid programs. A first requirement is the provision of large numbers of foreign specialists to fill the gaps in many important fields of endeavor until well-trained nationals are available in sufficient numbers to assume complete responsibility. The magnitude of this undertaking is appalling, especially, in view of the fact that no country has an excess of the type of manpower necessary to undertake these responsibilities of such major importance. Enough is known today about malaria, smallpox, yellow fever, tuberculosis, and other diseases of comparable importance, and about the methodology of agriculture so that, with adequate planning and financial resources in combination with sufficient trained manpower, it would be possible to make rapid strides in the control of major diseases and the substantial improvement of agricultural production and hence nutrition on a worldwide basis. However, qualified personnel are not available locally in significant numbers, and it is simply not possible to export them in sufficient quantity to carry out the required tasks at an optimum rate. Even if an adequate supply of foreign personnel were available, it would still be necessary to create or reinforce educational systems in order to complement all technical phases of foreign aid through the production of increasing numbers of competent individuals in all fields of learning and technology. This is impossible without liberal doses of time, regardless of the financial investment or the techniques applied.

SOCIAL AND ECONOMIC PATTERNS

Efforts to protect the health of large social groups have always met with some degree of resistance based on ignorance, superstition, religious convictions or, occasionally, greed. Well remembered in our country are the struggles to establish quarantine procedures, compulsory vaccination, and anti-venereal disease campaigns. When sanitary regulations were promulgated to assure pure meat, milk, and food supplies, they have in the past been fought or evaded by some who feared financial loss. The battle is continuous, since a few hard cores of resistance persist, and public apathy usually follows a successful breakthrough leading to the control of a major communicable disease.

In the modern scene the public health pattern is changing. Continuing surveillance and action are required to protect public water, milk, and food supplies and to prevent the outbreak of epidemics. However, the classic problems have been joined with others still more complex. The fallout of ionizing radiation, public health hazards from increasing population density, and the gradual shift from communicable disease as the major threat to health to that of mental disease and the organic conditions which afflict a society under increasing tensions are of growing concern.

Accepted social practices in underdeveloped communities are likely to be the product of tradition derived from limited experience, plus at least a modicum of superstition. The disciplines and practices of tribal and caste systems are frequently in conflict with modern concepts of public health measures, and the lack of understanding of even the simplest health precautions exposes the populace continuously to all local health hazards. It is not an easy matter to institute a whole spectrum of reforms or modern techniques with the expectation that these will be readily understood and accepted.

165

Most common obstacles are a variety of taboos, some quite obviously based upon experience and others completely nonunderstandable to the Western mind. These often involve local concepts of heat and cold, clean and unclean, and the cause and control of disease. Food preferences and restrictions affect nutrition, often adversely, and habits of work are conditioned by custom rather than efficiency.

In highly authoritarian societies it is sometimes possible to impose upon communities or societies sanitary and regulatory procedures for their own protection. Although effective, this is not necessarily the most satisfactory procedure.

Few social systems occur in unadulterated form, since a kaleidoscopic series of migrations, intrusions, and conquests has been in progress for centuries. There are still many isolated areas in which primitive patterns of society have become relatively stable as tribal cultures with their roots in antiquity. Dwellers of the plains, forests, or mountains; they are to be found in widely scattered areas of North and South America, Asia, and Africa. Out of touch and forced to depend on limited resources and their own ingenuity for a continuing existence under difficult circumstances, they are understandably conservative, superstitious, and fatalistic.

Since over two-thirds of the world's population is directly involved in the practice of agriculture, systems of crop production and animal husbandry regulate to a substantial degree the life of the individual farmer, his family, and the community in which he lives. Public health problems may derive largely from occupational practices, and their solution must be approached through an understanding of rural patterns of life. Obviously nomadic and stable communities present quite different sets of problems. The former are difficult, if not impossible, to keep under medical surveillance, and although they may escape some of the health hazards of village life, they may encounter others of equal severity and may also function as migrant reservoirs of communicable diseases. In more stable agrarian communities, crop production is frequently a family enterprise in which men, women, and children work side by side in the field from dawn to dark. This system militates against the education of children and of family life in which the mother plays the central role. Home and village sanitation are frequently nonexistent, with the result that intestinal parasites are universal and dysentery, schistosomiasis, and other diseases common occurrences.

Dietary habits in many of the more isolated communities are conditioned by ecology and custom. Wildlife provides food for hunting tribes; others depend principally upon fish, but the vast majority of people depend upon plants for their bulk foods. The most important of these are rice, wheat, corn, cassava, potatoes, and sweet potatoes. All are starchy and are usually complemented with one of the pulses and when possible with small amounts of meat and fish. When these are unavailable protein hunger may manifest itself in the consumption of exotic foods such as ants, grubs, maguey worms, and tadpoles. The use of alcohol is not uncommon, and narcotics such as hashish, opium, coca, peyote, marijuana, and certain fungi are regularly used by some groups.

In much of the world subsistence farming is the rule, and cash income is minimal or nonexistent. Relative wealth may be calculated in wives or cattle or the ownership of land, and essentially all exchanges within or between communities are through barter. More progressive societies have developed some form of division of labor to the extent that they contain both farmers and artisans. Ultimately, surpluses may accumulate and village markets be established for their exchange or sale, but as long as primitive methods require total effort for submarginal existence, economic progress is impossible. In some areas overpopulation, relative to available industrial and agricultural resources, deters economic progress and in others unstable social patterns may be a decisive factor.

CONCLUSIONS

Although the task is an enormous one, there is no doubt that progress is being made in the geographic extension of the benefits of modern public health measures. Much more rapid advances may be expected in the future as larger numbers of qualified personnel become available and as the emerging states make decisions and take action for the protection of the health of their citizens. Western nations can continue to help through the provision of leadership and resources in attempts to bring under control the major diseases which afflict the underdeveloped nations. Concurrent improvements in world food supplies and steady progress in the strengthening of educational facilities at all levels can assure continuing progress toward humanitarian goals.

Socio-Economic Factors That Limit Needed Food Production and Consumption

Statistics of world food production, distribution, and consumption emphasize the extraordinary disparities among human dietary patterns. The picture is a gloomy one, since it indicates that the sum total of social and scientific progress to date has failed to provide an adequate nutrition for one out of two members of society. The prospective future explosive increase in the world population portends problems of much greater orders of magnitude unless drastic improvements can be achieved promptly. And the frequent statement that the universal application of modern technology could double or triple world food production, although comforting, is unrealistic. Blind reliance on science and technology for the solution of basic human problems is both unreasonable and dangerous.

More than 50 per cent of the world's labor force is engaged in some aspect of agriculture. The less well-developed areas of the world are characteristically agrarian, and in the least privileged areas the struggle for mere existence is so severe that the vast majority of the population is forced into practice of subsistence agriculture. This situation effectively prevents the production of surpluses which could be used to support other facets of social progress and economic growth.

As long as the world population was insignificant in terms of available resources, the situation was a simple one, but as the numbers increased, complications set in. The most striking of these has been the evolution of geopolitical patterns, and today the world picture of political units is both kaleidoscopic and illogical. The range

Address given on September 6, 1960, at the Fifth International Congress on Nutrition, Symposium on World Needs and Food Resources, Washington, D.C.

in size, available resources, population, and social and economic development among the nations of the world is fantastic, and neither the political nor the natural conditions within these enormous extremes can readily be altered for calculated benefits. Individual nations can develop within the limits of population, climate, topography, and available renewable and nonrenewable resources. Those countries with great natural wealth and relatively small populations have been able to create the highest known standards of living which are compatible with human dignity.

The temperate regions have in modern history presented the greatest attraction to mankind as sites of human habitation. As he has progressed, man has learned a great deal about ways in which to improve his standards of living. In so doing, he has found ways by which to utilize more fully the resources of the tropics and the subarctics. The modern technologies developed by industrial societies comprise the greatest single resource for increasing world food production. This has become increasingly important in support of programs designed to speed the rate of economic progress in many of the less well-developed countries.

An international study of the socio-economic factors limiting food production and consumption reveals great similarities in patterns prevailing in widely separated areas. These reflect evolutionary stages in social development within the several countries. Each is the product of the interaction of natural phenomena and people. In land management the classic but destructive shifting system involving clearing, burning, planting, and eventually a move to a new area and a repetition of the process is widespread. Elsewhere, land may be laboriously tilled with the traditional Egyptian plow, the planting stick or iron hoe, resulting in an inadequate seed bed and low yields. Hillside cultivation is an ancient practice in many countries, which in its highest form consists of ingenious terracing and in its lowest of crude land preparation for two to three years followed by soil erosion. Pastoral systems are common, and where pressures on the land are heavy, overgrazing is a common phenomenon frequently accompanied by sheet erosion.

Similar landholding patterns are repeated throughout the world. Where populations are sparse and resources substantial, precise ownership systems are lacking. However, as population pressures increase or as new elements enter the scene, several types of ownership emerge, depending upon local circumstances. These may be tribal or some form of communal ownership; the latifundia under which great expanses of agricultural soils are held by the elite of the community, with the bulk of the population relegated to the role of a labor force; large numbers of small or medium-sized landholdings; and, at the lower extreme, the division and subdivision of land parcels until individual cultivators are forced to till one or several minute plots of land often quite distant one from another. This system represents one of the lowest efficiency levels, but is difficult to change where it is brought about by deeply rooted traditional systems of inheritance, credit practices which approach usury, and the treatment of land as patrimony rather than as a resource.

The management of biologic species by agrarian societies is critical to their progress. In many locales there has long been a process of selection resulting from a combination of ecological conditions with empiricism. Most commonly, food crops and domestic animals are indigenous or long ago introduced species which are well adapted and productive under local conditions. Plant food species are primarily the cereals, but other high-carbohydrate food crops predominate where cereals are not well adapted. Rice, wheat, maize, sorghum, the millets, rye, and barley are principal foods in the cereal-producing areas, but elsewhere cassava, the sweet potato, potatoes, coconuts, and bananas are basic foods. Although over 3,000 plant species have been used for food and over 300 are widely grown, only about 12 furnish nearly 90 per cent of the world's food.

A common phenomenon is the line selection of crop plants in response to local conditions. These may be low soil fertility, drought, or the incidence of disease. And over the years there has been a tendency to select domestic animal types which will persist, if not always thrive, under local conditions. Heat tolerance, resistance to pests and pathogens, along with the ability to utilize low-grade forages are among the most common characteristics of animal species in less advanced agricultural societies.

The social habits of communities in underdeveloped areas vary widely but fall into several patterns which may be repeated from country to country even though their origins are unrelated. Essentially, all societies have experienced periods during which superstition dominated local customs. The response of the human mind to mysterious natural phenomena is historically well documented, and it is disconcerting to realize the degree to which superstition and mysticism still pervade a major sector of the world's population. Although there may be great variety in local beliefs and customs, the similarity of the cause and effect is frequently apparent. Mysticism ultimately gives way to empiricism, which ideally should be replaced by the scientific method. Unfortunately, however, this stage in the evolution of human thought is neither universal nor even predominant in terms of total numbers.

Local beliefs dictate customs, and these include personal, food, work, and social habits. Again, the patterns repeat themselves in widely separated areas with minor dissimilarities. The use of drugs such as opium, marijuana, hashish, peyote, and cocaine have originated independently in different cultural groups, although these habits have become widespread through migration. The insistence upon certain foods for reasons of health, ritual, or taste preference is a well-established phenomenon. Work habits and marital and family patterns have many counterparts in social groups which have not had previous contact.

All of the foregoing factors have their impact upon food production and social and economic progress. They sum up to the conclusion that today the greatest cause of malnutrition is underproduction. Each agricultural unit which does not yield its full production potential represents a permanent irreplaceable loss to human nutrition and welfare. This loss may derive from unsatisfactory soil management, the use of low-yielding food crops and animals, attack by pests and pathogens, and the lack of storage facilities, transportation facilities, and markets for the preservation, distribution, and exchange of surplus commodities.

There is another form of underproduction which is even more serious than the material kind. This is the loss to society represented by the inability of millions of people to apply their total potentials to the improvement of standards of living individually and collectively. Just so long as there are these vast numbers whose opportunities for intellectual development are severely limited, it will be impossible to meet the increasing demand for food and other human requirements by the expanding populations of the future.

In dealing with world problems of health, nutrition, and technology, the scientist and engineer are able to establish specific goals and design projects leading to their attainment, but ultimate success

171

must be predicated upon the skill with which the social sciences and the humanities are integrated with the physical, biological, and engineering sciences. Each day it becomes more imperative that the problems of the underdeveloped portions of the world be considered in their total context and that efforts to ameliorate undesirable situations be established on an interdisciplinary basis calculated to combine advances in science and technology with those in economics, sociology, and the humanities.

The most formidable barrier to further social and economic progress is the low level of education of peoples in many parts of the world. Education is the key that unlocks the door of understanding and provides opportunities to apply human ingenuity to the solution of social problems. Reasonable progress in bringing the less privileged members of society to acceptable standards of living can come only as rapidly as the educational process is extended and intensified. And progress in education must be matched by increasing opportunities for useful employment so that social progress and economic growth may proceed in concert.

There is no short cut to education and understanding, although it is possible to intensify educational and training patterns in order to speed the rate at which levels of education are raised. However, regardless of the magnitude of effort, there will inevitably be a lag between its application and the desired achievement. The human misery resulting from malnutrition, disease, and social patterns built upon ignorance will persist, although hopefully on a diminishing scale, for many years into the future. The persistence of all the old problems along with the introduction of new ones, as well as the increase in population, clearly indicates that concerted and enormous effort and substantial periods of time will be required to gradually ameliorate, if not eliminate, existing situations incompatible with human dignity.

In the past there have been many instances of population pressures becoming explosive, with the results strife and warfare. At the moment, even though these pressures are already manifest in some areas and are definitely increasing, there appears to be greater agreement than ever in history that they can, and must, be resolved through the process of social, scientific, and economic development rather than conflict. However, unless rapid strides are made in education, science, and technology on an integrated basis, popula-

172

tion pressures will ultimately pose a new series of menaces to world peace and all facets of human welfare. Although the threat to the future of society is clear, the solution is not apparent. However, certain essential elements to the solution are quite evident and may be stated as follows:

1. Agreement among nations as to the irrationality of the investment of massive resources in armies and armaments at the expense of human welfare.

2. Increasing international cooperation in all matters affecting the rational utilization of agricultural resources and the production and exchange of agricultural commodities, goods, and services on the most sound economic basis.

3. Herculean efforts in the field of education in order that new knowledge shall continue to become available in response to the needs of mankind, and that more nearly all of the world's citizens acquire educational opportunities to permit them to take maximum advantage of available resources in support of decent standards of living.

4. An understanding of the threat posed by explosive population increases in the knowledge that sheer numbers can ultimately outstrip our productive capacity and at the same time create intolerable social problems. Serious and successful efforts must be made to stabilize populations so that we do not reach a situation of chaos.

Freedom from hunger implies a great deal more than increased food production. Although food is the basic ingredient in support of life, it is more importantly the source of the energy which enables mankind to take full advantage of its physical and intellectual potential. In the vital struggle to provide improved nutrition for the population of the present and of the future, there must be included comparable efforts to broaden and deepen the understanding of increasing numbers of individuals so that as we win the battle with hunger we will at the same time and as a part of the same effort win the goal of social progress.

Technologic Revolution in Agriculture

The agriculture which is practiced today is as unlike that of 50 years ago as are our modern systems of communication and transportation different from their counterparts at the turn of the century. Although the nostalgic concept of agriculture as a way of life is still expressed on occasion, the fact is that modern crop and animal production is a highly competitive business, and unless producers are either highly efficient or heavily subsidized, they cannot remain long in the business.

The major contribution to the evolution of agricultural practice over the past half century has been derived from basic research in the biological, physical, and engineering sciences in conjunction with improvements in educational patterns, agricultural services, and transportation facilities. Among the most striking are engineering developments which have enabled the agricultural producer continually to improve his productivity and at the same time reduce manpower requirements. A variety of modern machines, singly or in combination, prepare, plant, and fertilize the soil, carry out necessary cultivation operations, apply pesticides, fungicides, or herbicides, and ultimately harvest the final product. A myriad of other mechanical devices are involved in the procedures of preparation, preservation, or transformation essential to the conversion of crop and animal products into foods or other materials essential to modern standards of living. The next development in mechanized agricultural production will undoubtedly bring an increasing degree of automation into the entire pattern.

Of at least equal importance and dramatic benefit to agriculture has been the broad spectrum of chemical compounds which intervenes at every stage of the agricultural process. Modern fertilizer

From a talk delivered December 8, 1960, in Washington, D.C. at the Food Protection Committee symposium entitled *Science and Food: Today and Tomorrow*

practices have contributed enormously to increased production as a continuing result of research on essential micro- and macro-elements. Similarly, animal metabolism has been controlled to an increasing degree through the use of compounds with specific effects. The protection of crop plants and domestic animals from predators, pests, and weed competitors has reached a high level of efficiency through the use of elaborate chemical substances designed to provide external or systemic protection or prophylaxis. The result has been increasing quantities of high-quality products and a gradual diminution of the annual tribute levied upon the business of agriculture by pests and pathogens.

Most plant and animal products require the applications of chemistry to essentially every step in their conversion into consumer products, and modern foods, feeds, and fibres have all benefited from chemical transformations or enrichment. In fact, the food industry has undergone major evolution, if not revolution, during the past two decades, with the result that high-quality, attractive domestic and exotic foodstuffs are available to the American public in continuing supply at reasonable prices.

Without in the least deprecating the benefits of technology in the agricultural industry, it is evident that the success of agricultural production is in essence a triumph of research. The advances which have been made during recent years in biochemistry, plant and animal physiology, microbiology, nutrition, and related disciplines have produced the knowledge upon which present progress has been built. The efficient utilization of this increasing body of knowledge is fundamental to further developments and emphasizes the necessity for continuing and intensified effort for research on all fronts.

Superficially, it appears paradoxical that in spite of the spectacular progress which has been made in the more developed areas of the world, there are still vast numbers of people who are underfed, insufficiently clothed, inadequately housed, and barred from reasonable opportunities for decent standards of living. Many factors combine to permit this deplorable situation, and these cannot be easily and immediately changed. The frequently expressed thesis that the application of the modern scientific method to agricultural production on a worldwide basis can readily double or treble world food production is meaningless in the present social context. The problem is not purely one of manpower times mechanics, but rather one

175

consisting of an array of complex considerations, including climate, geography, resources, social and political systems, educational patterns, and economics. Thus, while science has much to offer in contributing to the alleviation of undesirable human conditions, science and technology alone are insufficient to the task. They must be joined with intensive and extensive efforts in related disciplines in order that humanitarian efforts may not become simply veneers over unsatisfactory situations but, rather, growing points which can develop into patterns of continuing progress and excellence.

The scientist has a great opportunity and responsibility in the matter of applying his knowledge to situations where it is urgently needed. His opportunities come through his ability to use his understanding and experience for desirable results. His responsibilities involve the understanding of problems in their broadest context and the willingness to interpret his own field so that it will be understood by others and to coordinate his activities with those of representatives of other disciplines in order that advances can be made on the broad front essential to social and economic progress.

The more developed countries of the world cannot indefinitely preserve the *status quo* without reference to the demands of the less fortunate nations of the world. This fact is recognized, and serious efforts have been launched with the object of helping to improve standards of living and opportunity in those nations where the needs are manifest. We are learning each day that this is a most complicated and difficult endeavor, and that scientific, technical, and other skills are only part of the variety of tools necessary to success. Of great importance is an increasing body of individuals who can practice their professions or apply their knowledge successfully to other cultures in such ways as to contribute demonstrably to material and other forms of progress and at the same time create patterns of excellence which will in themselves ultimately be taken over, continued, and expanded by the qualified nationals of the country concerned.

The dramatic success of modern science and technology has brought with it both massive benefits and major responsibilities. If human welfare is to advance globally, the benefits deriving from science must be made to apply effectively to the responsibilities which confront all the more favored nations toward helping others to work toward national goals compatible with their potentials.

Unhappy Paradox

Modern agricultural production is a triumph of the application of knowledge, derived from basic research, to problems of human nutrition and welfare. During the past quarter century agricultural practice has undergone a full-scale revolution as a result of the integrated application of many technologies to the total problem of crop and animal production, nutrition, protection, and utilization. Advances in the engineering, chemical, physical, and biological sciences have in the most highly developed countries of the world permitted qualitative and quantitative improvements in agricultural production in new orders of magnitude and, at the same time, have pointed the way to future improvements of similar or even greater dimensions.

The secret of this success story lies in men rather than machines. The outpouring of trained scientists and others destined to work in some aspect of agriculture has made possible extraordinarily creative and exceedingly rapid advances in science and technology. The agricultural producers in the industrial countries are highly sophisticated groups who have taken full advantage of available knowledge and tools, with the result that production has steadily increased while manpower requirements and costs have simultaneously declined. Thus, today the citizens of Western and certain other nations are able to enjoy appetizing, high-quality, and nutritious domestic and exotic foods without seasonal limitations and at reasonable prices. However, regardless of past achievements, it is entirely clear that future advances in response to the demands of a growing population are going to require more extensive and greatly intensified scientific research and development.

Editorial appearing in *Science*, March 10, 1961

With the knowledge and tools now available to society for the satisfaction of agricultural requirements, it seems paradoxical that a large proportion of the world's population lives at substandard nutritional levels. It is frequently suggested that the massive application everywhere of modern technologies could readily eliminate the specter of hunger which stalks so many lands; theoretically, such massive application could be carried out, but in practice this is impossible.

The great barrier is now, and will continue to be for a substantial period in the future, the lack of sufficient numbers of nationals able to participate in research and to contribute otherwise to the development and application of technologies in support of progress on all fronts. Thus, the future economic growth of many of the less well-developed nations of the world will depend precisely upon the rapidity with which their citizens can be trained for the multiplicity of responsibilities related to agricultural production, distribution, marketing, and utilization and attendant occupations.

Friendly nations cannot resolve the problems of the less well-developed or emerging countries, but they can help to speed the processes of social and economic growth. Efforts should include industrial and engineering projects, but more fundamentally they must emphasize education at all levels. Especially important is the utilization of technical assistance programs as intensive training media. Training abroad for special purposes is vitally important, but the broad base for economic growth and social progress is to be found at home through interrelated programs designed to prepare growing numbers of nationals to respond to the demands of evolving social patterns.

Current Developments in the Area of Foreign Aid

Foreign aid and technical assistance under various auspices have been practiced within less developed nations for more than a century. The motivation has on occasion been religious, philanthropic, economic, or political, but in each instance there was a degree of effort to extend knowledge and skills to areas in which these were lacking and to individuals who had not previously had the opportunity to develop them.

The role of the religious groups in bringing education and training to a vast number of individuals in many parts of the world has been a major one. Having been among the earliest foreigners on the local scene, they have over the years, through their schools and vocational programs, opened educational doors to many persons from among whom have emerged outstanding present-day leaders. Charitable and philanthropic agencies have long been active in the foreign field and have accomplished much in the areas of public health, education, agriculture, and general technology. The business and industrial community with overseas interests has been another pioneer and important force in the extension of technical knowledge to many parts of the world.

As might be expected, the entry of government and consortia of governments into the field of technical assistance added an entirely new dimension to this aspect of international cooperation. As a result of the many bilateral programs established between governments and of the multilateral activities carried out under the auspices of the United Nations agencies, the Colombo Plan, and other agen-

Address presented at the American Assembly on
National Goals, Duke University, May 20, 1961

cies with similar objectives, the funds, personnel, and material devoted to foreign aid or mutual assistance have multiplied many-fold during the past decade or more.

Today, although the subject is still being debated, many of those who are most aware of the international situation are convinced that there is extraordinary need to assist certain of the less-developed nations to make more rapid progress toward the goals of a decent standard of living and increased opportunity for all. Certainly, it is evident that there are vast numbers of individuals who are diseased, ill fed, poorly housed, and illiterate. Moreover, opportunities for education and the full development of individual potentials are in many instances exceedingly limited. In face of these situations it is imperative that those nations more favored with economic and industrial resources, well-developed institutions, and high living standards act to the limit of their capacities in alleviating circumstances elsewhere which are incompatible with human dignity and opportunity.

The principle of foreign aid is sound, but the practice is an extraordinarily complicated undertaking. The needs of emerging nations tend to be multiple, diverse, and urgent. New leadership strongly feels the necessity of contributing rapidly and generally to the well-being of all citizens, and is therefore receptive, or even insistent, concerning offers of foreign aid. It is not axiomatic that recipient nations always know exactly the orders of priority with respect to their own future progress, nor is there evidence that the donor is always competent to judge local needs abroad. On past occasions failure to recognize these facts, compounded with a sense of urgency on both sides, has resulted in decisions and actions which on more sober forethought might have been deemed unwise.

Superficially, it may seem a simple matter to mobilize the resources and technologies of the highly industrialized nations and to transfer those elements most useful in the rapid achievement of desired advances within recipient countries. However, experience has taught that there are many initial incompatibilities in culture, understanding, and *modus operandi* among nations with widely divergent histories, and that these must be reconciled to a reasonable degree if representatives of two unlike cultures are to work together effectively and harmoniously toward important national goals. Language, food patterns, social habits, and many other factors must all be reckoned with in the design of successful foreign assistance programs. This requires a careful approach, extensive and intensive preliminary study and planning, organization which is meaningful within the local mores, and a period of adjustment prior to full-scale operation.

There has now been sufficient time and experience to permit a reasonably thorough examination of the record of a substantial variety of foreign aid efforts in progress during the past 15 years. These have been carried on under the auspices of a wide spectrum of agencies, large and small. Projects range from some which are exceedingly modest in terms of coverage, personnel, and resources to others of national or regional dimensions involving large numbers of participants, quantities of material, and major financing. Some have been of short duration, whereas others have been continued over a substantial period of years. As a result, patterns have emerged which have been thoroughly tested, and some of these have now been shown to be effective in reaching established goals.

The critics of foreign aid have been able to find many examples to support their contention that in the past such programs have often involved poor planning, inefficiency, waste, inordinate delays, and unsatisfactory recruitment practices. These same critics could, however, match many of the failures or partial failures with other projects or programs which have been entirely successful and have contributed substantially to the well-being of the peoples concerned. The massive entry of government into the field of foreign aid, with the feeling of urgency and the desire for rapid accomplishments, inevitably created some difficulties and magnified others which could perhaps have been largely avoided if time had permitted a more deliberate approach. Admittedly, both the concept and practice of foreign assistance were new to government and grew out of a desire to share more substantially with less-privileged nations the economic and other achievements of highly industrialized nations such as our own. There may have been some naïveté in the original notion that American "know-how" could readily be exported and built into the social and economic patterns of the less-developed nations with great rapidity and ultimate permanence. This concept has now been considerably modified.

Today, when the needs are greater than ever, we are better able to meet them because of 15 years of experience, both successful and otherwise. Perhaps the most important product of this experience is the large body of individuals who have now had useful training in some phase of foreign assistance and can therefore carry out their part in such programs more effectively than in the past.

These 15 years have also provided valuable information regarding the development of concepts and techniques for a successful foreign aid program extended to many countries throughout the world. We have learned, for instance, that aid must of necessity be directed toward local needs which are important, obvious, and feasible, and that local enthusiasm, early planning, full participation, and maximum contribution are essential to ultimate success. We have learned, furthermore, that haste makes waste in foreign aid as in other endeavors, and that the prevailing sense of urgency must be tempered by sufficient time to assure that progress is sound, continuous, and accompanied by intensive and extensive efforts to help educate and train indigenous personnel who may ultimately be expected to exercise full leadership and assure continuity as foreign assistance is gradually withdrawn or shifted to other important activities. There is no known substitute for sustained effort in all of those fields directly involved in social and economic progress. Although major engineering enterprises may be undertaken in a precise fashion with productive results, *i.e.,* bridges, dams, railroads, power plants, *etc.,* these important economic elements are only the tools of society; the measure of their usefulness is the effectiveness with which they are utilized for the benefit of all. In the fields of public administration, public health, medicine, agriculture, education, and the others which depend so exclusively upon trained manpower, ultimate goals can be achieved only as rapidly as it is possible to give selected individuals the education and experience necessary to reach their full potentials in the service of society.

In the past, perhaps for reasons which combine compassion, generosity, the belief that ours is the best way of life, and the desire to share it with others, we have in our inexperience created problems at the same time that we have been trying to resolve others. However, these experiences have been educational and have given us insights which we lacked before. It is now becoming recognized that we cannot help our friends overseas to develop their full national potentials without local understanding of the bitter facts concerned in a shift from a totally unsatisfactory social pattern in which the majority are ill fed, medically unattended, ill housed, illiterate, and without hope or expectation, to one in which an increasing proportion will receive more of the benefits of modern social organization and be given opportunities to contribute their share to national well-being. No conceivable amounts of money or of personnel can accomplish breakthroughs in such ways as to suddenly convert admittedly deplorable situations into utopian ones. Those nations which, through government and private enterprise, except to contribute to the well-being of less fortunate nations must act in the knowledge that the effort will have to be large, long, and wise. Recipient nations must be brought to understand that achievement of the desired social and economic gains will require changes in many traditions and customs. Individual and national sacrifices must be made willingly and eagerly if the heavy sacrifice represented by the contributions of donor nations is to be justified. While the facts of life as they are today force an understanding of emergency situations which may have to be treated as special cases, the long-range view is of necessity one which contemplates mutual understanding and participation in sustained and intelligent effort toward humanitarian goals.

Current trends suggest that there is now general agreement on the principle that the various elements which make up the foreign assistance formula must for best results be carefully coordinated. Thus, loans, grants, gifts of food, and the use of personnel and equipment in the development of projects and programs can, if applied in an integrated fashion, produce a synergistic effect and at the same time minimize waste, duplication, and conflict of efforts. Included in the developing philosophy of foreign aid is the realization that all the factors which in combination may lead to success should be identified and marshalled prior to their application. The bedrock of this philosophy is the concept that foreign aid is a form of alliance for progress and one which carries with it the implicit understanding that donor nations are interested in helping recipients to achieve those goals which they themselves have determined to be of greatest social and economic value and to which their own efforts are fully dedicated. The sometimes held belief that foreign aid consists of doing something good to or for a recipient nation is being replaced by the more appropriate philosophy of working together toward humanitarian objectives.

There is a growing and desirable tendency toward the idea of foreign aid as a multiple responsibility in which many agencies are playing an active part. There is increasing communication among the organizations concerned in an effort to avoid excessive duplication and confusion and to assure that numerous programs and projects in force may complement or supplement each other. Further progress in this direction will result in greater efficiency and more rapid achievement. Multilateral efforts may well prove to be the most effective and the least controversial and to offer greatest flexibility as well. Hopefully, there will be growing evidence of progress on all fronts in the form of social and economic developments which will make it possible for those nations now seeking more rapid economic growth and improved standards of living to carry their efforts forward increasingly with their own national resources, thus enabling the foreign partner to withdraw gradually from the scene with the assurance of continuing accomplishment.

Aid Abroad: Some Principles and Their Latin American Practice

In seeking to aid underdeveloped nations through technical collaboration—in agriculture, in other natural sciences, or in the social sciences—there are certain principles which should be kept in mind. For one thing, it is important to distinguish between need and opportunity. Vital human needs are easily recognizable and readily demonstrable in many parts of the world, but real opportunities for foreign agencies to alleviate these needs are not always so clearly defined. Compassion and good will are laudable virtues, but they can become misleading if allowed to blind one to fundamental problems. It is inaccurate, as well as tasteless, to talk about the application of foreign "know-how" as the complete solution to human requirements, since most commonly demonstrated human needs are not of such simple solution.

Unfortunately, but understandably, too often there is a sense of urgency involved in foreign aid programs, accompanied by heavy pressure to achieve maximum accomplishment in a minimum period of time. But the very facts responsible for lack of development may themselves mitigate against rapid solutions. It is wise to spend both time and thought in preliminary surveys and in evaluating current and long-range problems, as well as their possible solutions. For this, competent individuals must travel widely in the country in question, consult extensively with leaders in all relevant fields, and ascertain the thinking of the political and social leaders of the state. Slowly, critical problems become apparent and what local people would like to have done about them becomes known. Finally, there may be

Article appearing in the September, 1962, issue of *Foundation News* agreement on the over-all type of program to be initiated, the identification of projects of greatest importance, those of collateral emphasis, and details of effective organization.

LOCAL RESOURCES

It is important to keep in mind the economic and technical resources of the country receiving foreign aid. No such program should require greater expenditures than the local budget will readily sustain. Neither should it contemplate rapid growth to dimensions that will outstrip the number of available national personnel who can be trained, with the view of ultimately taking over entire responsibility. It is very much better to initiate technical aid projects slowly and permit them to grow only as rapidly as accomplishments dictate. Periodic review and modification to suit changing conditions are essential to continued vitality, and the entire project should fit itself into the cultural pattern of the host country. And at some point the effort should become such an integral part of over-all local activities that foreign technical aid is no longer urgently needed; it will then be possible to begin to withdraw, with the assurance that the work will continue and expand under completely national auspices.

PERSONNEL

Technical competence alone is insufficient in the selection of foreign aid personnel. It must be accompanied by an international viewpoint, a determination to learn local languages and customs, the ability to see local problems in their logical framework, and the willingness to work within this framework. Recruitment of appropriate personnel is one of the most difficult tasks of technical collaboration in the foreign field. If urgency and expediency are substituted for a careful process of selection, eventual disadvantages will far outweigh any brief and transitory gains.

The greatest contribution any foreign technical aid program can make does not lie in technical accomplishments themselves, but rather in total impact on the recipient nation. People must first become convinced that the program is one of good will and of real value; that foreign operating personnel desire to become a part of the community; that empire-building is not contemplated; and finally, and most important of all, that there is in fact a definite and sustained effort to transfer imported knowledge and skills. Only then will there be general acceptance of the results obtained, and only then will these be applied to the amelioration of local conditions.

TRAINING

The formal and informal training of young nationals is the most vital single factor in this type of program. Admittedly, this must sometimes be started at a very elementary level, often with many delays and discouragements. But every trained national becomes one more person who may devote his life and efforts to the solution of his country's basic problems; the number and competence of such individuals developed by a technical collaboration program will in the long run determine its total success.

There are several ways of helping to train the nationals of the host country. The first and most fundamental is through the strengthening of local institutions. A second method is by training graduates of local institutions within the technical aid program, overlaying their academic experience with practical application to local situations. This process tends to focus attention upon national requirements; it also carries over into any training these men may receive abroad, since they begin with better knowledge both of their country's problems and some of the possible solutions. A third training technique is the use of external fellowships or scholarships, and an essential fourth method involves the strategic utilization of such persons after their return from abroad. Helping to place trained nationals in positions of usefulness is of maximum future benefit, and it is often necessary to continue to aid these young scientists both morally and materially, helping them to become established, to direct or to carry out locally significant projects and programs, and to aid in the training of subsequent generations.

All four techniques have been utilized in The Rockefeller Foundation's collaborative agricultural programs with the governments of Mexico, Colombia, and Chile.

MEXICO

The agricultural operating program of The Rockefeller Foundation had its beginnings in a 1941 request for technical assistance from the Government of Mexico. After preliminary stages of study, orientation, and selection of projects, a small group of American scientists of proven ability and accomplishment was brought together in Mexico, the several individuals to serve as nuclei for the development of basic sectors. By mutual agreement these men initiated interlocking projects aimed at the improvement, both in quantity and quality, of basic food crops, attacking all those factors of greatest importance in limiting yield. Each of these men was surrounded by a group of young Mexican agricultural graduates who acted as both colleagues and trainees. All the work was carried out on a completely cooperative basis; the entire operation was organized as a semiofficial office of the Ministry of Agriculture. The young trainees participated in every phase of the research from the most elementary to the final step. Many of those with special aptitudes were subsequently granted Foundation scholarships for further training abroad; others entered directly into various phases of agricultural science and production. They were then replaced by younger men, and the cycle continued. Almost 250 have thus far been enabled to complete advanced degrees abroad; over 600 have had practical in-service experience.

Most recently, the establishment of a National Institute of Agricultural Research has served to consolidate the program with other Ministry of Agriculture research units. It also places major responsibility for technical and administrative matters in the hands of Mexican scientists. And a locally based graduate school has been created; advanced training can now be obtained in Mexico, and in Spanish. As the graduate school expands, it can be expected to assume regional and then hemispheric significance.

COLOMBIA AND CHILE

As the program in Mexico developed, other countries became interested in this type of collaboration. In 1950, together with the Ministry of Agriculture of Colombia, the Foundation set up a second cooperative agricultural research program. This has now grown to substantial proportions—and one of its most gratifying aspects has been the demonstration that the improved materials produced, after years of intensive research, in the Mexican program were immediately useful in other areas with similar climatological conditions. The background experience gained in Mexico has made possible much more rapid progress in some areas of Colombia. And the still newer program, established in Chile in 1955, has been able to profit from the accumulated data of both the earlier efforts.

188

Information and improved materials produced in all three countries have been distributed widely and exchanged wherever it appeared they might be useful. The exchange of visits by agricultural scientists representing the several Latin American countries has been encouraged, and important international scientific meetings have been sponsored. Moreover, more than 75 young scientists from some 10 other countries of Latin America have received in-service training, principally in Mexico. These men, on their return, have assumed posts of high responsibility.

The Inter-American Food Crop Improvement Program (formally initiated in 1959) is still in the embryonic state. At first concerned with maize, and then with wheat, it has now been expanded to include attention to potato improvement. This new type of hemisphere-wide program seems likely to help maximize the effectiveness of Foundation staff and funds.

SUMMARY

Friendly nations cannot resolve the fundamental problems of the less developed or emerging nations, but they can help to speed the processes of social and economic growth by collaborating in projects of readily demonstrable benefit that can be completed or ultimately transferred to local agencies. Intensive preliminary planning of such projects, and careful selection of the personnel assigned to them, are essential to success. The most basic consideration of all, however, is the extent to which each project can serve as a training facility for the nationals of the countries concerned. Only by emphasizing the training aspect of foreign assistance is it possible to develop permanent roots and to achieve continuity and multiple benefits from an enlarging force of competent personnel able to serve national needs.

Making the Most of Human Resources

The mere act of existing is a totally unrewarding human experience. Through most of history, life at a level scarcely above that of the animal has been the lot of most of the people. Not until a stable agriculture began to give society a surplus supply of food beyond that necessary to feed individual producers could what we call civilization begin to develop on this globe, and the early civilized societies appeared only in those few places where a generous nature allowed primitive producers to grow a surplus large enough to support the gradual development of the arts, sciences, commerce, and industry.

Nature is no more lavish today than eons ago, but man has managed to increase the margin of food beyond that needed to feed himself until the next harvest so successfully that, in one country at least, the word "surplus" has become almost anathema. Even so, over most of the globe and for most of the people the idea of surplus food is an unrealized dream, an objective whose attainment seems still in the distant future. But the idea is abroad in the land that for all people in all countries production should grow to such proportions that all can share in the satisfactions of life beyond the bare material necessities.

The revolution of rising expectations means simply that people think that life is truly meaningful only when it is given more purpose than mere subsistence and when the individual has opportunity to seek maximum achievement within the limits of his potentials. Ideally, the complete realization of the rewards of effective social organization requires the full participation of all members of society, contributed to the maximum of their individual abilities. The con-

Talk given at Miami Beach on October 15, 1962, at the American Public Health Association Symposium on Health Today in Social and Economic Development

cept of full achievement by society and by individuals is obviously utopian, but some factors prevent even partial attainment of this goal and keep us from making the most of our human resources.

It is unnecessary to argue with this audience that of the three checks on population growth listed by Malthus—war, pestilence, and famine—it is pestilence that especially merits our attention because of the curious double role it plays in creating the situation in which we find ourselves. On the one hand, the practical eradication of some diseases and the containment of others is the factor chiefly credited with triggering the population explosion. While this is probably too simple an explanation, ignoring as it does the improvements in agriculture and transportation which have virtually eliminated famine, the net result is that a vast increase in the sheer numbers of people per unit of area holds back and may even defeat all efforts to close the gap between present extremes in standards of living. Malthus eventually came to admit that there might be a fourth check on unrestrained population growth, a factor he called "moral restraint." In considering possible controls of too exuberant population growth, we might reread Malthus on this point.

The other side of the paradox of pestilence is that in those very countries where unprecedented population growth is threatening living standards disease remains one of the chief deterrents to increased economic productivity and to enriched satisfactions. The dramatic onslaughts of the spectacular killers among the communicable diseases, sometimes so terrible as to alter the very course of history, have now been brought within more tolerable limits. But quietly and insidiously the chronic ills persist, debilitating and destroying gradually, their effects often perceived only indirectly.

The Rockefeller Foundation has had several opportunities to participate in efforts to study one of the most important of the debilitating diseases, bilharziasis. This "country cousin" among diseases, once thought to be prevalent only in the region where it was first observed, is now known as a wide-ranging crippler whose toll in terms of lowered human energy and productivity can only be guessed at. The question is, "Can the unpromising outlook for its control be changed to a more hopeful one?" A recent attempt to organize a coordinated and integrated attack on its problems, in which The Rockefeller Foundation has been privileged to share, will at least probe possible answers.

It is a curious coincidence that at the time of its establishment in 1913 The Rockefeller Foundation made its first venture in the health sciences with a full-scale attack on another debilitator, hookworm, in the southern states of this country. Most of us have probably never seen a case of hookworm, but the campaign against it deserves comment for its relevance to some of the problems we face in present aid and assistance programs to improve the well-being of mankind in less developed countries overseas.

Oddly enough, the hookworm campaign of The Rockefeller Foundation was not directed primarily toward the conquest of disease. The resources of the Foundation, vast though they seemed in those days, were totally inadequate in comparison to the dimensions of the job. Rather, the aim of the director of the campaign, Mr. Wickliffe Rose, was to use the project as a public education device, or demonstration, to inform the public about the seriousness of the disease, its importance as a depressor of productivity, and to cajole local communities into undertaking not just hookworm control but the general improvement of public health through better sanitation. Specifically, the aim was to persuade rural county officials to appropriate funds for the employment of full-time health officers. Through demonstrations and the offer of initial financial assistance, the Foundation aided the setting up of health departments with professional staffs in hundreds of counties, chiefly in the southern states.

The American Public Health Association recognized the importance of this county health unit campaign by electing to its presidency Mr. Rose's long-time associate who had been in immediate charge of the work, Dr. John A. Ferrell. Other pioneers in the establishment of the county health department system in this country are still alive and vigorous—Dr. Andrew J. Warren, Dr. Benjamin E. Washburn, and Dr. W. P. Jacocks—all of them, like Dr. Ferrell, from the state of North Carolina. Perhaps there is some subtle correlation between geography and longevity.

Incidentally, hookworm disease was never conquered in the usual medical sense of the term. It simply disappeared as slowly increasing prosperity allowed the southern communities, under the guidance of their new health departments, to alter the environment to one in which the parasite could not flourish, or more specifically, to install water and sewerage systems in the towns and sanitary privies in the country.

May I point out another lesson this almost forgotten chapter in American history might teach us? The South of that pre-World War I era was much like the underdeveloped countries we know today— its per capita agricultural income was as low as one-sixth of that in a state like Iowa; its illiteracy rate among white people was 27 per cent; its economy was dependent principally on a single crop, cotton; and its educational system was pitifully inadequate. To document these appalling conditions, I cite the published history of The Rockefeller Foundation's sister organization, the General Education Board. Written by Raymond B. Fosdick and entitled *Adventure in Giving,* this book will make interesting and heartening reading for those who may be discouraged by the slow pace of social improvement in some of the countries among our overseas neighbors. We have been pretty slow about some of these improvements ourselves.

When you read Mr. Fosdick's book, you will find emphasized what you already know, that social advance is conditioned by a complex of interrelated factors. The General Education Board, as its title implies, was devoted primarily to the improvement of education, "without distinction of race, sex, or creed," and with particular emphasis on southern education. But Mr. John D. Rockefeller, Jr., with the wise guidance of Frederick T. Gates, soon realized that public education can never be strong or good until the taxable wealth of the state becomes sufficient to produce adequate revenue, not only for education but also for health and other protections and services. Hence, the Board stepped in to change the Seaman A. Knapp farm demonstration program from one devoted to cotton boll weevil control to one devoted to broad rural improvement, with the aim of increasing the tax base in the southern states. Between 1906 and 1914 the Board invested nearly one million dollars in the Knapp farm demonstrations in 636 counties and in 16 southern states. In 1914 the United States Federal Government, convinced of its worth, assumed the full financial responsibility for continuing the county agent extension system, not only in the South but also for its expansion to the rest of the country. Seldom has a private technical assistance agency so brilliantly worked itself out of a job, or a cooperating government so enthusiastically picked up the burden and carried it forward so vigorously and successfully.

Most malariologists are familiar with the Sardinia story (1946-1950, inclusive) in which The Rockefeller Foundation played a rather important role. Once described as "the hell hole of the Mediterranean" because of its long history and almost universal prevalence of malaria, the island was made the scene of a massive campaign directed to the eradication of the malarial vector. Scientifically, this five-year effort must perhaps be described as a failure, since it did not prove possible to eradicate the mosquito species totally from Sardinia through this program. Nevertheless, the dramatic reduction in the incidence of malaria and the corresponding improvement in the health of the population have changed the entire economic and social pattern of the island. Today it enjoys economic prosperity, which is supplemented by income from the tourists who now visit the island, attracted by its climate, comfort, and beauty.

While The Rockefeller Foundation does not maintain programs in public health of the dimensions of some of its previous activities, it is by no means out of or away from this field. The Foundation is now putting a great deal of emphasis on the strengthening of medical education in underdeveloped areas, in connection with a plan for across-the-board university development. In the schools with which it collaborates, the traditional teaching hospital experience of the students, interns, and residents will be strongly supplemented by training experience in a community health center. Here the student sees the patient as a whole person, as a member of a family and of a community. I am sure you will recognize in this pattern our heritage from a great teacher and educational innovator, Dr. John B. Grant, formerly of The Rockefeller Foundation and, until his death, of the University of Puerto Rico Medical School.

I should mention also in this connection the arthropod-borne virus research program of the Foundation, with its field stations in a number of tropical countries and its headquarter laboratories in this country. When this investigation began in 1949, some of the few arboviruses then known were not associated with any recognized infection—they were sometimes referred to, almost derisively, as infectious agents in search of a disease. Since that time, more refined methodology, more precise procedures for classification, and a vast amount of descriptive and empirical data gathered through field work have shown the public health importance of the arboviruses and opened up an almost new field of investigation which is rapidly attracting new workers and strong support.

It is not difficult to illustrate through specific examples the fact that public health programs in numerous instances have contributed to the rehabilitation of large populations by increasing their comfort through the control of disease and, by extrapolation, their productive potentials. It is difficult, however, to cite statistical analyses which clearly measure these gains. Still more complicated and less understood is the interrelationship of public health, agriculture, and education as factors in the complex of social progress.

From time immemorial the primary duty of the physician has been to heal the sick and of the public health physician to protect the community from illness and premature mortality. Many may feel that these humanitarian mandates are sufficient unto themselves, require no explanation, and admit no question. However, today we are witnessing the struggle of a number of developing countries to achieve economic growth and stability. They need essentially everything in order to provide their rapidly growing populations with food, housing, schools, health services, transportation, communication, and industries. These are all needed quickly in response to rising expectations, and there is pressure against acceptance of the gradual process of exchange and evolution characteristic of the England of the Industrial Revolution and the United States of a hundred years ago. Today things move so fast and the rate of change is so rapid that those who delay fear that they will only fall further behind. The dangers inherent in the attempt to telescope history are apparent, but the attempt is under way and must be recognized.

This situation is further complicated by the always present specter of limited resources of all kinds. Under such circumstances it is not possible to indulge in decision-making which might be described as purely humanitarian, as contrasted to judgments and action dictated by the best economic criteria. It is increasingly evident that although any single aspect of human welfare could absorb all available resources, major amounts must be channeled in support of those elements which can effectively contribute to the over-all area of economic development. This may often mean that considerations of program in medicine and public health may have to be subordinated to the needs of other sectors of social and economic planning.

When we search for figures to illustrate the conservation of human resources through disease prevention in the less developed countries, we find that there are few useful data which would be acceptable to the economist and at the same time generally applicable. There has, it would appear, been an unfortunate lag in the interaction between the health sciences and economics, which has prevented each from taking advantage of the skills of the other in a joint effort to establish sound guideposts to the road ahead. It is true that the malariologists, as early as 50 years ago, asked themselves questions concerning the economic and social consequences of their control programs, but these questions have largely gone unanswered in precise terms. Certainly, empirical formulas were established, which gave at least an indication as to what might be expected as a result of a successful malaria-control program in a stated locality. However, such formulas have been largely a combination of tangibles and intangibles which gave answers somewhat short of the mathematical ideal. Nevertheless, we owe a great deal to the interest of such persons as Watson in Malaya, Gorgas in Panama, Sir Gordon Covell in India, and my own former colleague, Dr. Paul F. Russell, on the relationship between disease prevention and economic productivity. Dr. Russell concluded that it is impossible at the present time to make any authoritative statement bearing on the relationship between disease prevention and economic productivity.

Another former colleague, Dr. Walter Salant, an economist, now at the Brookings Institution, has inquired into the question of disease prevention and economic productivity. He concludes that there should be a serious study of the relationships between health and social and economic development, and says:

> "It may be argued that such studies would have little practical value because public health expenditures are made for humanitarian, not economic, reasons and would not be influenced by the results of any study. Although I recognize that there is a good deal to the premise of this argument, I am disposed not to accept its conclusion. One reason is that so long as resources are scarce, choices must be made among alternative forms and amounts of such expenditure and economic consequences are relevant to the choices. . . . Another reason that I do not accept the conclusion is that even if the undertaking of public health expenditures is not affected by their economic consequences, these consequences should be known if economic planning is to be conducted intelligently."

It is encouraging to note that in recent years skilled professional economists have become preoccupied by the interrelationship between health and economics and have sought approaches to evaluation methods in order to determine the facts and, more importantly still, to help chart the course of the future for maximum human benefit. Weisbrod at Princeton, Fein of the Council of Economic Advisors, Mushkin of the Advisory Commission on Intergovernmental Relations, and Alice Rivlin of the Brookings Institution have made considerable progress in developing a theoretical framework and a quantitative methodology for the study of the economics of public health. Although most of the work done thus far has dealt with this country, it seems clear that, when successfully worked out, the general concepts and technics might well be applicable to the situations which exist in many of the less developed nations.

A most recent and significant development in theoretical economics relevant to this discussion is being carried out under the leadership of Professor Theodore W. Schultz of the University of Chicago. A new theory of human capital, now in process of formulation, bears very closely on the maximum use of human resources and on their value to social and economic development. The theory treats the costs of education as an investment in human capital rather than as consumption, that bugbear of the economist and the economic planner in underdeveloped countries. It has already been extended to consideration of health expenditure, which closely resembles expenditure for education as an investment in human capital. Indeed, there are very strong similarities between the analysis required for the economics of public health and that for education. Schultz states:

> "Although it is obvious that people acquire useful skills and knowledge, it is not obvious that these skills and knowledge are a form of capital, that this capital is in substantial part a product of deliberate investment, that it has grown in Western societies at a much faster rate than conventional (non-human) capital, and that its growth may well be the most distinctive feature of the economic system. It has been widely observed that increases in national output have been large compared with the increases of land, man-hours, and physical reproducible capital. Investment in human capital is probably the major explanation for this difference."

In summary, I believe there is indisputable evidence of the many occasions upon which the principles and practice of public health have returned health and vigor to millions of mankind. In so doing, the re-establishment of productive potentials has been made possible, and without doubt this has contributed to economic progress.

197

On the other hand, as pointed out, it is extraordinarily difficult to weigh each of the factors concerned and to determine whether the figures are accurate and whether the results have fully justified the expense and effort. This is especially true in a situation in which resources are so limited that many basic human demands must long remain unsatisfied.

In the light of the complexities of modern society, it becomes clear that decision-making is taking on new dimensions of importance and that no aspect of human experience or circumstances can be considered in isolation from the others. Painful as they may be, decisions will have to be made which are calculated to produce maximum social and economic progress at all possible speed. Thus, each facet of social organization will have to be tested in terms of the whole and supported within the limits of available resources to the level compatible with its estimated services to the social good.

Bread and Peace

In 1963 missiles are commonplace. Man expects to land on the moon seven years and thirty billion dollars from now, and interplanetary exchange is apparently just around a cosmic corner. Modern technology is dazzling in what it has done and what it can do, not only in space but here on earth in the creation of new sources of energy, new methods of production, and new products for those who can buy and use them.

But in the meantime, the melancholy fact is that half the people in the world go to bed hungry every night. While man forges ahead in his technological conquest of the universe, efforts to provide even minimum acceptable standards of living lag tragically behind. If this lag is not corrected, and reasonably soon, all the rest of human accomplishment may end in chaos.

Mankind's path to peace is through the creation of an ever-improving environment for people everywhere. In a world in which traditionally the strong have exploited the weak, denying them opportunity, liberty, and often life itself, an equitable environment for all is not to be easily achieved. The heritage of centuries of conflicts, large and small, is the disparity of economic and social progress among nations.

Although man's basic nature is much the same as in an earlier, more primitive stage of existence, education and greater understanding are gradually changing the values most esteemed in human behavior. Once considered totally expendable, the individual human being is now more highly regarded, his rights protected, and his

Speech delivered at a meeting of the Nutrition Foundation, New York City, March 6, 1963 aspirations respected. But powerful forces are still arrayed against each other, direct confrontations still occur, and sporadic conflicts erupt. In times past, these frictions could and did flame into open war. Today, as a result of awesome technological accomplishments, we have reached the point at which total self-destruction is possible —a tragic accomplishment, indeed, in a society which values individual life as never before and where more people can at last enjoy enriched personal satisfactions and fulfillment.

The problems which currently beset the world are many and complicated, and not often clearly understood. In order to overcome them and improve the lot of all citizens of the globe, men of good will must persist in engaging the forces which destroy rather than advance civilization. Our faith must rest upon the march of knowledge and its application for human benefit. Ultimate success in the achievement of human satisfaction and social progress must be through the full participation by all of society in the responsibilities of national and world citizenship.

One of the great emergent forces working for rather than against the fulfillment of mankind's ideals is private philanthropy. The product of the deepest human compassion and intellectual sophistication, this force has had a gradual yet vigorous evolution as the concept of human equality slowly gained ascendancy over the philosophy that "to the victor belong the spoils." And it is in the United States during the short span of the past 50 years that the highest expressions of private philanthropy have been reached.

Although the programs of philanthropic foundations are usually defined as falling in the fields of education, health, nutrition, economics, or the like, what each seeks is the alleviation or elimination of some negative factor in human experience. They attempt to remove certain basic causes of human tension and suffering which, unless changed at the source, may bring conflict or social deterioration. Their ideals are positive—to increase the well-being of mankind throughout the world—but their methods take the form of campaigns against specific ills like disease and hunger and ignorance.

The word "campaign" brings us to the practicalities of the situation—how does one get things done in raising standards of health or nutrition or education? Almost exactly fifty years ago The Rockefeller Foundation began experimenting with various answers. Its early campaigns were directed against the major infectious diseases

—hookworm, malaria, typhus, yellow fever. The officers of the Foundation soon learned that continuing protection must depend on local health agencies staffed by competent people. The next step, therefore, was to build up training institutions, a chain of 23 schools of hygiene and public health from Tokyo to Zagreb, from Oslo to Sao Paulo, which today stand as monuments to this insight. Medical education, research in the medical sciences, and the training of other health care personnel followed logically as objectives in the over-all campaign.

The opportunity to enter the field of nutrition came in the early 1940's with an invitation from the government of Mexico to cooperate in a campaign to improve the quantity of production and the quality of the basic foods essential to the national diet.

The Rockefeller Foundation accepted this invitation in the belief that private philanthropy could play a role in seeking to remove, or at least move a little further away, the specter of hunger from the many peoples over whom it had loomed since time immemorial. If the effort were successful, it could be hoped that a pattern might develop which could relieve some of the tensions which have in the past led to major conflicts. The Foundation, having long given battle to pestilence, the first of the three dread specters, now joined issue with the second, hunger, in the belief that progress on these two fronts might diminish the ominous threat of the third, war.

Revolutions are run on slogans, and the Mexican Revolution which began in 1910 had two which well express the phases through which it passed. The first slogan was *Tierra y Libertad*—Land and Liberty. Through the military phase of the revolution, land distribution and political freedom were the constant aims of the Mexican people. In the next the cry was *Paz y Pan*—Peace and Bread, civil order and food. But to get the bread another revolution was needed. In the words of Don Marte R. Gomez, the Minister of Agriculture who issued the invitation to The Rockefeller Foundation to come to Mexico, his country had solved its land reform problem; now it needed an agricultural revolution to increase food production. The population day by day was outgrowing its food supplies—a 19 per cent increase between 1930 and 1940, a 31 per cent increase between 1940 and 1950. Mexico was forced to import large amounts of corn, her basic food, and of wheat, at great cost in scarce foreign exchange. To grow more food was an imperative.

How to create an agricultural revolution? This is the question The Rockefeller Foundation tried to answer in intimate cooperation with its Mexican colleagues. That the answer devised there has relevance elsewhere will, I think, become apparent as the story unfolds.

An agricultural revolution cannot be a single breakthrough, a great leap forward depending on a miracle of science. Yet we must have faith in miracles, since all that we now know has accumulated from past breakthroughs based upon scientific miracles, both large and small. Some day science can make the deserts blossom with de-salted water from the sea produced by nuclear power. Some day we may convert solar energy through systems more efficient than photosynthesis, or harvest the infinite resources of the sea.

But while we must always hope that some major discovery will significantly hasten the progress of food production, it simply is not possible to ignore opportunities to apply all the knowledge we now have to conventional agricultural practices, with the understanding that this can lead to great increases of food production.

The simple truth is that we know enough—today—now—to transform the food production of the world. The earth today can produce at least three times what it is now producing on present arable surfaces by the known methods of conventional agriculture. The cry for Bread could be answered now. So far as scientific knowledge is concerned, there is no reason why any human being in the world should not be well fed, and there is no longer any excuse for human starvation. The stumbling block is man himself—his prejudices and misinformation, his lack of education and ability to put to work the accumulated scientific and technical knowledge that lies at hand.

Begun in 1943, the modest effort in Mexico first focused upon the improvement of maize and wheat, the principal food crops of the country. I was the first staff member of the joint Ministry of Agriculture-Rockefeller Foundation program. My first associate was a young Mexican graduate of the National School of Agriculture, commissioned to the joint program for advanced practical experience in scientific agriculture. Later we were joined by additional staff specialists in corn, wheat, soil science, entomology, and plant pathology. Each of these specialists became the leader of small groups of young Mexican agronomists assigned by the Ministry for training. The experience they received was in research methods on problems which limited the production of food crops in their own country, under the supervision of specialists in each discipline. We operated through a semi-autonomous agency of the Ministry of Agriculture called the Office of Special Studies. As one project showed it was on the way to success, we added others, until, in addition to corn and wheat, we had sections dealing with potatoes, vegetables, sorghum, barley, and forage and pasture legumes and grasses. The last step was to extend our work into the animal sciences, with research on poultry, dairy and beef cattle, swine, and sheep.

In each crop improvement project we followed the same pattern. It began with collection and testing of indigenous adapted varieties and the selection of the best for quick release to farmers. From other countries we brought in and tested materials that appeared promising. From the germ plasm banks thus created we began hybridizing to create higher-yielding, disease-resistant varieties intimately adapted to the Mexican regions for which they were recommended. For this work physical facilities were needed, and as results began to show and farmers began to demand more materials and information, the government supplied funds for building and improving central and regional experiment stations and laboratories and for the necessary technicians and labor. The Foundation supplied its own staff and funds for equipment, supplies, and salary supplements.

As we were seeking and testing seeds and methods we were seeking and testing young Mexicans. Our problem basically was to cultivate personnel and crops at the same time. We brought in young men from the agricultural schools to work during vacation periods. From these we selected the best to join our office for more systematic training, and from this group we chose others to receive fellowships and scholarships for study abroad. Always we saw to it that there were jobs waiting for them upon their return to Mexico.

Generally speaking, when we had improved seed and could recommend better methods, we began by helping those farmers who would respond. We did not necessarily start at the bottom, where it takes one missionary to make one convert, but at the level where one man with an idea can lead others toward progress. We were sure that the best way to help the subsistence farmer was to begin to create a new agricultural climate, a climate of hope and progress and success. As the ideas of seed and soil improvement became more and more familiar and widely accepted, the extension work necessary for the acceptance of the improvements at the base of the agricultural pyramid could be more productive. And, so I believe, it has been.

Gradually we won converts. We had regular field days at the experiment stations. For our first one, I think 22 people appeared —most of them our own people and their friends. Ultimately, we were to have up to 4,000 farmers come on a single day to see for themselves what could be done and to learn. When the Ministry decided to expand its organization to include an extension service, recommendations for materials and methods were ready, and a corps of knowledgeable agronomists to undertake the task of persuading their own countrymen to try the new ways.

I won't attempt to give a more detailed description of the Mexican program. When we began, it was supposed that the Office of Special Studies might go on for at least ten years, though those of us most closely involved soon saw it would take longer. As results began to be seen, we continued to move ahead. This year the program celebrates its twentieth birthday. The Office of Special Studies no longer exists, having been absorbed into the newly created National Institute of Agricultural Research, directed and administered by Mexican scientists, almost all of whom are Office of Special Studies alumni. The Institute will soon become associated with the undergraduate and postgraduate divisions of the National School of Agriculture and the national extension service. Together, these can become a great national and international center for agricultural research, education, and extension.

During these 20 years, 700 young Mexicans served internships in the Office of Special Studies. Of those who were given fellowships for postgraduate studies abroad, more than 100 have earned Master of Science degrees and over 30 have completed their doctorates. Every one of them has returned to Mexico to a position of leadership in teaching, in research, in extension, or in commercial agriculture—a growing sector of strength in the Mexican economy.

The impact of this cooperative program on the agriculture of Mexico has produced demonstrable results. In general, it can be said that food production has doubled. Wheat production has more than doubled, corn harvests are up almost as much, bean production has doubled, broiler production has tripled, eggs have increased two and a half times, and the end is not in sight. Mexico could stop importing wheat in 1956, when harvest balanced demand for the first time in history, and corn is no longer in deficit supply.

Twenty years ago Mexico's 21 million people averaged 1,700 calories a day. Today Mexico's 37 million people average 2,700 calories, and they have a more varied diet that increasingly includes animal proteins.

From the experience gained in Mexico The Rockefeller Foundation has carried the pattern of cooperation to other parts of the world. The program in Colombia, established at the invitation of the government in 1950, and the one in Chile, similarly begun in 1955, have taken full advantage of the experience gained by their predecessor. Together they have been able to accomplish a great deal more than would have been possible had each had to start at the point where the Mexican program began. Each owes a great debt to Mexico and the cooperation there, and in turn each has contributed to a wide variety of efforts elsewhere.

The program in India, begun in 1956, follows the Latin American pattern in two crop-improvement plans, one for maize and the other for sorghum and the millets. It broke new ground in another respect; from the first, its staff members worked directly in the establishment and development of a postgraduate school of agriculture, the Indian Agricultural Research Institute. Following a curriculum plan much like that of land-grant colleges in this country, the Institute has already awarded 60 Ph.D. degrees and 246 M.Sc. degrees.

The program in the Philippines takes the form of an international institute devoted to the problems of rice production and its distribution and utilization. The International Rice Research Institute, dedicated early in 1962, is a cooperative effort of the government of the Philippines, which supplied the land and other facilities; The Ford Foundation, which supplied the funds for its plant; and The Rockefeller Foundation, which supports and administers its scientific program. The Institute has already drawn upon Latin American experience for some of its staff, but most of its Trustees and the bulk of its scientific staff consist of distinguished officials and scientists from the several countries of Asia. Some 60 young men from rice bowl countries will obtain advanced training each year in rice improvement methods. Working closely with other Asian countries, and intimately associated with the University of the Philippines, the Institute, it is hoped, will each year become a more powerful tool for the alleviation of hunger in the area where untold millions depend upon rice for their daily bread.

Perhaps the most significant product thus far obtained from the concerted programs in Latin America and Asia for the improvement of maize, wheat, rice, and potatoes has been their natural proliferation into world-wide efforts for the betterment of these crops elsewhere. Vast depositories of genetic material of these plants have been accumulated. Lines and varieties are being tested in uniform yield and disease-resistance nurseries in essentially all the important production areas. Superior materials are being selected and utilized both for immediate production and as foundation stocks for still better varieties.

In terms of total world need, the results of the work of The Rockefeller Foundation and of those with whom it has been associated can only be described as modest. Nevertheless, they have, I believe, created a pattern of operation which can be and, in fact, is being emulated by others. Particularly influential have been the scientists who have come from other countries to associate themselves for periods of various lengths with one or another of the Foundation operations. On returning to their own countries, these men have established similar projects, with direct encouragement and support from the Foundation. Through proliferation of this kind there are today a growing number of projects and programs set up by local scientists alone or in collaboration with other national or international agencies. Together, these are making significant contributions to the well-being of growing numbers of people.

Important though it may be, a successful solution of the problems of agricultural production can satisfy only part of the requirement for giving human life greater dignity and richer meaning. If we have learned any lesson from the ecologists, it is that progress in one sector must be accompanied by advances in others, to preserve the subtle balance which in societies as in nature maintains the harmony of the social order. Ideally, a pattern of technical aid to emerging countries should catalyze all the main aspects of cultural and economic progress; along with improvements in agriculture should go others in education, in public health, in employment, and in opportunities for self-realization. If to these could be added the full protection of the rights of citizenship and the advantages of freedom of communication and of individual enterprise, then it would truly be possible to make fullest use of national resources for the well-being of all the people.

The pressures of population increase upon the resources of many nations are every day becoming greater and greater, threatening the bankruptcy of their social economies. Unless concerted, organized, and intelligent effort is directed toward the prompt amelioration of the causes of human suffering and the stabilization of population, the advance of civilization may be halted. Such patterns of technical assistance as I have described here may provide guidelines for future successes. Alone, however, they are not enough.

The example of Mexico may be illuminating in this regard. Over a ten-year span Mexico's agricultural production has increased at an annual rate of seven per cent. In the same ten years her population increased annually by three per cent. Mexico has thus "bought time" in the race against engulfment by the flood of sheer numbers.

The infinite projection of agricultural improvement can never keep up with the infinite projection of unchecked population increase. But if the improvement of food production through better agriculture can gain time for mounting an integrated attack on the forces which endanger the ecological balance of the human species, it may be the key to a more hopeful future. We must live, and work, in the faith that the widespread application of the benefits of knowledge and technology will in the end contribute fundamentally to the well-being of mankind throughout the world.

New Ventures for Private Philanthropy

The Rockefeller Foundation this year completes a half-century of activity toward "the well-being of mankind throughout the world." During these 50 years hundreds of millions of dollars have been spent by foundations—some of them established before, and more since, 1913—on education, research, and related efforts in the cause of human welfare.

This may be an appropriate moment to examine the purpose and the value of private philanthropy as it has developed in these decades, and to speculate about its future.

The philanthropic foundation as we know it today is an invention of the early 20th century, although its roots go back at least to 14th-century England where wealthy merchants were urged to gain remission of their sins by leaving perpetuities to "repair hospitals, mend bad roads, put scholars to school, help maidens marry or make them nuns."

In our country, organized private philanthropy was the response of a small number of men—long before income taxes—to a conviction that the accumulation of great wealth bore with it an obligation to public service. Andrew Carnegie, in his essay "The Gospel of Wealth," published in 1889, said, "The man who dies rich dies disgraced." One of his readers, John D. Rockefeller, wrote Carnegie to assure him that "your example will bear fruits, and the time will come when men of wealth will more generally be willing to use it for the good of others."

Mr. Rockefeller was encouraged to establish private philanthropies with his wealth by his most trusted adviser Frederick T. Gates,

Article appearing in *The New York Times Magazine,* June 9, 1963 who told him, " Your fortune is rolling up, rolling up like an avalanche! You must distribute it faster than it grows! If you do not, it will crush you and your children and your children's children."

The conviction that private wealth must be put to work to advance human welfare was not characteristic of the time. Popular opinion held that, by and large, men were rewarded according to their own efforts, and that poverty and ignorance were the result of shiftlessness and lack of initiative. In assuming moral and social responsibilities which were not thrust upon them, men such as Peabody, Dodge, Carnegie, Rockefeller, Guggenheim, Rosenwald, and Sloan defined obligations of wealth far beyond personal giving.

As the Carnegie Corporation said in its 50th-anniversary report two years ago, "Wealth is nothing new in the history of the world. Nor is charity. But the idea of using private wealth imaginatively, constructively, and systematically to attack the fundamental problems of mankind *is* new."

Chief among the ills of Americans 50 years ago were ignorance and disease. Fewer than nine per cent of the population were high-school graduates. Only one in 20 could hope to continue education through college or professional school. America's illiteracy rate was more than seven per cent.

Dysentery and typhoid were commonplace and accepted with resignation. Smallpox was an ever-present threat. Hookworm, an anemia-producing parasite, took an immense toll in human potential, especially in the South. Malaria, venereal infections, and many other diseases plagued millions. Public health services, especially in the rural areas, were minimal and sanitary conditions primitive. Of 190,000 homes inspected in the rural South in 1911, one-half did not have even an outdoor privy.

The sick were in the hands of physicians who were ill-educated and poorly trained. When Abraham Flexner, under a grant from the Carnegie Foundation for the Advancement of Teaching, personally investigated every one of the 155 medical schools in this country, he found that the vast majority consisted of "a few local practitioners and a few bones." Only 50 schools required even a high school education as an entrance requirement. In 1913, the year The Rockefeller Foundation was incorporated in New York State, life expectancy in this country was 52 years, and one out of every 10 children died in the first year of life.

Clearly, grave national deficiencies existed in education and health, which able leadership and large sums of money might help correct. The scarcity of public money for these purposes was one stimulus for the creation of private foundations. Thus, the Carnegie Corporation carried on the library-supporting tradition of its founder; the Duke Endowment appropriated large sums of money toward higher education and medical care; the John Simon Guggenheim Memorial Foundation was organized to increase the literary, artistic, and scientific power of this country; the W. K. Kellogg Foundation concerned itself with the health and welfare of children. John D. Rockefeller endowed four independent boards with more than $400,000,000 to pioneer in almost uncharted areas.

To be effective, the funds of foundations could not be invested in relieving symptoms of human misery. As Mr. Rockefeller once put it, "The best philanthropy involves a search for cause, an attempt to cure evils at their source."

To the early trustees of The Rockefeller Foundation disease appeared as "the supreme ill of life . . . and the main source of almost all human ills." Somewhat optimistically, the Foundation determined to "eradicate" the great mass diseases wherever they were to be found.

A start was made by establishing in the South (under the Rockefeller Sanitary Commission), and ultimately in 52 countries and on 29 islands, a program for controlling hookworm, which affected an estimated 1,000,000,000 people. Although hookworm was never completely "eradicated," it was brought under control.

In this first organized attack against widespread disease, and in subsequent worldwide campaigns against malaria and yellow fever, the Foundation formulated step by step the pattern of public health services. These included full-time health officers, well-staffed laboratories, and postgraduate schools which, with Government support, made possible the control of mass disease.

Taken together, the work of the private foundations has filled a gap in the development of better health, better education, and social progress in our country, which could not have been closed otherwise.

Yesterday's "root evils"—ignorance and endemic disease—are no longer the major problems of our society. Today some 60 per cent of our teen-agers complete high school, 30 per cent go on to higher education, and the figures are rising. Life expectancy is up to 70 years from 1913's 52 years, and is rising; infant mortality is down to one in 40, and is going lower. The conditions of life for the American people have certainly changed for the better, but the rapidity and drastic nature of the changes themselves have created problems which 50 years ago were either nonexistent or far less complex.

The domestic problems of our times and of the foreseeable future are primarily those of adaptation rather than deficiency. Rapid population growth has fundamentally altered America's social and natural environment. In 1963 more than 60 per cent of some 180,000,000 Americans live in cities, most of which have been allowed to grow haphazardly for decades. Problems of urban development, transportation, and recreation, of individual and group tensions, of shifts in moral and social values flow from so many people living in such close quarters as to jeopardize the well-being of contemporary man. The arrival of 3,000,000 new citizens each year adds to his burdens and strains his abilities.

Fortunately, government has begun to move heavily into a number of the historic areas of health, education, and welfare. This change has been a prime factor in enabling foundations to broaden their role in social progress.

The evolution of public opinion which dictated that government should be more responsible for social well-being began after the First World War, was vastly accelerated during the Depression, and has grown to its present proportions since the Second World War. In 1962 government funds appropriated for health, education, and welfare came to some $21,000,000,000. Federal research and development grants to American educational institutions totaled more than $1,000,000,000.

Not only are public funds becoming available in greater dimensions, but their application for human benefit is changing in pattern. Basically, public funds must be utilized to provide health protection and educational opportunities for all the people. Modern interpretation calls for the support of research in health, medical education, and the biological sciences, of graduate scholarships, the construction of new health and educational facilities, and special provision for children, the aged, and the handicapped.

To the senior foundations, the gradual transfer to public agencies of responsibility for the continuing support of programs, institutions, and projects which, in their early development, were nourished by private funds, is satisfying evidence of the wisdom of their previous decisions. From the beginning, their goal has been to identify key problems and to demonstrate means for their solution with such clarity that increasing public support would be generated, thus enabling the foundations to turn to new opportunities.

In general terms, the trend of programs of private philanthropy is to search, on the one hand, for answers to domestic problems caused by an increasingly complex social structure, and, on the other hand, for applications of knowledge and technology that will benefit underdeveloped areas abroad.

At home, in our industrialized and urbanized society, foundations have unprecedented opportunities to encourage fresh thinking and experimentation in fields for which support from public funds will probably long be meager. Government support for certain of the social sciences, for example, is limited at best. The humanities—history, philosophy, languages, literature, art—share very little in the flow of public funds. Disciplines like sociology, anthropology, and archaeology find support hard to come by. The stickier and more controversial aspects of race relations, constitutional government, legal and political philosophy, the communication processes, and the management of natural resources need the aid of private resources.

In response to these needs, foundations are today supporting a variety of research and development projects. They have, for instance, aided basic research in linguistics, they have helped finance the International Press Institute's efforts for better worldwide news flow and understanding.

A major activity of foundations has been the support of basic and applied research at the university level to advance the study of regional planning and urban design and renewal. Foundation-supported studies of land use, for example, resulted recently in Congressional authorization for the establishment of three National Seashores, among them one on Cape Cod.

In the field of health, private funds and leadership still are needed to move boldly into little-known areas of investigation and to follow every possible lead. Perhaps most important is intensification of research into the mind of man in relation to his behavior, history, and environment.

In the field of science generally, there are many obvious gaps in our knowledge which must one day be filled. Principal among these is the understanding of what we are doing to ourselves through the changes in our environment—changes brought about by efforts to increase our comforts, pleasures, and standards of living as well as to accommodate more people each year. Our technologies, while serving us well, have implications which have progressed far beyond our understanding. The development of environmental science is of paramount importance to our continued well-being. Here, again, foundations may well serve as pacesetters.

Educational methods need to be restudied, and every effort made to use all the techniques available, plus whatever others can be discovered, to assure that the educational process fully serves the needs of society. Foundations have long recognized this need. They are, for example, leaders in the support of educational television as a sharp tool for spreading understanding.

Already, we are feeling the need of greater opportunities for the constructive use of leisure time. Foundations are increasingly engaged in the support of projects or programs in the humanities and the creative and performing arts. It is to be expected that during the years ahead private philanthropy will put still greater emphasis upon ways to enrich the cultural experience of society in the understanding of its great significance to the well-being of the nation.

Throughout much of the world, the population explosion is the greatest problem. Foundations were among the first to recognize this threat to world peace and prosperity. They have sought to clarify the many facets of the population question, to support research, to provide avenues of action, to encourage public examination and discussion of the subject in the knowledge that ultimate decisions must be made by an informed citizenry. Increased attention is being—and will be—given by foundations to this fundamental concern.

Unhappily, progress toward population stabilization will not come rapidly, and foundations must strive to help find the solutions to the problems of accommodating those new millions who join us each year and of providing opportunities for them. The logistics of the accommodation, employment, and normal movement of people, goods, and services becomes more complex and difficult each year. Social problems arising out of economic, cultural, ethnic, or religious differences become more complicated as our numbers increase.

More immediately, in the developing countries of Latin America, Africa, and Asia the adaptation of already existing knowledge to local conditions can be of greatest importance in meeting popular expectations. Working with governments and universities, foundations are among the most vigorous forces in the improvement of health, agricultural production, and professional education in such areas.

In the "rice bowl" of the Far East, a great International Rice Research Institute created by the Government of the Philippines in collaboration with the Ford and Rockefeller Foundations, gives hope for more food for over half the world's population. Foundations in cooperation with governments are strengthening medical centers for teaching and research in East Africa, West Africa, India, and Colombia. Foundation-supported studies of land economics in South America will provide a background of solid information for approaches to one of the most pressing problems in the region.

For meeting such challenges, the unique assets of foundations are of special relevance. They have not only experienced, highly-trained staffs and continuity of effort, but the freedom from political considerations and the willingness to take risks that government cannot readily undertake.

The record of foundations is clear. With relatively modest resources and small but highly-trained staffs, they have long been a major force in the struggle against ignorance and disease. They have undertaken pioneer efforts and paved the way for much larger undertakings under national and international auspices. Thus, although operating with a high degree of autonomy, they have, in effect, worked in concert with many other agencies, including those of government, for the public good. In the years ahead, foundations can be expected to continue to operate at the forefront of human experience, to add to the body of knowledge, to assist in its application at critical points, and to develop programs which may become pilot projects for the future.

Foundations fulfill their highest purpose only when they support innovation and experimentation. Since they are free to act without the restraints of either profit making or official policy, they can assume the risks and controversy involved in working on the growing edge of things. In the years ahead, the tried and true will eventually be supported by the public purse, but the untried and new will continue to require venture capital and venturesome people.

Moving Frontiers of Applied Microbiology

Few realize the extent to which we live in, and are surrounded by, an invisible sea of microorganisms—a sea as important a part of the total environment of man, plants, and animals as are the oceans which surround the continents. As René Dubos has noted, recent calculations indicate that the total mass of this microbial life on earth is approximately 20 times the total mass of animal life. And, like the oceans, this microbial component of our environment is, in some aspects, favorable to higher organisms; in others, inimical to them.

The impact of microorganisms upon the comforts, well-being, and even the life span of man has been felt, if not understood, since the dawn of civilization. As man's intellect and his curiosity combined to cause him to examine the phenomena of nature, he gained an impression of occurrences which, although painful and sometimes lethal, were not brought about by any visible force. Illness and pain have always been with us, and primitive man certainly must have realized often that he was the victim of a power which he could neither understand nor describe. The pains of wounds, burns, and bruises could readily be related to cause, but aches and fevers not related to visible symptoms created a new mystique. Efforts to relate cause and effect were empirical, and remedial attempts were motivated either by superstition or by bitter experience.

Although man's earliest encounters with microorganisms were principally unhappy ones, he also derived early benefits from their activities. Most prominent among these were the by-products of fer-

Address given July 30, 1963, in Stockholm at a symposium sponsored by the International Association of Microbiological Societies and the Royal Swedish Academy of Engineering Sciences

mentation. Alcohol seems to have been associated with human experience throughout recorded history, and primitive husbandmen, without a real understanding of the process, learned by observation and experience at least some of the secrets of the fermentation process. The production of alcoholic beverages from the wide variety of fruits and grains, the curing of hay and silage, and the production of lactic and acetic acid were among the early domestic applications of microbial activity. Conversely, it was soon learned that the process of fermentation could be retarded by desiccation, hence the advent of cured meats and fruits.

There are numerous illustrations of the march of the microorganisms in the progress of man, but modern microbiology had to await the invention of the microscope, the elaboration of the germ theory of disease, and the development of techniques for the control of microbial fermentation and other processes. Only then did man begin to become vaguely aware of the cosmos of invisible life around him. Fortunately for succeeding generations, a group of brilliant scientific minds in the mid-nineteenth century focused upon the phenomena produced by microorganisms and laid the basis for all that has been learned since of their role in relation to the rest of the living world. Society owes incalculable debts to Pasteur, Lister, Koch, Jenner, and the others who, together, created that golden age of science.

As might be expected, most early microbiologists were principally concerned with the cause and cure of disease, and the magnificent achievements which have accrued to human health over the years are adequate testimonials to their devotion, abilities, and numbers. Along the way they were joined by scientists interested in the health of plants and animals and in domestic applications of microbiology. These investigators, in turn, have contributed many and major advances to the understanding and progress of plant and animal pathology and industrial microbiology. Once the invisible world of microorganisms became at least partially visible, and a little was learned of their roles in a variety of chemical transformations, increasing numbers of leading scientists were attracted to the task of unraveling their secrets.

The recognition of microorganisms as a hostile force that threatened the health of man made it certain that intensive and extensive study of all the factors involved in this perilous relationship would quickly follow. As new tools for research and refinements of experimental techniques were developed, knowledge of the life processes of the microorganisms increased. As the bacteria, the yeasts, the fungi, and, later, the viruses were intensively studied as the causative agents of diseases, a body of knowledge began to accumulate which led microbiologists down many related pathways toward the understanding of their life processes.

Today we realize as never before the role which microorganisms have played and are playing in the natural environment and in support of human progress. We recognize, to a degree, the extent to which we are dependent upon them and the fact that we must fear and attempt to overcome those which threaten our health and possessions. In the past the power of the unseen bacterium, fungus, virus, or protozoan has frequently been manifest in catastrophic form. The scourges of smallpox, bubonic plague, cholera, and influenza, among others, have killed millions and intimidated and panicked large sectors of society when they attacked in epidemic form.

The protean spirochete, the lethal viruses of smallpox and yellow fever, the insidious schistosome, and perhaps the greatest killer of them all, the *Plasmodium* of malaria, have decimated populations or robbed them of health and vigor for centuries. In the field of animal production, the losses caused by the insidious brucellosis, the violent hog cholera, and the persistent foot-and-mouth disease and rinderpest are typical of the ravages which hostile microorganisms may wreak upon important animal food resources.

Food and other economic crops have traditionally suffered from the destructive forces of plant pathogens. The "late blight" of potatoes created havoc and famine in Western Europe and especially in Ireland, in the last century; the South American leaf disease of the rubber tree wiped out an entire industry, and bacterial canker has destroyed millions of citrus fruit trees. Black stem rust of small grains, root rots, and other virulent plant pathogens—fungal, bacterial, and viral—still levy an annual toll of agricultural production in excess of 15 per cent, and all too often their attack in epidemic form has resulted in total crop loss in the area affected.

Probably the greatest single boon rendered to society by microorganisms is what is generically described as the process of organic decay. In this process, multiples of unlike microorganisms combine to reduce organic substances to simple soluble compounds or elements. Although taken for granted, our dependence upon the continuity of this process is total. It restores the soil, and without it we should soon be living in the morass of the accumulation of dead biologic forms.

Among the best known activities of microorganisms are those within the general framework of the agricultural process. The roles of bacteria and fungi in the fermentation process are well known and widespread throughout the entire agricultural industry, and industrial microbiology is an increasingly powerful tool in the service of society. The chemical changes occurring in the preparation of coffee, tea, and cacao, the curing of cheese, the retting of flax and jute, and the production of alcohols and acids from fruits and grains have all been recognized for many years. And the destructive effect of microorganisms on stored grain and innumerable manufactured products is thoroughly established and is the cause of heavy annual losses. Some, notably the clostridia, are capable of synthesizing lethal toxins as the metabolic by-products of their association with preserved foods. Others whose metabolic activities cause plant and animal diseases are responsible for the creation of the scientific disciplines of plant and animal pathology.

Although still not well understood, the role of microorganisms in the rhizosphere is without doubt the most important biologic phenomenon associated with the practice of agriculture. Soil microflora and fauna are bewildering in their numbers, diversity, and complex of activities. Although substantial emphasis has been placed on soil microbiology, we have as yet barely scratched the surface of knowledge with respect to the chemical transformations which occur in kaleidoscopic fashions with changing conditions in all soils and, most particularly, those managed for agricultural purposes.

Most notable among known activities of soil-living microorganisms is the complex of nitrification and nitrogen-fixation. Much less is known of the cycles involving other major nutrient elements, such as phosphorus, and a host of minor elements including copper, sulfur, and manganese, in which certain soil-borne microorganisms have been found to intervene. Because of their size, numbers, and the rapidity with which they multiply, the minor ecological successions which occur in the soil proceed rapidly and may be repeated within a single crop cycle. These biological chain reactions are difficult to evaluate with precision.

Not all soil microorganisms are beneficial, and there is a plethora of those which are responsible for root rots and seedling blights. Although the fungi are the principal organisms concerned, there are many bacteria which attack root tissues, and a host of nematodes are active in causing root knot and other pathologic conditions. Viruses, too, get into the act—both through their persistence in plant materials in the soils and through their association with vector microorganisms. There is little doubt that much greater emphasis should be given to the study of soil microbiology so that new knowledge gained from research can show ways to use soil microfauna and flora more advantageously and to control inimical forms.

In the fields of medicine and public health, microorganisms have generally been thought of as the enemy, and the progress of the biologist, pharmacologist, physician, and public health doctor in meeting the threat of pathogenetic organisms with drugs, vaccines, and a variety of other techniques has been one of the great success stories of the past half-century.

The discovery that microorganisms could be pitted against each other for the benefit of man, animals, and plants created a whole new concept of what might be called biochemotherapy. The phenomenon of antibiosis, long observed by mycologists and bacteriologists, finally was recognized as a possible biological tool for the control of pathogenic organisms. This story is now well known, and modern refinements have led to the production of a broad spectrum of antibiotic substances from diverse species of fungi, bacteria, and other microorganisms which enable the successful conquest of many diseases of man, animals, and plants, and offer hope and expectation of other discoveries of still greater significance. And we are now encouraged to apply imagination and investigation to the search for still other ways to take advantage of the biochemical properties of microorganisms in the fight against disease.

Industrial microbiology is a relatively young science but one which has grown with great rapidity. Industrial fermentations of many types are commonplace and essential to the production of many food and non-food products. The well-known use of microforms as sources of enzymes, amino acids, and protein concentrates leads the rapidly growing field of industrial biotechnology. Another growing application of microorganisms to industrial processes is their use in the elimination of unwanted by-products and certain industrial and domestic wastes. Without doubt, increased emphasis on research upon the role of microorganisms in manufacturing processes will result in multiplying their use many-fold.

The applications of the science of microbiology to the needs of society will continue, as in the past, to depend, in the first instance, upon the quantity and the quality of the research in this area. Although some of the earliest achievements in harnessing microorganisms for human needs were the result of a combination of observation and empiricism, the forward march of microbiology is deeply imbedded in a body of knowledge coming from careful and painstaking fundamental research.

One of the most striking accomplishments of microorganisms is their ability to synthesize substances which, for the moment at least, cannot be economically produced by other means. This knowledge opens up a whole new world within which to seek those that may serve man in the synthesis of critically needed materials. Opportunities for discovery are everywhere, and many such microorganisms have already been identified. We know that the normal bacterial flora of the human intestinal tract synthesize various chemicals, especially vitamins, which have important roles in human health. This suggests immediately that other species of bacteria exist which, although not yet identified nor studied in depth, could materially contribute to man's well-being. It is intriguing to speculate upon the possibility that microorganisms may synthesize compounds which could protect against disease such as cancer or that others might slow down the process of aging. The possibilities are infinite, and there is no limit to what might be accomplished with an advancing understanding of the metabolism of microorganisms.

In recent years, the science of microbiology has provided the tools and techniques which have made possible one of the great historical landmarks of modern biology. A rapidly progressing, cumulative series of investigations has begun to shed light upon the ways in which genetically determined inheritance is affected and controlled and to penetrate into the molecular basis of life itself. In effect, all of these great advances have depended upon the use of microorganisms as essential and living research tools. They have made possible a study of genetic, biochemical, and biophysical factors in fundamental life processes at the cellular and subcellular level. The classical work of Beadle and Tatum on metabolic derangements in artificially produced mutants of *Neurospora* show that a single gene exerts its effect by controlling the synthesis of a single enzyme. Avery, MacLeod, and McCarty at the Rockefeller Institute demonstrated, again working with microorganisms, that the chemical substance fundamental to the gene is deoxyribonucleic acid. Their brilliant experiments proved that DNA characteristic of one pneumococcus type was capable of transforming another type into that from which the DNA was obtained. Lederberg used bacteria for the study of certain molecular processes by which genetic material is transferred from one generation to another. Watson, Crick, and Wilkins have established the structure of the giant DNA molecule, which leads directly to a reasonable theory of the molecular mechanisms underlying inheritance, replication, and reproduction. These workers and others have proceeded to use microorganisms as research tools to analyze the genetic code by which information is transmitted through DNA from one generation to the next.

The striking advances being made in the understanding of the organization and function of microorganisms offer a promise of new applications of microbiology to the needs of man. The work of Monod, Brenner, Jacob, and Meselson and others on *E. coli* has shed new light on the ways in which DNA and its related compound, ribonucleic acid, govern the synthesis of proteins in subcellular structures within the cell. Benzer and others, also working with *E. coli* and its associated viruses, have been able to map the fine structure of the gene itself. As a result, a beginning has been made in the application of certain of these techniques to higher organisms such as maize. Eventually, genetic fine structure analysis of man will undoubtedly become possible in response to progress in handling human cells in cultures in appropriate manner.

Although giant strides have already been made in the fundamental investigation of the metabolism of many microorganisms and in their use in agriculture, industry, medicine, and manufacturing, it is tantalizing to realize that all that has been accomplished thus far is infinitesimal compared with the untapped possibilities. All of the species, strains, varieties, and forms of microorganisms thus far investigated represent but a minute fraction of the total numbers. Among these it is logical to assume that there are myriad diverse types which could have a harmful effect on health and many others which could, under appropriate circumstances, be most beneficial.

221

We know that innumerable microorganisms tend to be biologically amorphous and subject to fundamental changes brought about by natural hybridization or mutation. Some, on the other hand, are highly stable and extraordinarily specific in their action. All of this suggests that so long as life exists all living forms will be menaced by others; that chief among the parasitic or pathogenic forms will be the microorganisms, and that we must continue to develop knowledge which will enable us to cope with new forms of disease or, better still, to prevent their establishment within populations.

Although the injurious potential of microforms is great, continuing, and important, surely it is enormously overbalanced by the benefits which could be derived from the better understanding and utilization of their biochemical powers. It is exciting to contemplate the fact that where man commands thousands and millions of individual plant and animal organisms to do his bidding, he can readily obtain with incredible speed the services of multiple billions of microorganisms with both ease and economy. The power potential here is beyond imagination, and if we can learn to harness it in an ever-widening variety of ways, future achievements for the benefit of society will quickly make those of the past pale by comparison. In the early history of microbiology, the process of the economic utilization of microorganisms was akin to mining in search of the mother lode. Today, through the sophistication of modern research, the mining technique has been joined by conscious effort to control and direct the biochemical capabilities of microorganisms to desired effects.

Probably no one can successfully predict all the directions in which the frontiers of applied modern microbiology will move. It might, however, be interesting to speculate a little. Reaching for what today seems impossible is predicated on the hypothesis that as he accepts the Biblical injunction to "have dominion over the fish of the sea, and over the fowl of the air, and over every living thing that moveth upon the earth," man should seek dominion also over the invisible world of the microorganisms. If successful, he will have captured a biochemical power greater than any thus far subservient to his will.

Perhaps the greatest single accomplishment which microbiologists could hope to achieve would be the control and management of the nitrogen-fixation process. Currently, we are limited to the slight

222

influence we can bring to bear on free-living, nitrogen-fixing organisms in the soil through patterns of soil management. And, in a somewhat similar fashion, we can at least take advantage of symbiotic nitrogen-fixation through the insertion of legumes into crop rotation patterns.

Although a substantial amount of research has been directed to the study of various systems of biologic nitrogen-fixation, we appear to be far from any deep understanding of the biochemical organization of this phenomenon and still further from being able to direct it to our own desires. As might be expected, principal research emphasis has been placed upon nodular-fixation, with relatively less on the phenomenon of nitrogen-fixation in certain non-nodulated higher plants. Little is known of the capacities of the algae to fix atmospheric nitrogen in forms available for assimilation by higher plants. If one is willing to concede the possibility that there could be developed species of those crops which feed the world (principally the small grains) with the capacity for nitrogen-fixation, it at once becomes clear what this could mean to available world food supplies.

Obviously, the all-out attack on the problem of nitrogen-fixation would require a multidisciplinary approach. Primary emphasis would involve the same intensive and extensive research which has been devoted to the photosynthetic process over a period of many years. And, indeed, there is evidence that there may be some similarities between processes in photosynthesis and in symbiotic nitrogen-fixation. Bacteriology, cytogenetics, genetics, and numerous other branches of science would inevitably be drawn into the total effort, which, if successful, could be one of the great achievements of man in exerting his dominion over microforms of life to his incalculable benefit.

The sea has long been an intriguing subject for the biologist, the oceanographer, the geologist, and others. There has been a great deal of speculation and substantial theoretical calculation of the biological power of the sea, particularly with respect to food production. The total investigation of marine food resources to date, although significant and worthwhile, becomes insignificant when contrasted with unsolved mysteries of the sea and the progress which might be made in controlling and directing marine resources for human benefit. If, on an increasing scale, the sea could be used as a giant medium for the culture and harvest of microorganisms synthesizing products desired by society as foods, feeds, or raw materials, an almost unlimited new resource would come into being. And this is but one of the multiple possibilities for taking advantage of marine microbiological resources directly or as elements in the food chain.

Under controlled circumstances the phenomenon of antibiosis has been effectively put to work in the service of man. Perhaps, one day, it may be possible to associate living microorganisms symbiotically with higher forms in order that they may be afforded continuing protection from the attack of pathogens. There are numerous examples of permanent association between higher plants and viruses with no evidence of detrimental effect and at least some evidence of benefit. It is not illogical to assume that such associations could be induced for specific purposes—including disease protection and improvements in nutrition.

In conclusion, let me suggest that there would seem to be no reason why a greater advantage should not be taken of the synthetic potentials of the bacteria, fungi, yeasts, viruses, including phage, and protozoans. To do so will require greatly intensified and more extensive research on these different groups and deeper understanding of their biochemical capacities. The ease with which many can be grown in artificial culture, the rapidity with which they multiply so that they can be used in essentially any quantity, and the fact that many microorganisms readily hybridize and that others are highly mutable all indicate infinite possibilities for creating variants—even for controlling to a degree the direction of variation. If science can succeed on an increasing scale in domesticating microorganisms and putting their energies to work on chemical transformations of economic importance, the massive resource of the invisible world will contribute incalculably to man's future well-being.

Nutrition and Numbers

Between 1960 and 1980 the number of human beings on this planet will increase from 3 billion to 4.3 billion. In the following 20 years the total world population will grow to 6.9 billion. That is, within the next 40 years there will be more than twice as many people in the world as in 1960.

The peoples of all lands are today demanding not only the basic necessities of life, but those amenities essential to adequate standards of living. And yet, although more food is being produced in some parts of the world than the people who live there can possibly eat, roughly half the people of the world go hungry even today.

Two giant and relentless forces have thus combined to threaten human existence as we know it, and growing awareness of this fact has become a dominant concern throughout the world. Prompt and major success in increasing world food supplies has become critical to human progress.

Ironically enough, the greatest single barrier to the satisfaction of man's most basic need—enough food—is his own success in the numbers game. Modern medical miracles and herculean efforts in other fields of science have done glorious battle with the specters of infant and juvenile mortality and the traditionally accepted short span of life. These successes, in combination with the enthusiastic social response to the injunction contained in the first chapter of Genesis, "Be fruitful and multiply and replenish the earth," have now thrust upon us a dilemma which must be understood and met squarely.

Address made in Edinburgh, Scotland, on August 9, 1963,
at the 6th International Congress of Nutrition

It seems strange that man, whose special instrument of intelligence has enabled him to vanquish other animal species and, to a degree, to harness and control the forces of nature itself, should have thus far so completely failed to understand the implications of his own successes. He has converted his wildest dreams into reality in terms of social and technical progress. But unless the same persistent logic and ingenuity are applied to the problem of unlimited population increase, future progress may be seriously impeded.

After all, it was more than 3,000 years ago when man was advised to multiply. That was a time when the natural environment still acted cruelly and promptly to impose checks and balances upon numbers. Famine, pestilence, war, and other forces held populations in check—although they brought with them misery, poverty, and hopelessness for millions. When man removes or limits the controls exerted by these natural forces, he creates a situation in which vastly larger numbers of individuals are provided with comforts and opportunities, but he also permits the massive reproductive capacity of mankind to operate like a motor without a governor and to begin to race out of control.

For many years men of vision have foreseen this situation. Beginning with Malthus in 1798 and continuing to the present the consequences of unlimited procreation have been predicted, and mankind has been warned to take early and appropriate action. The proponents of population stabilization have, by and large, been treated with public apathy. They have even been ridiculed as prophets of doom, nonbelievers, and inveighers against divine laws. Many who believed that numbers and progress were totally compatible cited the spectacular advances in agricultural technology following the Industrial Revolution of the nineteenth century as proof of the fallacies of Malthusian doctrines.

But we are now approaching the end of the pleasant path. We can no longer wishfully think that there is no limit to production which can be imposed by numbers. The predictions of unpopular prophets are gradually being recognized as having the sound of truth. Many, who formerly vilified as inhumane the persons who taught the value of population stabilization, are now grudgingly admitting that the greater inhumanity lies in condemning millions upon millions of human beings—living as well as unborn—to lives of misery and degradation.

Fortunately, in spite of apathy and active opposition, there are emerging thoughtful coalitions of forces directed toward the solution of the problems of overpopulation and world hunger. These coalescing groups are not as yet sufficiently integrated, but there is general agreement among them that the furious increase in sheer numbers is a menace to present and future peace and prosperity. They recognize that the necessity to feed, clothe, house, and employ the thousands upon thousands of new citizens joining the world population each day is an immediate, grave, and growing challenge to society.

Even though we can hope for progress toward population stabilization, the battle to increase the production and equitable distribution of food supplies must now be pressed to the limit. The world today is sadly out of balance in this respect. Total production is still inadequate, and distribution patterns are out of phase with reality. Men of intelligence and good will must redouble their efforts on every front if civilization is to achieve within the foreseeable future any reasonable ratio between nutrition and numbers.

There are many related approaches to the solution of agricultural production patterns, but perhaps the first consideration is the elimination of the traditional, nostalgic, but today totally unrealistic concept that farming is simply a way of life. Perhaps more than any other of man's major occupations, agriculture is overlaid with thick layers of myth, memory, and romance. To gain proper perspective on the contemporary scene, we must somehow excavate these layers to expose the bedrock of reality.

According to John Cohen,* St. Augustine refused to believe that Adam's back was bent in toil, but held that he gave himself to the agreeable occupation of agriculture, partly because it afforded wonderful opportunities for close communion with nature. Cohen reminds us also that Milton poeticized about farming as a "pleasant labour" but that Abelard thought of agriculture as a penance imposed upon Adam at the time of the Fall. Abelard may have been closer to the truth, as one recalls the sheer drudgery of trying to wrest a subsistence from an often resistant nature.

In our own time it is still popular to think of agriculture as a stronghold of morality, and the farm way of life as more ruggedly

* *Nature,* vol. 198, pp. 1028-1033, June 15, 1963

virtuous than urban occupations. Actually, although farm communities in the Western world have been the backbone of society in many ways, the farmer is fundamentally much like his contemporary in the city. His storied virtues may derive as much from long hours of manual labor, early rising and early retiring, and his highly developed self-sufficiency, as from his so-called "daily communion with nature."

The hard fact of the matter is that, from the beginning of civilization, agriculture has been a way of life by imposition rather than by choice. Millions upon millions have subsisted through agriculture, but relatively few have flourished. Admittedly, in the presence of abundance and the absence of intense and competitive pressures for land and the other adjuncts of agricultural practice, farming was for a period of time, especially in the West, a way of life for millions of families who were willing to work hard and put in long hours to achieve productive success and personal satisfaction. And societies blessed by a favorable combination of ecologic factors and natural resources have been enabled to develop an agricultural technology backed by all the forces of education and science and leading to a high degree of efficiency.

Today, agriculture is still the largest direct employer of human energy, and a substantial additional fraction of the world population is employed in industry or business related to agriculture. But agriculture, when it is successful, is a business, benefiting from major infusions of capital. And where unsuccessful, it may indeed be a way of life which few would choose if given alternative opportunities.

The concept of agriculture as a business enterprise must be recognized, fully understood, and popularly supported if the world pattern of food production is to advance in response to human need. Time after time in the past, the fact that agriculture must be managed on the same principles as any other successful business enterprise has been overlooked. The notion that there is some marked difference between business and industry, as ordinarily defined, and what has frequently been called the "art of husbandry" has too often worked to the disadvantage of the production of those agricultural commodities which form the economic base for other forms of industrial development.

Where agriculture has been unsuccessful, it is usually axiomatic that climate is less than benign, natural resources limited, and rural populations restricted in their educational opportunities. It is usually true also that national leaders have placed insufficient emphasis upon the development of the agricultural production pattern as a sound business enterprise. Even today, many seem to persist in the naïve concept that farming is simply man taking advantage of nature's bounty, and that the easy combination of soil, water, seed, and farmer results in food supplies. As a consequence, the agricultural aspects of industry in nation after nation have been badly neglected in favor of unbalanced investments in other segments of industry as the true road to prosperity.

This is most unfortunate, since the agricultural nations can build their industrial economy only upon a successful agricultural-industrial economy that requires investments in education, research, technology, materials, and credit like any other sound industrial enterprise.

In order to insure the success of the agricultural businessman, his country must provide him with economic units of arable land suitable for crop or animal production. He must be assured insofar as possible of dependable water supplies, either through the appropriate location of his holdings or by the availability of supplemental water from wells, dams, rivers, and the like. He must be able to obtain fertilizer, adapted seed, tools, equipment, and information readily and at realistic prices. He must have some form of insurance protection against crop loss and, ultimately, ready access to markets in which to sell his products.

Obviously, the individual farmer cannot undertake to provide all these requirements through his own initiative. He must be part of a system in which there is continuing investment leading to greater production and higher standards of living for the farmer as well as for those he serves through his toil. A basic assumption involves the provision of ever-increasing educational opportunities for the farmer, his children, and his children's children.

In our country there is still a great deal of sentimentality about the family farm, and we have spent hundreds of millions of dollars to protect the family farm whether or not it is an efficient economic unit. Forty-four per cent of those classified as farmers in the United States market less than $2,500 worth of farm goods a year, while nine per cent of the farms—the large, heavily capitalized units— produce 50 per cent of total farm production.

Unhappily, perhaps, but inevitably, the small undercapitalized farm must one day follow the path of the small, undercapitalized business. This does not suggest total disappearance, since there are always opportunities for the imaginative entrepreneur. The trend, however, will continue to be toward the consolidation of the agricultural industry, paralleling that of the retail food, the automotive, the textile, and many other basic industries. In an increasingly competitive society it is simply not possible to protect uneconomic enterprises, whether they be manufacturing or agricultural, unless society is prepared to pay the price of perpetual public subsidy.

In the United States the gradual disappearance of the small farm is taking place naturally, even though the pace has been delayed and sentimental regrets are still voiced. All of us have seen changes come about which we regret, and we share a sense of nostalgia for much of what we once knew and enjoyed, but the swift rush of progress through technology and the pressure of increasing numbers do not permit the preservation of the world as it used to be. We can but try to use our new-found strengths and skills to make it still better.

Among the sciences which serve the world, nutrition is a distinguished leader. As civilization has advanced, nutrition and its attendant technologies have made available to us foods superior in every way to most of those enjoyed by our forefathers. They are more attractive in appearance, freer from pests and diseases, and richer in nutrient qualities than ever before in history. The choice of domestic and exotic foods available to the citizens of the most developed nations is bewildering in its array. The food and nutrition sciences have taught us ways in which greatest advantage may be taken of the inherent qualities in our foods, have shown us how to transform them into myriad diverse products, how to transport them safely, and how to preserve them in their state of maximum freshness for extended periods of time. This has helped lift canning and related food processing and preserving industries to levels never before achieved, so that today we have a continuing supply of high-quality foods, and are able to export large quantities to others and even to acquire surpluses beyond our needs.

These signal successes achieved by the whole spectrum of food scientists have at times, perhaps, lulled the public mind unintentionally into a false sense of security. Enthusiasm for their science and dedication to its goals, along with major accomplishments, may have tended to blur their consideration of certain basic collateral issues. Frequently the scientist speaks with confidence of what could be accomplished in assuring adequate food supplies for all if given the opportunity and sufficient support. And there is little doubt that these predictions could be made good under appropriate *circumstances*. But it is these *circumstances* that are critical, and the most basic of them is full support to the agricultural industry in order that it can maximize its potential.

Much of the food crop and domestic animal production today is carried on under severe restrictions. Landholding patterns are frequently uneconomic, supplies of water, fertilizer, tools, and implements inadequate, and credit and market facilities strictly limited. All too often there is a combination of negative forces which essentially assures underproduction. And failure to achieve normal yields during any crop cycle represents a permanent loss of food, feed, or fiber which can never be replaced in subsequent years.

It should always be remembered that nutritional short cuts can never satisfy the deficiencies brought about by an inefficient subsistence agriculture. Synthetic foods, food supplements, enriching procedures, and all of the other techniques applied to the amelioration of nutrient deficiencies among peoples can at best only buy a little time. The multiplication of their numbers and the size of these programs cannot alone provide the answers to the nutritional problem and must be accompanied by substantial and continuing progress in the improvement of the local agricultural industry. While individual and often unrelated efforts to provide nutritional supplements to food-deficient populations may furnish temporary surcease in rather special situations, they are not a substitute for individual and collective enterprise directed to the efficient use of local resources and manpower.

Extraordinary progress has been made during the past 30 years in the development of adapted and high-yielding crop plants and animals, with the result that in the more developed nations the agricultural production curve has gone steadily upward both in total output and in yield per land unit. During this period careful attention has been paid to the nutrition of crop plants and domestic animals in order that they might flourish and produce in the service of mankind.

Had we during this same period combined the knowledge and

imagination of the biochemist, the geneticist, the soil scientist, the economic botanist, the zoologist, the food technologist, and the medical scientist, in all probability many of today's foods would be of substantially greater nutritional value than those we currently consume.

There is clear evidence that through this sort of cooperation it would be possible to identify and select those plant and animal stocks of superior quality and to tailor genetically new varieties to higher yield potentials and increased content of desired nutrient compounds. Great future possibilities exist in this type of cooperation and through association between the several scientific disciplines concerned and the extension specialist and the farmer.

Although great strides have been made in the improvement of conventional agriculture, the broad reaches of nonconventional agriculture have not yet been deeply penetrated. There has been a great deal of imaginative speculation and estimates of possibilities for increasing food supplies through progress in the control of climate, the conversion of saline waters to fresh water for agricultural purposes, improved "farming of the sea," and the marshaling of microorganisms for the synthesis of vast quantities of nutrients for the benefit of man. Consideration has also been given to the utilization of noncrop-plant materials as a reservoir of protein substances and the chemical transformation of nonedible components of plants and animals into supplementary foodstuffs or feeds.

Certainly few would argue that the food potential of the sea is almost unlimited within the immediate terms of reference and that ingenuity applied to management techniques could yield manifold dividends. It seems clear also that the food potential properties of the invisible world of microorganisms are but vaguely understood and that the future holds forth hope that vast additional quantities of food may one day be the result of the greater domestication of microorganisms in the service of man. Perhaps as we learn more about the peacetime uses of atomic energy, we may find still other and as yet unconceived approaches to substantial increments to world food supplies. In all of these investigations, the science of nutrition will inevitably play a leading role; its success will depend to a major degree upon the extent to which the investigators and practitioners of the several scientific disciplines associate their skills in the total effort.

It has frequently been said that the answer to the world's food problems lies in the prompt and universal application of the scientific method to agricultural production. As a principle this point of view is defensible, but as a practical possibility it has no validity. The fact is that if through some series of miracles all that is now *known* in the field of agricultural technology could, along with appropriate materials, be applied universally and economically to agrarian societies, world food production could be expected to double or treble quite promptly.

Unhappily, there is no hope of any early and major progress toward this utopia. This is not because of lack of scientific information, but because the scientist cannot function independently of the other sectors of society. The operation of science is permissive and greatly dependent upon the understanding and support which the public should and is prepared to invest in it. Decisions as to the role of science and the extent of its participation in national and public programs are usually, and often must be, taken by nonscientists in positions of power and influence. In the final analysis the successful application of science to food production generally depends upon adequate communication among scientists, national and local leaders, and the general public, and upon the understanding and acquiescence of the man who tills the soil. All of the injections of modern science and technology, if not based on understanding which leads to their acceptance, application, and continuity, cannot far advance the cause of food production. They can only temporize and delay the inevitable unless accompanied by these appropriate social approvals.

The greatest single deterrent to the advance of world agriculture is to be found in the educational process or, too often, in the lack of it. Wherever in the world agriculture is a successful business, it is backed by a highly developed system of education at all levels and investments in research and technology which have paid for themselves many-fold in increased production. And the need for vast educational improvements is in no way limited to the rural peoples of the globe. Every sector of society is involved, and ultimate success will depend upon the interaction of all if substantial gain is to be made.

Nations with rising expectations must accept rising responsibilities for the development of their own national resources. Fundamental to these is the training of the individual in order that he may understand and accept responsibilities and discharge them with efficiency in his own interest and those of his community and nation. Even if successful, the process will be painfully slow, and millions of citizens of today and tomorrow are doomed to lives of underprivilege and dissatisfaction.

If we can make definite progress rapidly on the educational front and in all that is associated with it, we may hope for a better future. If we do not, and if we fail to recognize and meet the threat of unlimited population increase, we will be on the road to engulfment by our own numbers. The mills of man and his environment grind on slowly, but there is hope that reason, responsibility, and energy will permit the ascendancy of man over his contemporary challenges.

Foundations and the Public Interest

Philanthropic foundations are once again under government scrutiny. Two Congressional inquiries into the operations of tax-exempt foundations were held in the last decade; a third inquiry, under the leadership of Representative Wright Patman, has been in progress for many months.

Such reviews are part of the democratic process, and provided they are objectively motivated and dispassionately handled, they cannot be resented by foundations proud of their record.

There has been evidence, in connection with the current study, that some foundations are being used by individuals and groups not to advance the public welfare but to serve private interests. Such a possibility is most serious and deserves careful and objective consideration by public representatives.

In appraising the performance of our foundations, however—and especially in contemplating the possibility of restrictive measures—it is well that we remind ourselves of the nature of this uniquely American institution and of what the people of the United States have received from it in the past and have a right to expect from it in the future.

The foundation, as we know it, came into its own in the first decade of this century when a few men of great wealth, who were also men of vision and compassion, saw that their wealth had grown far beyond their own needs and could be turned to the welfare of mankind. It should be recalled that this highly civilized idea took form before there were any income or estate taxes at all. Men like John D. Rockefeller and Andrew Carnegie were here concerned with the

From an address delivered at the Annual Dinner of the
Cosmos Club, Washington, D.C., November 16, 1964

condition of mankind, not with the avoidance of tax payments. As a result, Carnegie organizations built thousands of free libraries and pioneered retirement benefits for teachers. The Rockefeller Foundation established the pattern of modern public health practices and conducted worldwide campaigns against mass diseases and hunger; today both The Rockefeller Foundation and the Carnegie Corporation continue in the forefront of private effort for public benefit.

There can be little doubt that this same impulse guided the formation of subsequent philanthropies, even though many important ones were formed after the income tax amendment of 1913. Among these have been the W. K. Kellogg Foundation, with its great contributions to the fields of medicine, nursing, rural health, and nutrition, and to American education generally; the John Simon Guggenheim Memorial Foundation, which for almost 40 years has provided fellowships to young scholars, scientists, writers, and artists; the Julius Rosenwald Fund, which has helped education in the rural South and has worked to improve race relations; the Twentieth Century Fund with its major contributions to economic and social research; the Milbank Memorial Fund, long active in public health, especially population research and nutrition; the Russell Sage Foundation, a prime mover in the professionalization of welfare and philanthropic activities; the Alfred P. Sloan Foundation, active in medicine, mathematics, and the physical and social sciences; the great worldwide activities of the Ford Foundation, concentrated especially on improvements within America's educational systems, and on economic and social progress abroad; and many others.

The achievements of America's foundations, reaching back collectively more than a half century, have established the soundness of the idea that private wealth can be expended effectively for the public welfare through programs privately conceived and administered.

A second and complementary idea has also been confirmed: the public interest is well served if incentives to the establishment of these philanthropies include tax exemptions for such organizations, as well as tax reductions for their contributors. As the number of privately endowed foundations has risen over the decades of this century, so have their programs devoted to public advancement. And with experience gained, these programs have become increasingly effective.

At the same time, it is clear that in our time of rapid social change philanthropies must be prepared to meet the changing requirements of society. These must be constant sensitivity to the problems of contemporary society and to standards of performance that can keep foundation effectiveness always at its highest.

There must also be public guarantees that the privilege of tax exemption is not abused by anyone in order to exploit the foundation idea for private ends. When any part of this extraordinary instrument for social progress falls into the hands of cynics who use it for self-serving purposes, the instrument itself is jeopardized.

The Rockefeller Foundation has welcomed the Treasury Department's recently concluded study of private foundations. Its recommendations deserve careful consideration. The Treasury has already gone far to deter misconduct and to expose it when it occurs by revising the information-return forms filed by foundations so as to call for fuller disclosure with respect to foundation operations and by starting a program of more frequent and searching audits of these returns. Under the law, as it now stands, a foundation is not entitled to tax exemption unless it is operated *exclusively* for authorized tax-exempt purposes.

Most of the conduct which has come under attack in the current investigation fails to measure up to this standard. Stricter enforcement of the present law may remove or reduce the need for stricter laws. If additional legislative controls are to be considered to protect the public interest, we urge the lawmakers not to restrict the independence of the vast majority of foundations, which seek only to advance the general welfare, and to encourage, not stifle, the philanthropic impulse to which humanity owes so much.

The fact is that much remains to be done by the privately endowed, general-purpose foundation; and this ingenious social instrument must not be hamstrung as it seeks to apply its unique resources to human need.

Our private foundations represent only a small fraction of the massive welfare resources of the American people and their government. In the year 1961, for example, all the privately endowed foundations in the country disbursed only about one penny of every welfare dollar spent in this country. But we have learned that this comparatively tiny fraction of the total American welfare expenditure has an effectiveness far beyond its size. The philanthropic dollar spent by the experienced and imaginative private servants of the public interest who are working in the foundations can trigger great movements in the interest of mankind.

But if they are to perform this vital function of pioneering human progress, foundations plainly require the understanding and the support of the society they serve. They must have the flexibility of broadly framed charters which enable them to move promptly to seize opportunities across the whole range of human need. They must be able to risk failure in opening new vistas of progress. They must not be limited in size, for there is work for the large foundation as well as for the small. They must retain the freedom to move to the point of need—including places abroad. We have learned, perhaps bitterly, that attending to human problems in a land we hardly know today can spare the tragedy of greatly magnified problems touching us closely tomorrow.

And just as a founder should not be denied the right to determine the amount of his endowment, so also he should not be denied the right to endow it with longevity. The gradual evolution of the foundation as a tool of progress during this century has resulted in the accumulation of a totally new reserve of experience devoted to the service of mankind. But this has taken time. The techniques of organized philanthropy are today far more sophisticated and effective than those of a half-century ago, and they are far less so than they will be a half-century from now. If the life of The Rockefeller Foundation had been limited at the outset and if its mission had been restricted to an attack on epidemic diseases, mankind would have lost the incalculable benefits of the Foundation's programs in aid to education, agricultural development, population stabilization, and assistance to the arts, among many others.

There are still many trails yet unblazed—new vistas for constructive giving. We live in an age of seemingly overwhelming problems —the products of the past in newer, larger, and more complex form. Few, if any, have burst upon an unsuspecting world; rather, they have become impossible to ignore.

Other than total war, the greatest threat we face is the impact of unrestrained population increase upon the world's resources and social structure. Hindsight tells us that efforts to improve sanitation, disease control, food production, and the like should have been carried on long ago with an awareness of their impact on population increase and in conjunction with measures toward its stabilization. Today, even though apathy and opposition are diminishing, and despite a great deal of expressed concern, progress almost everywhere is still too slow.

Some private foundations have accepted the challenge and are doing all in their power to work toward the stabilization of population. Because of the nature and sensitivity of the problem, foundations are in a special position to give support on several fronts, including demographic research, studies on the physiology of reproduction, and direct action projects where the need is greatest. They can also promote public consideration and social and economic research focused on the problems of population and their solution.

As we work toward population stabilization, we must continue our efforts to combat hunger, disease, and ignorance which condemn so many millions to degradation and misery and tax a multitude of others for their support. Here again private philanthropy can and does work toward the establishment and development of sound programs, adaptable to local conditions and resources, which in combination with efforts to stabilize population offer hope for a brighter future for all.

The stagnating effect of educational disadvantage is clearer today than ever before. Newer nations and resurgent ancient states are painfully aware how difficult an obstacle they face in the lack of people trained for the many forms of leadership and responsibility essential to national progress. The need is so critical and vast that massive and coordinated effort is required to achieve even a moderate advance. Foundations have been among the first to recognize this and to act, and today private and public organizations, working together, are making encouraging progress.

In this country, despite great achievements on many fronts, our people have still to solve grave current problems and to overcome earlier failures. Most critical is the struggle for equal rights and opportunity. In this area some foundations have a long record of concern and action, but gains made over the years have been slow and inadequate. Private philanthropy would seem by definition to have a stake in helping to resolve long-standing inequalities in imaginative and significant ways.

The quality of our society is a matter of interest to all. Even today, support from private sources for the performing arts and for outstandingly creative people is hard to come by. Yet it is from these sources that we can expect stimulating contributions to the tone and substance of our times. Furthermore, there is substantial evidence that, given the opportunity, large numbers of citizens, especially young people, would like to have greater experience in the creative and performing arts as participants or spectators. This is a fertile field for experimentation and assistance, and one in which the interest and involvement of a number of foundations are growing.

There are innumerable other ways and fields in which private foundations can contribute to human progress. A few examples might include further research in the new needs of education; greater encouragement of the humanities; economic research and its present application to disadvantaged nations; confrontation of the problems of the arid lands of the world, which are coming under greater population pressure; participation in basic studies of water resources; aid to research on the increasingly critical problem of air and water pollution; efforts to reduce or eliminate certain epidemic diseases of domestic animals in the interest of increased protein production; continuing studies and progress in the area of human nutrition; greater effort to understand and utilize marine, brackish- and fresh-water resources for sustained food supplies.

Other subjects which lend themselves to study under the auspices of private philanthropy are: international relations, modern diplomacy, political and constitutional institutions of underdeveloped areas, economic and political history, the causes of war, and methods of disarmament, and the behavioral sciences as they relate to current social ills.

There are many more; no single foundation can tackle more than a few. But fortunately the number and diversity of foundations' program interests enable them to range widely, particularly in areas in which other support is not yet at hand. If constantly self-disciplined by imagination, flexibility, and a dedicated willingness to venture in good cause, foundations can continue to pioneer toward constant improvement in the well-being of mankind.

The Race Between Procreation and Food Production

The purposes of human life are not fulfilled simply through the provision of appropriate quantities of foodstuffs to supply energy. The human experience achieves meaning only when the individual enjoys an opportunity to develop the full potential of his personality. Though life cannot be equated solely with food, it is, nevertheless, a hard fact that the former depends squarely on the latter and that over half the world's people must occupy their full time and energy in growing the food they live on. This alone emphasizes dramatically that food production is basic not only to human existence but to the quality of human experience. The precarious balance between populations and their food supply represents a critical relationship which may well determine the course of history.

In 1751 Benjamin Franklin prepared a manuscript setting forth his "Observations Concerning the Increase of Mankind, and the Peopling of Countries." We know that Benjamin Franklin's ideas definitely influenced the thinking of Thomas Malthus, Adam Smith, and the English founder of the modern birth-control movement, Francis Place. These men took a far more gloomy view of the world's population growth than did Franklin. Sanguine about America's rapidly growing population, Franklin surveyed his country's demographic future with confidence and equanimity because of a plentiful supply of land to support its large families.

In Franklin's day the revolutions in industry, science, technology, medicine, and public health were hardly in their infancy in

From a paper presented at the Spring Meeting of the
American Philosophical Society in Philadelphia, April 23, 1965

the Western world. Close on the heels of each revolution came major increases in the numbers of human beings. These increases did not exert detrimental effects in the Western nations because the rise in numbers took place over a period of several decades, and expanding economies were able to absorb a major portion of their populations. Moreover, population pressures in Europe were in part relieved by emigration to the less crowded regions of the globe. Today, standards of living in the advanced nations of the West have reached unprecedented heights.

When Franklin wrote his paper 214 years ago, the population of the world stood at an estimated 700 million. Today it is nearly 3.4 billion. Each week sees a *net increase* of over 1.3 million. To put it more forcefully still, this growth amounts to about 192,000 each day, or nearly two and one-quarter persons per second. If this growth rate of over two per cent continues to be compounded annually, the world's population will be more than doubled by the turn of the century.

The job of simply providing bare subsistence for all these people is in itself one of frightening magnitude. The total implications of enormous populations, and the stupendous task of assuring meaningful experience and opportunity for all, might well cause men of good will to confess themselves helpless. Nevertheless, the task must be essayed with all the reason, understanding, and intelligence mankind has at its disposal.

The people of Western nations do not yet suffer the pangs of hunger or the extreme pressures of overpopulation. But in many of the non-Western nations a dismaying degradation of the human experience worsens each day. The conditions in these nations might well be prophetic. The old feeling of fortunate people that the painful problems of faraway lands are too remote to be meaningful to them, is today unrealistic and unenlightened. As never before in history the concerns of any nation become to some degree the concern of all nations.

The less developed areas of the world have several common denominators. Theirs are fundamentally agrarian economies, with rural classes largely isolated from the urban centers. Vast numbers of rural dwellers live at extremely low standards. Most of these areas possess severely limited renewable and nonrenewable resources. All too many of their governments are politically unstable. An added

242

deterrent to progress is that large segments of the population are illiterate or have totally inadequate educational and training opportunities. Moreover, it is just these countries which are experiencing extraordinary increases in rates of population growth.

The nations which were formerly colonies, in the past had served principally to furnish food and raw materials to industrial nations. They were long regarded not so much as societies in stages of evolution as sources of supplies for the expanding needs of the metropolitan powers which, in return, provided protection and certain other political and social services. Perhaps the first and key change in this situation was the extension into the less developed areas of advances in the fields of medicine and public health. These advances had doubled life expectancy in the West and soon began to increase the life span of people everywhere. Throughout the developing world the expectation of life at birth is rising from the traditional level of 30 or 35 years prevalent only two decades ago toward the more than 70 years characteristic of the most advanced Western nations.

Medical benefits have had the secondary effect of bringing about huge annual additions to the populations of the developing areas, along with large-scale social and economic disruption. From today's point of vantage it may well be regretted that early advances in public health were not coupled with the foresight to initiate measures to help stabilize the populations that benefited from them.

The adverse effects of rapid population increase have fallen most heavily on the nations least able to handle staggering numbers of new individuals. In many of the poorer nations the net rate of increase is more than three per cent per year. Even a rich nation would have a difficult task in accommodating that many new people annually. In 1900 the populations of the less developed regions made up about 67 per cent of the world total; in 1960 they comprised about 70 per cent; in 2000 the population of these same regions will be almost 80 per cent of the world total. A 10 per cent increase over a forty-year period may not seem very ominous on paper, but numerically it represents the addition of almost three billion people to the less developed regions, but of only 436 million in the developed countries.

A most frustrating phenomenon associated with uncontrolled and massive population growth is the "soak-up effect." This is the discouraging situation in which herculean efforts to bring about economic development and improved standards of living are nullified by growing numbers. In its microform this effect can be illustrated by the subsistence farmer whose every improvement in efficiency of production is offset by increases in the size of his family. On a national scale this situation can doom a government's most careful planning for economic development.

Not only sheer numbers, but also the distribution of age groups puts a severe strain on poorer lands. In many of the underdeveloped countries 40 to 45 per cent of the population is under the age of 15. The national economies of these countries must depend on the labor of only 50 to 55 per cent of their population, since another three to four per cent are too old to be productive. In most of the highly industrialized countries the proportion of children under 15 is only 25 to 30 per cent, and the economy may draw upon the productive capacity of 55 to 60 per cent of the population.

Food production is similarly out of balance. The less developed areas, with 70 per cent of the world's people, produce only 47 per cent of the world's food grains, using .43 acres of land per capita to do so. The advanced nations, only fractionally as large in total land surface and with only 30 per cent of the world's people, grow 53 per cent of the world's grain, devoting .85 acres of land per capita to its production.

Despite all the progress in science and technology of the past 150 years, there are today many more people who live in hunger, misery, and deprivation than at the turn of the century. There is a tendency to emphasize the growing numbers of people who are enjoying more adequate standards of living each year, but the tragic fact is that the world's disadvantaged people are increasing in much greater numbers than those with rising living standards. This year, half the world's population is hungry—either undernourished or malnourished. The Food and Agriculture Organization of the United Nations has estimated that there must be a global annual increase in food production of about 2.25 per cent above the rate of population growth to provide a decent level of nutrition for all the world's people. Thus, a four to five per cent annual increase in the rate of food production will be required to provide an adequate diet not only for the estimated 1.5 to two billion who are now hungry, but also for the hundreds of millions of new human beings who will be born within the next few years.

Clearly, measures must be taken now if the world is to retain any sort of balance between nutrition and numbers. Acceptable ways must be found to decrease population growth rates and, simultaneously, to increase world food supplies. These are the two fundamental and interrelated elements of the modern dilemma.

POPULATION STABILIZATION

To achieve a stable and controlled population growth rate must be a goal of modern society. In the past, sporadic increases in mortality rates and a short life span interacted to control population growth. Modern civilization fights valiantly and continuously against famine and plagues, and in other ways seeks to prolong life and increase the dignity of the human condition. Voluntary reduction of births is the only road open to population stabilization. Its effectiveness depends on three essential factors: the level and intensity of motivation (the social factor), the utility and availability of procedures (the biomedical factor), and the means of reaching promptly the myriad individuals who might wish to take advantage of available procedures (the organizational factor). Since World War II the greatest advance has been in improving the biomedical factor. Given motivation, a family in a developed nation is now, more than ever before in history, likely to have access to some effective biomedical procedure.

The social factor still continues to impede rapid progress toward population stabilization. Cultural attitudes, religious beliefs and restrictions, economic limitations, family organization, and sexual practices are all resistant to change and loom large as obstacles to the control of population growth. This is the case even in the highly developed countries where large segments of the public already seem to be well ahead of their leaders in the matter of family planning.

In all parts of the world in which population stabilization is of vital importance, and especially in the heavily overpopulated areas, the missing element is organization and the development of patterns of operation to make generally available the concepts, information, and materials essential to family planning. It is increasingly clear that many underprivileged and disadvantaged families, even though they may not be educated, welcome simple, inexpensive methods to effect family planning and to reduce the burden of families of excessive size. Leaders in the field believe that greatly stepped-up efforts to reach the millions of families who could profit through family planning would show prompt and ultimately spectacular benefits.

There are several encouraging indications that the world is slowly becoming aware of the dangers inherent in uncontrolled population growth. Long suppressed by various forces strongly opposed to any suggestion of family planning, the whole problem has now become the subject of a continuing dialogue, discussed openly in various forums throughout the world. Recently the Senate of the United States held a series of public hearings on the Gruening bill, which provides for two new assistant secretaries for population problems in the Department of State and the Department of Health, Education, and Welfare. These two public servants would concern themselves largely with the collection and dissemination of information on the activities of federal and state governments, and of foreign governments, in the birth-control field and with stimulating the development and flow of new information.

Another promising development in this country is the recent Supreme Court decision which declared unconstitutional a Connecticut law of 1879 forbidding the use or sale of contraceptives. This decision guarantees freedom under the law to those people who wish to limit the size of their families, but it does not abridge the freedom of others. The responsibility for family size has now been placed squarely where it fundamentally belongs in a democratic society—not on the state, but on each individual couple in its private capacity.

Among the states, since January, 1965, 11 legislatures have taken action to provide family planning services or to repeal archaic and obsolete birth-control laws. Since these 11 states include some of the nation's most populous areas, virtually half the population of the United States—around 100 million people—may now, under certain legal provisions, seek and utilize birth-control information and devices. The most recent example of legislative action is in New York where the legislature has just removed from the statute books an 1881 law which, though in fact largely ignored, banned the dissemination of birth-control devices and information.

In some Asian countries national governments have begun to sponsor active programs designed to reduce population growth rates. The Government of India incorporated into its Fourth Five-Year Plan (1966-1971) a sterilization and intrauterine device program which has yielded significant data. It is expected that at least a million of these devices will be used during the next 12 months, with the ultimate hope that considerable progress may be made toward reducing India's annual population increase of 10 million. South Korea and Pakistan have also initiated programs directly aimed at family planning and population stabilization, using the intrauterine device as a primary means. Japan, by means of a highly effective program of legalized abortion, succeeded in cutting its birth rate in half between 1947 and 1955, and recently other less drastic methods have found acceptance there.

In Latin America, where the population is increasing faster than in any other region of the world, there is growing alarm over the high rate of induced abortion among women of the disadvantaged classes. This and other social and economic problems have served to focus increased attention on the perils of uncontrolled population growth and to provoke widespread and serious discussion of family planning. A dramatic example is the First Pan American Assembly on Population, held in Cali, Colombia, in August 1965. Among the participants in the Assembly were educators, doctors, sociologists, businessmen, and clergymen from all over the Americas. Never before in Latin America has there been open debate on such subjects as birth control and the relative merits of various contraceptive devices, and it is hoped that the Assembly will have far-reaching and beneficial results.

Even in the Communist nations government population policies begin to give some indication that they no longer strictly adhere to the Marxist-Leninist view that overpopulation is a problem only in capitalist nations and that a truly Communist state, because its means of production are socialized, can accommodate an unlimited number of people and, indeed, should encourage a large population. China, with 700 million inhabitants, found its Great Leap Forward seriously hampered by the need to provide for an annual population increase of 12 million. The government, after protracted debate within the party on an official population policy, now appears to advocate later marriage and smaller families.

In December, 1962, the United Nations served for the first time in its history as the forum for an open debate on world population problems. A resolution entitled "Population Growth and Economic Development" was passed, which expressed general concern about growing populations and their threat to economic development. Its passage was an important indication that many governments are reconsidering their previous stand on population increase and would not actively oppose international measures to examine its ultimate effects. Twenty-seven nations, including the Soviet Union, other members of the Communist bloc, and certain predominantly Roman Catholic countries, abstained from the vote, and the resolution was passed 69 to 0, thus registering the decision that the whole problem should be further studied.

During the three and a half years since the resolution was passed the U.N. Economic Commission for Asia and the Far East, the U.N. Population Commission, and an *ad hoc* committee established by the Secretary-General to advise on a long-range program of work in the field of population have all been active in planning and holding conferences, making surveys and reports, and gathering data. It is now expected that a much stronger draft resolution will be placed before the General Assembly later this year, calling for assistance to be provided to any country requesting it on the formulation and operation of family planning programs and other population policy measures.

Other hopeful signs are the spontaneous activities conducted around the world by private agencies to stimulate public interest in averting the consequences of unlimited population growth. In a number of the advanced countries both private and government funds are being earmarked in steadily increasing amounts for research on the biomedical aspects of reproduction and on family planning. The funds allocated for such studies by the National Institutes of Health of the United States have been modest at best, but may well increase. Recently developed technologies make it possible to manufacture contraceptive devices at minimal cost; in South Korea, Taiwan, and India plastic intrauterine coils can be mass produced at a cost of two to three cents each.

The Malthusians and Neo-Malthusians, once labeled prophets of doom, who warned of the ultimate dangers of uncontrolled population increase, have of late been appreciated by more and more of the world's spokesmen who have come to realize the importance of population growth in determining man's destiny. Final success can come only when political and other leaders understand the necessity of continuing the support of research and education, and of developing organizations responsible for ever-expanding action programs.

Major attention should be focused on the young people of all nations. It is they who will determine the numbers of the next generation, who must comprehend the disastrous effects of uncontrolled population growth on their and their children's lives, who must accept the fact that they themselves can make appropriate decisions, and who must have access to the techniques of family planning. Obviously, to reach them will require massive effort, which should be accompanied by other endeavors directed toward economic progress and expansion of educational networks.

In view of the important role of government in social action, it is obvious that national governments should take the lead in formulating and putting into effect policies and programs to encourage family planning. If general agreement on this point could be reached, it would be possible to establish national agencies and a specialized agency within the United Nations system which would concern itself with all aspects of the population problem. Such an agency could even be empowered to assist nations in developing blueprints to solve overpopulation problems and in establishing action programs to help promote family planning. Currently, the United Nations is limited to the dissemination of information, to training personnel for demographic studies, and to promoting public discussion. The World Health Organization, for instance, has not been allowed to consider the effects of population density on health because of disagreement on policy among member nations.

Although we can hope for more rapid progress toward international recognition of the population problem and toward agreement on approaches to its solution, the battle is still far from won. Where the situation is most acute it is least understood. And although partial success may be won by persuasion and special incentives, the ultimate solution can be found only in universal understanding and social planning with world opinion united behind it. Any and all efforts to reduce the rate of population growth in the already crowded nations depend upon organized national effort involving extensive programs which would reach the public generally, acquaint people with the basic concepts of family planning, and facilitate direct action.

Nor do the advantaged countries have immunity against the population problem. If they are to avoid the crises which exist elsewhere, they will have to act now to preserve for future generations much of what they have enjoyed and to ensure continuing progress toward the fulfillment of the human experience. Failure to act intelligently and promptly can only bring ultimate chaos, as numbers eventually stifle both individual and collective enterprise.

If people of this generation fail to recognize the problem and do not take positive steps for its solution, their descendants may well look back upon this time as a golden age forever gone. The path man treads today leads to diminishing importance of the individual and declining respect for human dignity. Along it lie inherent dangers of greater world instability and increasing severity of life on earth for all mankind.

INCREASED FOOD PRODUCTION

If the prospect of achieving a stabilized population is melancholy, that for early and major improvements in worldwide food production is equally discouraging. The two components interact. The strong probabilities are that within 15 years world population will exceed 4 billion; that high density populations such as those in India, Pakistan, and China will double before current trends can be changed; and that at the end of the century we will have achieved the dubious miracle of multiplying world population by a factor of ten in 250 years. In the face of a deficit food-production pattern in 1965, there is good reason to be concerned about the future.

It seems paradoxical that the knowledge, methods, and materials needed for efficient food production are available in plentiful supply at a time when half the world's citizens live on substandard diets. It is frustrating to realize that, from the standpoint of technology, world food production could readily be doubled or trebled without bringing one additional acre under cultivation. If agricultural potentials could be translated into realities in all lands, food could be removed from the list of man's worries and he could concentrate on limiting population increases and improving the quality of the environment through social and economic measures to benefit the individual. The formula is simple but, too often, the essential ingredients are missing.

Most of the advanced nations have learned that agriculture is not only an art and a science but primarily a business. The agricultural industry not only satisfies man's hunger but supports his technologies. But without the introduction of the essential elements required for successful and continuing production, agricultural practice may become destructive.

In seeking to modernize their agriculture, the leading industrial nations have recognized their total dependence on efficient systems for general and specialized education and on broad applications of modern technologies. They have invested vast sums to make education available to all persons throughout the country and to provide cheap power, adequate transportation, accessible markets, and ready credit in support of the agricultural industry. Unmistakably, this is the industry which is fundamental to all other economic endeavors.

In contrast, the disadvantaged nations are commonly still bound to traditional practices in agriculture, farming solely as a way of life, as the simple reaping of nature's bounty. In these lands agriculture has been a subsistence enterprise for centuries; today it contributes little to national economies. Efforts to hasten economic progress through heavy emphasis on nonagricultural industries, ignoring the agricultural sector, have usually led to increasing deficits rather than to the desired economic gains. The curious attitude that agriculture does not require the same attentive effort and economic support given the mining, construction, and fabricating industries must change if there is ever to be hope that the world can be adequately fed.

Poorer nations usually have inadequate communication and transportation systems, and their rural populations are largely isolated. The farmer cannot readily sell his surplus products, nor can he easily buy the goods and services he might desire. As a result, he lacks incentives to increase productivity. The same isolation makes it axiomatic that the farmer is the last to benefit from social advances, particularly in the realm of education. Until farmers everywhere are able to understand and communicate there can never be hope that food production will approach total agricultural potentials.

It is interesting that the factors which apply most directly to the problems of population stabilization are similar to those involved in agricultural production. Social, technological, and organizational considerations are of paramount importance in seeking to increase world food supplies. Here, again, the technologies are the most advanced of the three, and if they could be applied generally, the food deficit could be corrected. The techniques of education and related social phenomena are understood, and they, too, if generally applied, could with relative speed advance the individual and collective accomplishment of rural populations. However, as with population control, the mobilization of knowledge and the organization of programs to be applied promptly and widely represent the greatest single bottleneck to the satisfaction of world hunger. What is needed is increased understanding, not only among those who till the soil but also among their leaders, who often fail to appreciate the necessity for sound agricultural planning and practice and for the investment of adequate funds in support of the development of the agricultural industry. Funds appropriated for public works, industry and commerce, and the military are all too often out of all proportion to the woefully meager amounts provided for agriculture.

The panaceas offered for agriculture in underdeveloped nations are many, but none thus far has achieved its avowed purpose. At various times great emphasis has been placed on land reform, credit organizations, extension services, and mechanization. It is repeatedly stated that a broadening of the base of education must accompany these other developments.

Perhaps the basic reason for the failure of these prescriptions is the lack of realization that no single measure can correct the situation—that it is necessary to apply a variety of remedial measures in a timely and balanced fashion. Changes for the better can be expected only from well-coordinated efforts to improve the entire substructure on which modern agriculture rests—ready transportation, cheap power, high-quality genetic materials, effective marketing outlets, credit systems, and the like, and to provide greater educational opportunities at all levels. Finally, no country dependent on agricultural resources for economic growth can afford to ignore the necessity for mobilizing science and technology in support of agriculture.

Successful agriculture requires intelligent and logical planning and execution. Theoretically, a few leaders with complete authority and sufficient numbers of partially trained but highly disciplined people could execute such plans, but such authoritarian methods are not a part of modern democratic systems. Reliance must rest on rapid upgrading of the educational and economic levels of rural peoples everywhere. To do so will require herculean efforts, the sacrifice of certain national luxuries, and even, for a time, general austerity. Nations seeking to improve their economic and social positions will have to develop, often against great odds, elementary and secondary schools and colleges, in-service training, extension services, and other techniques to bring to isolated and disadvantaged rural communities the opportunity to learn and to apply learning to the improvement of production patterns as well as to daily life.

Many of the present deficiencies of agricultural production are clearly evident; so are their causes, and the remedies which might be applied over substantial periods of time. It is essential that these efforts be undertaken. But there are short-run possibilities for prompter accomplishment which should also be vigorously pursued. These will in themselves help support collateral efforts.

One direct and extremely important approach would be a gigantic effort to provide mineral fertilizers in adequate quantities wherever they can usefully be applied. Fertilizers can be manufactured readily and are easily transported. Perhaps the most important subsidy that could be given to farmers throughout the world would be in the form of fertilizers containing nitrogen, phosphorus, and potassium. If all organizations interested in improving food production in the developing areas would unite in a project for doubling, trebling, or quadrupling the amount of fertilizer used, the results could be spectacular. Surely there would be waste, surely there would be misuse, but once undertaken, the effort should grow each year with improved organization and the increased understanding by those who for the first time would learn the benefits of these essential elements. Organized on an international scale, with attention to the requirements of the nations concerned and the assurance of their enthusiastic participation and support, a fertilizer campaign could well be a master key to unlock one door to greater production.

Obviously, fertilizer alone does not guarantee successful agriculture. However, when fertilizer and high-yielding varieties go hand in hand the situation immediately brightens. One obvious but frequently overlooked essential for increasing production is continuous effort to develop improved crop plant and domestic animal varieties with yield potentials greatly in excess of average harvests. National average yields of cereal crops, even in the most advanced

253

nations, always lag far behind maximum potentials; as record yields go from 100 to 150 to 200 bushels or more per acre, national averages rise only from 20 to 30 and to 50 or so bushels per acre. Given the higher genetic potentials of improved crop plants, average yields can continue to rise. They can also rise by improved crop management stimulated by the promise of greater economic gain.

At least one billion pounds of animal protein, which might be used to improve human nutrition, are lost each year as a result of animal diseases. The value of the meat in the market place is unrealized, and the effort and capital invested in herds and flocks later lost to disease are wasted. Veterinary science and animal pathology are international concerns, and if they could be marshaled, reinforced, and applied on an ever-expanding scale, it is certain that the results, in the form of larger supplies of meat and meat products for hungry nations, would be dramatic. Here again, a vast body of research information is still unutilized in many areas of the world which, if promptly applied, would greatly benefit animal production. Effective regulatory programs already in existence, if enforced generally, could immediately begin to reverse the trend in animal losses from disease. Man has fought malaria, yellow fever, smallpox, and other widespread human diseases to a standstill during the past 50 years. Similar organized efforts for the control of rinderpest, schistosomiasis, aphthous fever, East African swine fever, bovine pleuropneumonia, and other major infectious diseases of animals, could produce incalculable benefits through increased food supplies.

Water has always been a limiting factor in the success of agriculture throughout much of the world. Many large land areas are unsuitable for agriculture because of too much water or too little. In many areas crops fail one, two, or three years out of five because of drought. Unfortunately, there is no easy or cheap way to supply water to moisture-scarce agricultural lands. Investments in power, material, and manpower must be heavy. Ultimately perhaps, almost unlimited sources of cheap power may help resolve both the problem of converting saline or brackish waters for agricultural purposes and of pumping them long distances. In the meantime, continuing effort should be made to develop crop plants with improved drought tolerance and shorter growing seasons. This approach, along with improvements in water conservation and utilization, could effect substantial improvements in production in the dry lands of the world. Such an approach, however, requires a kind of sophistication that can only come through continuing research and its application by those able to take advantage of modern methods and materials.

The search for new sources of food supplies must be continued and even intensified. Investigators should seek for methods of increasing the productivity of saline, fresh, and brackish waters for human nutrition. Further research on microorganisms of critical importance to nutrition, on plant genetics and physiology, soil science, animal science, and disease and pest control, must be conducted. Continuing studies must be made of food-processing techniques and product utilization. The application of the engineering sciences to agricultural production has had magnificent success in the advanced nations, and in the future it can be expected that proven techniques could be adapted to other lands.

To sum up: much could be done, although real breakthroughs probably can come only as the result of changes in social attitudes. Time is running out; the world cannot afford the dubious luxury of severe underproduction on lands which could yield two to three or more times their current averages and which could help sustain the added burden of millions of citizens who are now deprived of the opportunity to enjoy a reasonable standard of living.

CONCLUSIONS

The powers of modern science are finite, and governed by the purposes to which man is willing to apply them. In terms of scientific knowledge and its application, man could decide what rate of population increase would be acceptable, and he could achieve this rate, or change it, at will. Similarly, insofar as science and technology are concerned, man could double or treble current annual world food supplies.

Most of the great advances in public health and medicine have not required the active participation of all the people. The masses could remain passive and still reap the benefits of scientifically directed disease control campaigns and public works. The population problem cannot be resolved passively by reason of its highly personal nature and the necessity of individual agreement and active participation.

The barriers, then, are not technological but human. They are not the same everywhere, since social and economic conditions, cultures, and attitudes vary widely over the face of the globe. A common denominator would seem to be the lack of general agreement and determination to take steps to achieve clearly desirable human purposes.

Ultimate population stabilization can come about only through interactions within the entire society. Fractional accomplishment could at best delay the inevitable. Similarly, food deficits must be tackled nationally and internationally, for progress in a solitary situation contributes little to solving the total problem. Both the population and the food problems can be solved only through the active participation of leaders and people who must learn to accept new ideas and practices and to discard outmoded or even destructive traditional beliefs.

There may still be a chance to avert a Malthusian disaster. The auguries are not all unfavorable when viewed in terms of contemporary potentials for achievement. If the world's leaders in government, religion, education, and science become convinced of the need for action, agree upon appropriate methods, and take responsibility for the wide dissemination of information, as well as for the organization of positive effort, then there is still hope. At best, the apparently unequal race between human procreation and food production can be won only after an immense and prolonged struggle during which man will be ever more precariously crowding the margin of safety.

Whatever is done must be begun soon if we are to avoid the ominous situation where population numbers become so great and relative food supplies so inadequate as to bring about an unnatural rise in death rates and severe social deterioration. Man can still choose the kind of world in which he would like to live, and he can work toward it. The generations which follow will not have it within their power to make that choice if it is left until then. As members of the most intelligent species on earth, men ought to be able to foresee, on behalf of themselves and future generations, the consequences of biological complacency and social lethargy, and to take timely steps to forestall the dire consequences which could result from blindly playing the numbers game.

War on Hunger

The rapidly widening imbalance between world population increase and food production is a worsening situation that can become catastrophic for mankind. The community of nations is already falling behind in the task of providing an adequate diet for all peoples, while making only infinitesimal progress toward population stabilization.

Previous witnesses have emphasized the problems created by an explosive population increase. Therefore, these remarks will be confined to a discussion of some of the difficulties involved in producing vastly greater quantities of food and its prompt and equitable distribution in response to the demands of ever-growing numbers of people.

We have often been warned that, if the disastrous effects of widespread and growing hunger are to be avoided, immediate and massive efforts to increase production of food by conventional means and to improve distribution patterns are essential. Unfortunately, efforts to understand and remedy this situation have thus far been only partially successful at best. Today, approximately 50 per cent of the world's population is suffering from some degree of malnutrition, and this condition could not be corrected even if all the food currently produced throughout the world were regularly and properly distributed. Thus, between total production and total requirements, there is already an absolute gap which can be bridged only through universal improvement in present methods of agriculture, coupled with significant progress toward population stabilization.

Statement at the Hearings of War on Hunger,
House Committee on Agriculture, February 16, 1966

It would be unrealistic to believe that the current situation could be solved through some technological breakthrough which could bypass conventional patterns of agricultural production or make them unnecessary. Much has been said and written about the utilization of microorganisms, *i.e.,* bacteria, fungi, and algae, as potential major sources of protein; a breakthrough in the photosynthetic process has long been prophesied; greater and more efficient utilization of marine, brackish, and fresh waters for food production is often stressed; the conversion of certain petrochemicals to protein substances is a clear possibility; and there are many other ingenious ways to add substantially to world food supplies once the economic and technological obstacles have been overcome. All of these are potentially valuable. They merit investigation, experimentation, and, where economically feasible, application. Added together they cannot, however, be expected to reduce significantly demands on conventional agricultural practice in any foreseeable future.

DEFINING THE PROBLEM

If we can agree that immediate and major emphasis should be on rapid increase in the efficiency with which arable land and related resources everywhere are utilized to expand world food production, then at least the problem is clearly before us. It is possible to reach a reasonably accurate estimate of the world's food production capacity under present conditions and to measure this against the minimal nutrient requirements of current and projected future populations. The difference between the two figures will show that it would be necessary to increase world food supplies by approximately five per cent a year just to keep up with expected increases in population and to begin to correct the existing deficit. Those countries with a highly industrialized agriculture will continue to improve the efficiency of their production patterns. It is in the less developed nations where major improvements in agriculture must be brought about if this food gap is ever to be closed.

It is a humanitarian proposition to suggest that the more advanced and affluent countries of the world should assume the burden of feeding the hungry nations through intensive agricultural overproduction to produce surpluses. But taken alone, this course would place a continuing and growing burden on all of the producer nations involved and could at best be only a short-term expedient, as well as a force disruptive to the local economy. A more rational approach would be a well-organized effort toward overcoming the tremendous underproduction which plagues so much of the world today.

A REALISTIC ATTITUDE

The highly developed nations recognize humanitarian problems and want to do what they can to alleviate them. Thus, donations of surplus foods—and occasionally even of some that are not surplus—may be necessary to prevent calamities such as famine, disease, and strife. Ultimately, however, this process, if unaccompanied by self-help, can result only in a trend toward a common economic denominator detrimental to all concerned. The only workable plan requires the mobilization of knowledge, methods, materials, and technology in a consortium of effort to bring about improvements in all aspects of agricultural technology in those nations whose production figures are substantially lower than their potentials.

In any modern society those engaged in producing food must feed not only themselves but a large percentage of their fellow countrymen who are otherwise occupied, and as populations increase, so must the efficiency of the agricultural industry. Failure to take maximum advantage of the various factors contributing to successful agricultural production now results each year in massive losses to society, not only in the form of production losses which can never be regained, but also in the waste of its manpower and investment in totally unsatisfactory yields.

Most affluent nations have learned that their prosperity is in no small measure a result of the care and attention paid to the business of agriculture—the one industry fundamentally important to the economic development of all nations. They have learned that agricultural land units must be of a size to permit economically sound agriculture. They realize that the farmer, in order that he may take full advantage of the land and help increase the supply of agricultural commodities, must be better prepared through improved educational opportunities, and through the provision of services such as up-to-date information, modern technology, improved varieties, essential agricultural chemicals and fertilizers, ready credit, and easy access to markets. Standing behind the farmer is a whole array of related business and industry which both contributes to the total process and profits from it.

259

It is a simple matter to suggest that all that is necessary is the rapid conversion of the agricultural resources of underdeveloped countries to the production levels achieved in much of the Western world. Unfortunately, implementation of this basic generalization immediately runs into complex and widely varying obstacles, all of them serious. Agriculture in many parts of the world is the product of many hundreds of years of traditional practices, and to bring about modernization within any reasonable period of time is a task requiring herculean effort and great ingenuity. Yet this enormous task must be essayed if succeeding generations are to have any hope of achieving the standards of living currently enjoyed by few but sought by many.

USING AVAILABLE KNOWLEDGE

The first requirement is a clear understanding among the hungry nations of the nature of their problems and knowledge of what must be done with all possible speed to bring about improvements. Successful agricultural technology is today no mystery. Using available information, developing nations, with the will and the organization to do so, could make prompt and substantial improvements in their food-production patterns with resultant economic and social gains.

Some rapid accomplishments are perhaps reasonably possible, given the desire and determination on the part of the nations concerned to effect change for the benefit of all their people. Some of these changes may be painful, but all are essential and logical. When developing nations are determined and eager to modernize their agriculture, their friends with greater resources can engage with them in realistic plans to bring about required adjustments in agricultural production patterns which will lead to increased average yields and higher-quality farm products. No nation really desires to live by the charity of its neighbors, and many nations could achieve far more in the future than they have in the past by building their economies upon a solid base of productive agriculture which will in turn contribute to national economic vitality.

There are many major obstacles to the modernization of traditional and sometimes primitive forms of agricultural production. In some cases governmental activity related to the affairs of the agricultural sector is inefficient. In other cases national investment in the agricultural industry is totally inadequate to encourage modern efficient practices, and all too often the problems underlying successful agricultural production are neglected. There is no single solution to the problem, but rather there must be a balanced attack, involving government, private enterprise, and the agricultural community, directed to eliminating bottlenecks and to improving technology and efficiency.

FOUR CRITICAL STEPS

A fundamental condition for bringing about the transition from underproduction to a sound agricultural economy is a logical and carefully detailed national plan supported by legislation and public funds. With proper encouragement and fiscal support from government it becomes possible to convert soundly conceived plans into effective action with visible and increasing benefits to production. Some of the most critically important steps which could be taken by local governments, or with their support, in order to assure the success of plans to modernize agricultural technology might be listed as follows:

1. Emphasize and reinforce agricultural research, education, and extension in order to interrelate the entire agricultural community and bring to it the current knowledge, improved materials, and other innovations resulting from research. The successful farmer must have at his command the information and materials which are the basic tools of the agricultural industry. This means that there must be substantial numbers of individuals trained in the agricultural sciences who will impart their knowledge to others. There must also be a growing body of qualified investigators seeking solutions to agricultural problems, and, in turn, it is essential that there be an organized extension service staffed by qualified specialists who assure that the farmer is constantly and currently informed on matters which will benefit his production. Those individuals serving the agricultural sector of the nation should be attracted and protected by a well-planned and adequately supported career civil service, thus insuring a continuing supply of investigators, teachers, and administrators dedicated to the solution of national problems.

2. Provide supervised credit, permitting improved management and gradual escape from subsistence agriculture. In many situations farmers are condemned to subsistence levels of existence through their inability to obtain the credit which will enable them to im-

prove their practices through the purchase of equipment, adding to their landholdings, increasing their flocks or herds, or otherwise improving the efficiency of their operation. Careful and judicious use of supervised credit, along with price incentives where these are sound, are among the greatest stimuli to increased production.

3. Develop transportation and marketing facilities. All too often farmers find it difficult, if not impossible, to move their surplus goods to markets where they could be sold at fair prices. In fact, markets themselves are in short supply in many areas, thus discouraging the incentive to increasing production for cash accumulation. A by-product of inadequate transportation systems can be a situation in which it becomes extremely difficult to receive and distribute food supplies provided by friendly nations, due to lack of port facilities, railways, adequate highways, and roads.

4. Make available vastly increased quantities of inorganic fertilizers and necessary pesticides through agricultural areas. Perhaps the single most important, rapid, and effective way to obtain prompt increases in food production is the application of greatly increased quantities of fertilizer wherever indicated, coupled with plant protection through the use of herbicides, pesticides, and fungicides. Immediate and substantial improvements are possible if a determined effort is made to increase the annual production of fertilizers containing nitrogen and phosphorus; and the prompt and equitable distribution of fertilizers is an endeavor in which essentially all nations can participate to advantage. Inorganic fertilizers may be produced in many countries, and maximum effort should be made to develop the fertilizer industry in all nations which have the capacity. One of the most important single measures that can be undertaken by local governments to stimulate agricultural production is to provide adequate quantities of cheap fertilizers, perhaps even in the form of a subsidy to the farmer, in order that he may have the benefit of this powerful tool to increase his production.

There are many other factors to be taken into consideration in agricultural planning, but those listed above are of the most fundamental and immediate concern. Implied in them is the absolute necessity that landholding patterns be economically sound. Situations vary widely in different countries, but all agriculture which successfully supports a national economy requires landholding systems which permit the ready application of modern technology for efficient production. There is no single ideal system of land economics, but there are many possibilities for improvements in those areas where land units are too small or are otherwise unproductive.

THE UNDERPRODUCTIVE TROPICS

The improvement of current agricultural patterns and practices is fundamental and vital to future food production. Coincidentally, however, it is possible to consider the inclusion of some of the land areas not now in a productive condition within the agricultural resource. In many parts of the world vast expanses of the tropics, both wet and dry, as well as nontropical and semiarid lands, have not yet been brought under cultivation. New knowledge and modern methods suggest that slowly but surely some of these now essentially unused areas could become available for human benefit. Support for research and development and the prompt application of modern technologies and biological materials are the basic elements needed to convert unproductive lands into economic assets.

SUPPORT FOR SELF-HELP

The emphasis in this presentation is upon self-help in the belief that each nation must take advantage of every opportunity and resource which will contribute to its own economic development. Aid from the more advanced countries should be temporary and, except in the case of extremity, in the form of programs directed toward the goal of local self-sufficiency. In return, recipient nations will have to take whatever measures may be necessary and to request the kinds of assistance which clearly are directed toward this objective. Success is predicated upon a series of small victories which together are synergistic and which could largely be accomplished through the measures listed in the foregoing numbered paragraphs.

There are not enough funds anywhere for indefinite assistance through donation. Rather, foreign aid funds should be directed toward a variety of productive enterprises. Nations wishing to assist their neighbors can be most helpful by joining with them, upon request, in bringing about the conversion of unsuccessful or partially successful agricultural and related industries into efficient and economically viable productive systems.

It is too much to expect that such an approach could be readily and promptly embraced by all the so-called hungry nations. It is perhaps not too much to expect that among them a number would be eager to embark upon the effort, given the opportunity and the required initial collaboration and support. In such cases it could be expected that their success would point the way to others until, in time, there would be a significant and growing shift from the patterns of agricultural production which today contribute to what can only be called underproduction to those in which all nations will take ever-increasing advantage of their natural resources to emancipate themselves from the pangs of hunger which threaten increasing human degradation, disease, and famine.

Although some nations are hungry, all nations are inevitably concerned with the universal problem posed by explosive increases in population and the resultant widening gap between world food demand and available surplus. In the last analysis success in correcting this undesirable and ominous situation depends upon the degree to which outside help from the advantaged nations and self-help combine to bring agriculture everywhere into a state of increasing production, with emphasis on both the quality and quantity of the product. If, simultaneously, significant progress is made toward stabilization of populations, then the future will be brighter.

The Quality of the Future

As I stand here this morning, things, at least on the surface, appear to be in good shape. It would seem that most of you can continue to expect to achieve the good life—marriage, job, children, health, and some degree of success and affluence. Unhappily, the future may not be as auspicious and as certain as it now appears, for it is my regretful conviction that you may not enjoy this full life unless the hard challenges which face the world today are met and substantially resolved.

Every generation has had to make difficult decisions, decisions which affected not only that generation but succeeding ones as well. Your generation will be similarly faced with difficult problems. One of the most pressing is the need to take appropriate action toward establishing the quality of the environment in which you will live. Quantitatively, this country has progressed on every front—record population growth, vast industrialization, extensive urbanization, and mass education. Qualitatively, however, we have not done as well; and, unless we begin to pay sufficient heed to the quality of our existence and to conserve the resources, neither inexhaustible nor indestructible, which this great land has provided to so many for so long, we will not be able to escape the dire results of unlimited population increase, haphazard industrial expansion, unplanned urban growth, and deteriorating social mores.

It may, perhaps, be inappropriate to suffuse this happy occasion with a degree of prophetic gloom. We all like to think with nostalgia

Commencement Address, Emory University, Atlanta, Georgia, June 13, 1966 of the "ivied walls and hallowed halls" and the gay, carefree campus life which has indeed provided many generations of students with one of the happiest experiences of their lives. The privilege to pursue learning without other preoccupation, to make a variety of new friendships, to be introduced to the mysteries of new and exciting knowledge, and ultimately, perhaps to find the girl or boy of one's dreams on the same university campus can be a decisive factor in one's life.

I fear that those halcyon days may not persist in the same measure in the future, and perhaps this is as it should be. In many ways life, with all its present affluence, is a sterner and a much more serious affair than in the past. Youth must now grow up faster, accept heavier responsibilities sooner, and face greater challenges more often than was true when life in this nation was less complex and when our limited communication and transportation facilities effectively restricted the mobility of the population. Now we can have breakfast in London, lunch in Atlanta, and dinner in California on the same day. There are about 50 more sovereign nations in the world today than when I graduated from college, each with its aspirations, expectations, and national goals. In those days we were more concerned with wars originating in Europe, but by the 1940's we were fighting in many places on the globe. Today, conflict may break out anywhere and no country is immune from it. It is not clear that we know how to bring about the equitable distribution of opportunity for self-help and the realization of reasonable national goals which in their achievement will turn the forces of nations away from conflict toward peaceful and prosperous coexistence. To this end much will depend on what progress your generation can make and what bridges you can build to the future so that those who follow after you can take up your work with vigor and effectiveness.

Fortunately, the American college graduate of today is more mature, more sophisticated, better educated than he has ever been. As thoughtful citizens who are going to have to participate in decisions which will determine the future course not only of our own history but, to some degree at least, the history of many other nations, it is, I think, essential that all of you consider the qualitative problems you will face, as well as the future opportunities open to you.

During the past 50 years the face of our land has undergone many dramatic but not always desirable transformations. I refer principally to those changes associated with rapid industrialization, urbanization, and transportation. Many of us long took for granted the permanent availability of open spaces with all the delights they afford. Today city dwellers often must travel several hours in order to admire the rural countryside. Vast areas of land once supporting an abundant agriculture and wildlife are now occupied by sprawling cities, industrial plants, superhighways, airports, and military installations. All this came about because of population pressures, the need for enormously increased supplies of consumer goods, the necessity for rapid and easy interchange of people and articles, and because agricultural technology has made it possible for one farmer to provide enough food and fiber for himself and 35 other people. (In 1950, the figure was 15 others.)

A great pride of our nation has been our lakes and rivers, providing us with beauty, recreation, and the basic resources. Early in our history we began to harness our rivers to provide the power to support our infant industries, and we drew upon them and our lakes for the fresh water so essential to urban development. We even exported ice as far away as Persia and India, so famous was the purity of our water. In taking advantage of these great natural resources we have been wantonly careless of their future. We have befouled the same lakes and streams with industrial wastes, municipal sewage, detergents, and an extraordinary variety of other effluents, not only desecrating their natural beauty but destroying the wildlife, both aquatic and terrestrial, which once flourished in their waters and along their shores. And the problem is not an isolated one but is rapidly becoming nationwide. As we in the North have polluted the Hudson, which once inspired an entire school of painting, and the Merrimack, which inspired Thoreau, so you in Atlanta have contaminated the Chattahoochee, whose beauty and purity Sidney Lanier so admired.

We have strewn our roadsides with beer cans and other debris, and even the largest and most ugly of our roadside advertising cannot hide the still uglier automobile junkpiles and other unesthetic products of our technological age. We have destroyed hundreds of thousands of acres through surface mining without long-range plans for the restoration of the areas once the underground wealth has been exhausted. And we have destroyed millions of acres of forests through mismanagement and carelessness with fire.

We have added toxic elements to our soils, which then enter the "food chain" to the extent that there have been found in fish caught many miles out at sea traces of these chemicals which came originally from inland waterways adjacent to agricultural areas. Pesticides have been, and are, an extraordinary boon to agricultural production, and to no small degree have been responsible for the increased productivity of the American farmer. We must, however, learn how to design and fully utilize our pesticide technology so that it will not adversely affect our environment.

Finally, our industries, cities, and automobiles are contaminating the atmosphere with every conceivable form of matter, ranging from the gaseous and particulate by-products of industry to dust, motor exhaust, incinerator smoke, and compounds of sulphur, rubber, and other organic and inorganic materials, which, along with the radioactive fall-out, have created an entirely changed and unhealthy environment for human beings.

All of these changes, many of which have come about haphazardly with no conscious direction, have served to lower the quality of our physical environment, and these, along with social pressures, have contributed to undesirable changes in the quality of our total cultural environment.

Another major factor in our changing environment, which can threaten our future well-being, is a rapidly increasing population. We in the United States have long been at least vaguely aware of the dangers of uncontrolled population growth, but we think of this phenomenon as remote from us and as affecting only far-off and less fortunate nations. We tend to attribute the problem of overpopulation to local inaction and planning failures, without recognizing that there is nothing unique about this country, or any other country, which guarantees a stabilized population in balance with economic growth. We are, in fact, at times prone to instruct other countries as to how they should live, without first being sure that the quality of existence in our own country is worthy of emulation.

We all want those who come after us to have at least the same opportunities and satisfactions that we have had. This can only be accomplished if we lay the groundwork now so that they will continue to find it possible to achieve these benefits for themselves and their children. Therefore, it is not unrealistic to suggest that we should work toward the stabilization of our population in terms of our ability to provide choices and appropriate opportunities for each person. Otherwise, we may one day find ourselves confronted by a situation in which living space and sheer survival take precedence over the development of the individual and his contribution to his society.

In 1966 seven out of ten Americans live in an urban environment. By 1970 about 75 per cent of you will be living and working in or near a large city. This seems to be an irreversible trend, and most of us have accepted it as inevitable, not without a twinge of nostalgia for the way of life in rural America. However, many of our cities are becoming more and more unsatisfactory and unpleasant places in which to live; and in certain parts of our cities life has become almost subhuman, with environmental conditions below even the minimum standards of decency. Most of the steps that have been taken thus far are haphazard, stopgap solutions that do not treat with the basic causes of the deterioration of city life but only the symptoms. There is every indication that the only solution to our urban problems is to remake the urban environment as a whole and to decentralize both the physical and cultural environment. New directions for urban planning, which will utilize all the benefits of science and technology—with the essential but as yet lacking ingredients of understanding, flexibility, and imagination—are badly needed.

The bare facts of our environmental crisis are in themselves alarming, but I think no more so than the fact that over the years society has permitted all these things to come to pass. Widespread public apathy and lack of effective leadership have been the main causes for this wholesale destruction of our national resources; this worsening pollution of our rivers and lakes; this defilement of our atmosphere, which is daily becoming more unhealthful for human beings; and this deterioration of our cities, which have become tangled masses of humanity, vehicles, and waste, contributing to psychological and social tensions.

I believe that a sensitivity to the quality of society and its importance in our future lives begins in the home, with the aid and encouragement of the church and the elementary and secondary school. Refinement of this understanding should come with the university experience and continue on into adult life through intelligent examination of available facts and information by the educated, responsible individual.

In the future our educational institutions, and especially our universities, must continue to provide the best training possible in the sciences, humanities, and social sciences for *all* students. This training, in turn, should prepare a cadre of dedicated, vigorous leaders who will provide the guidance for growing numbers of Americans who are aware of what is happening to the quality of their own lives and the lives of their children, but do not know what to do about it.

Studies of the rise, growth, breakdown, and disintegration of the world's civilizations have brought us to a realization that all civilizations are confronted by various challenges which may either arise from outside or emerge from within. Unless a civilization is aware of these challenges and effectively responds to them, it may begin to break down and eventually disintegrate. The essential element which a civilization must possess in order to respond successfully to a challenge threatening its existence is a group of creative individuals—a creative minority who are sensitive to the values of their social system and capable not only of maintaining what is good in their culture but also of improving upon the available fund of beliefs, potentials, and techniques and using them to the better advantage of society as a whole.

I would like to leave with you my strong conviction that one of the most critical challenges to emerge today from *within* our civilization is the deterioration of our environment and the threat to the quality of our existence. Perhaps in our concern with *outside* challenges we have been blind to the serious danger threatening us from *within*. The new creative leadership which will play a decisive role in responding to this challenge, must come from among you—the young men and women who are to leave the campus this month for more worldly activities and responsibilities or to return to the academic life for further study and training. In a democratic and pluralistic society the impetus for a constructive public policy depends on "opinion-leaders" to provide the necessary thrust and guidance. Whether it is to bring the general public to a sharper awareness of the critical situation, whether it is to discover new methods of combating the problem, whether it is to demand new state and federal laws, or whether it is to improve the administration of the existing laws, an informed and responsible leadership is essential. The record of the past is illuminated with notable human achievements. In the wake of each achievement new problems will rise to challenge us. It is my hope and belief that your generation and future generations will meet them with imagination, vigor, and integrity.

Agricultural Development in Latin America

Latin America—beginning in Mexico and reaching through Central and South America to the tip of Chile—presents an infinite variety of climates, topography, and crops. Taken as a whole, this area has the capacity to satisfy essentially all of its food, feed, and fiber needs and to produce additional quantities of agricultural commodities for the world's markets. Its present condition of underproduction cannot be ascribed to any single major circumstance of geography, climate, or resources; it is rather the result of many interacting factors of time and place, history, and tradition.

To begin with, Latin America from Mexico southward does not have an unlimited abundance of arable land, rainfall, educated farmers, and well-developed economies. Much of the land area is mountainous, a great deal is arid or semiarid, and the arable soils are not uniformly rich. Communication and transportation systems, although advancing in some countries, lag far behind in others. Educational facilities are often insufficiently developed to meet anything like the total needs of most of the countries concerned, and kaleidoscopic political changes in a number of Latin American countries have over the years adversely affected the formation of stable economies.

THE NEGLECTED SECTOR

Unfortunately, throughout much of Latin America agriculture has been looked upon as a tradition, a way of life, rather than as business. In the competition for public funds agriculture almost invariably has lost out to what is called industrialization. Assembly and manufacturing plants and varieties of light and heavy industry have frequently been given favored positions, while agriculture,

Statement before the Subcommittee on International Finance of the House Committee on Banking and Currency, August 29, 1966

upon which they are based and which could provide them with essential raw materials, remains an orphan.

As is so often the case, the agricultural community in Latin America is not in a strong position to make its wants and needs felt. Generally speaking, the farmers have fewer incentives to increase their production than any other group in the labor community. They are likely to be remote from the centers of power and, even where they are not ignored, they receive relatively little attention. The net result is that the vast productive capacity of the rural sectors of Latin America never approaches its full potential. Yet there is a growing leadership within Latin America which has grasped in an exemplary manner that national investments in agriculture are essential to overall national progress and prosperity. In a speech given early in August, His Excellency Antonio Ortiz Mena, Mexico's Minister of Finance, declared:

"... the days when a choice between industrialization and agriculture was considered mandatory are gone. Today we know that farm progress is a requirement of vigorous industrialization and that the latter should be based on a growing internal demand.

"We cannot reach this massive demand within the next decades without increasing productivity and income at the farms. Despite excellent opportunities for exporting Mexican products, development of Mexico's economy must be based on the internal market.

"Agriculture must continue to produce food and clothing for our people and surpluses to be exchanged for capital goods we do not produce yet.

"If we ask all these things from the farms, we have to adopt measures to make them stronger and modern—among them, pay just prices for farm products."

This statement is a capsule blueprint which might be applied successfully elsewhere. If adapted to each individual case and translated into action, it could change the entire production pattern for agriculture in Latin America.

LOCAL LEADERSHIP

In my judgment the satisfaction of food and related agricultural needs of Latin America's ever-expanding populations rests squarely on the initiative and enterprise of its own leadership, its own institutions, and its own agricultural producers. Outside assistance can be truly effective only if it is focused to help achieve soundly based, locally supported, and well-planned projects of fundamental importance to the nations concerned. I do not believe that there is any template that can be placed on Latin America as a pattern for progress. I think, rather, that there must be serious and continuing conversation with the political, scientific, and economic leadership in each country in order to identify the critical problem areas and agree upon rational methods for their solution. Once this has been accomplished it becomes possible to plan and initiate action programs.

As a first step, I would suggest a country-by-country assessment of what is now available and what will be needed to raise agricultural productivity. By this I do not mean to suggest still another series of studies, but rather the prompt marshaling of known facts to arrive at clear decisions as to how rapid progress toward greater agricultural productivity can best be brought about in each country.

The next step would be to establish short- and long-range objectives and goals and to begin at once to implement programs directed to these ends. In most situations it is impossible, for economic and other reasons, to mount an immediate and massive full-scale agricultural development program, but priorities can be established and projects initiated which later, as progress permits, can be accelerated by bringing additional factors into play.

SIX VITAL MEASURES

If it is clearly understood from the beginning that the first goal is improved productivity at the farmer level, then it becomes possible to concentrate effort and perhaps to avoid the motion lost through an overly theoretical approach to broad economic problems. It is relatively easy to determine what the bottlenecks limiting production may be in any given country or agricultural area. Once this has been done it becomes possible to plan and take remedial action. Measures which I would cite as central to full agricultural production are the following:

The economic use of land resources—Farming is an entrepreneurial endeavor and its entrepreneurs must, in the first instance, have at their disposal land units of adequate size to enable them to carry out a successful business operation. Landholding patterns vary from country to country. No single system can be applied everywhere, but it is clear that unused arable land and uneconomic absentee landlordism are inconsistent with the food requirements of growing populations.

Applied technology—To be successful, farmers must have the benefit of a mobilized technology for the optimum utilization of their land units. This means there must be continuing research and prompt application of its results for benefits to production. Much of the underproduction encountered in Latin America comes from the utilization of inefficient varieties of crop plants and domestic animals as food sources. Many are highly susceptible to attacks by pests and diseases, some are poorly adapted to their environment, and some are inefficient in the conversion of available nutrients into food products. It is possible through research and its application to correct these conditions with reasonable rapidity.

Agricultural chemicals—The provision of adequate and timely supplies of nutrients and protectants at reasonable prices is absolutely essential in combining land resources and improved crop varieties and animal breeds for optimum production. Attention to plant nutrition and protection is as vital to their productivity as it is to domestic animals. Therefore, any attempt to bring about general and significant improvement in food production requires major effort in the production of fertilizers containing nitrogen, phosphorus, and potash, and the easy availability of fungicides, pesticides, and herbicides to combat insects, diseases, and weeds which on occasion destroy crops and every year take heavy tolls.

Water—Water is a controlling factor in most agricultural areas of the world. Its availability determines cropping patterns, and the efficient use of rainfall, ground water, or impounded water is critical to agricultural production.

Farmer incentives—To induce farmers to produce more, they must know that there are easily accessible markets for their products, adequate storage facilities to prevent glut and scarce periods, and price and other incentives which will continually stimulate them to improve their landholdings and their practices, with the expectation that this will provide added income for the needs of their enterprise and the requirements of their families.

Education—Finally, there must be a "back-up" support in the rural communities to assure that there is a continuing flow of information to the farmer for his benefit; that he can readily obtain the

275

implements and other materials he needs; and that social services, schools, and clinics are available to him and to his family.

ESTABLISHING PRIORITIES

It seems to me that any examination of a nation's economic opportunities should include a close scrutiny of the ways in which funds could be diverted from marginally productive uses to the agricultural and other basic industries. Ideally, clear-cut national priorities should be established and adhered to, even if this means curtailment of less essential expenditures. This would be courageous stocktaking, but it could pay multiple dividends to economic development. Some of the possibilities that might be considered would be the postponement of public works of symbolic rather than productive significance; limiting government operations which require continuing subsidy but which do not contribute significantly to the local economy; the examination of investments in military hardware to determine where they might be reduced without damage to the national safety and with substantial gain to economic development; examination of possibilities for common markets, customs unions, tariff agreements, and common development projects such as international highways, pipelines, and other economic inputs; inducing citizens to invest at home, thus cutting down on the export of capital and, simultaneously, the encouragement of private investment from abroad and the attraction of long-term, low-cost loans from international banks.

There is no mystery about any of the ingredients essential to successful agriculture; each can be identified and put to work by any country with the desire and the will to achieve higher crop yields and better standards of living. And as gains are made in each area, it becomes possible to add other elements which interact and accelerate the process.

When a developing country has shown evidence that it is taking constructive steps to improve its economic progress, it then becomes feasible for outside agencies to contribute to the total effort in a variety of ways:

Private assistance—The private sector has had a long record of interest and involvement in economic improvement in Latin America. Private foundations have cooperated directly in education, research, and extension in support of agriculture, engineering, public health, and general institutional development with many demonstrable benefits. Two examples of meaningful results are to be found in the greatly improved varieties of food crops (especially wheat, corn, and potatoes) which are now widely available and extensively utilized throughout much of Latin America, and the growing number of well-trained, competent agricultural scientists who are serving well the economic development of their countries.

Everyone can understand the profit motive and its contributions to progress. When wisely and equitably applied, there is no single force which contributes more to the development of a democratic society. The foreign business community has long been active in Latin America and has made vast investments in commercial, manufacturing, and industrial enterprises. This group today represents one of the most far-flung, most sophisticated, and most enlightened forces for economic development in all of Latin America. Possibilities for enormous increase in business partnerships within the Americas and between Latin American countries and nations overseas are clearly apparent. Properly designed and established, such enterprises would attract vast quantities of foreign capital with principal benefits to the recipient countries. These would be in the rational utilization of natural resources, a substantial increase in employment, and the profits from successful business and industrial complexes.

Bilateral assistance—Experience has taught that bilateral programs of foreign aid can be extremely effective in stimulating economic developments in countries where these are wanted. Each country's program should be designed in response to clearly demonstrated need and opportunity; it should be established and organized by full mutual agreement and should be geared into the basic economic planning of the recipient nation. Projects within such programs may take many forms, depending upon local situations and critical requirements. They might be investments in short-term economic accelerators or they might be programs directed toward long-range institutional development through the support of research, education, and extension. Some might involve direct and joint action in which qualified participants from both nations participate in high priority projects. These require clear identification, sound organization, career staff, and assured and stable support over adequate periods of time.

Multilateral assistance—Many multilateral efforts have been effective in the past, and this form of assistance has great future potential. These efforts may be highly effective when a group of nations, such as the Organization of American States, makes a concerted endeavor to solve common problems. One striking example of a problem common to many Latin American nations, and one which adversely affects their economic development, is the hoof-and-mouth disease of cattle, which can be successfully attacked only through joint action. Many other examples might be cited.

The United Nations specialized agencies are in a position to continue to be helpful through their statistical studies, the provision of consultants and advisers, through their training and communication activities, through international meetings, and other projects directed principally to agriculture and health. Action programs backed by the United Nations Special Fund have been, and continue to be, of assistance on many fronts.

International banks—International lending agencies can be a major force in raising the level of economic development. The careful investment of loan funds, where they may break bottlenecks or catalyze national development, serve to telescope other efforts to step up economic growth. Properly utilized, these loans can pay for themselves manyfold through increasing productivity. Both the Inter-American Development Bank and the World Bank have been operating in Latin America and, as their programs continue to expand and to be coordinated with other efforts already under way, their contributions to the economic development of Latin America can be expected to grow apace.

It seems to me that international bank loans can, in many instances, be decisive factors in helping the "turn-around" aspects of the local economy. They could well be critical in the support of projects designed to supply promptly a valuable component to the agricultural industry. Fertilizer plants, key transport facilities, food processing establishments, and many other facilities essential to the national economy are examples of viable objects for long-term loans.

The foregoing examples suggest that there is no single force or agency which could or should undertake the total responsibility for providing foreign aid to economic development in Latin America. The strength of current efforts is in their variety. And this strength is further enhanced if there is reasonable, voluntary coordination and complementation of effort. Excessive duplication, obviously, can lead only to confusion and waste.

Realistic assistance—Those who believe that successful economic development begins at home urge that it be built upon soundly conceived principles which are first identified and understood by national leadership—a principal requirement for getting the economy moving ahead more rapidly. When these conditions have been met, it becomes possible to provide aid in a variety of forms to carefully established objectives. This process has not always been followed in the past, and some of the dangers should perhaps be pointed out here.

Nations cannot have both cheap and adequate supplies of foodstuffs when "cheap" means that food prices are lower than local production costs. A number of countries of Latin America have, for political reasons, tried this, with the result that there has been a decrease in the supplies of basic daily foods and an increased demand for shipments from abroad, principally from the United States. These food supplies have occasionally served to depress further the local economy and price structure and have thus failed to accomplish their economic purpose. Another harmful practice, not unknown in Latin America, is the use of tariffs to the disadvantage of agriculture. A further error has been the attempt from without to assure that assistance funds are not invested in crops which would compete with imports, with the rationale that the deficit nations could purchase their food grains and other basic commodities more cheaply abroad. This restriction on assistance is unrealistic and illogical, since each nation should be encouraged to produce at least the minimum amount of its own basic foodstuffs, whichever they may be, in accord with its own soils, climate, and growing seasons. This is important for both economic and protective reasons. If successful, the nation will then become a better customer in the world markets for goods and services it cannot readily produce itself, as well as for machinery and other items necessary to the gradual improvement of its industrial potential.

CONCLUSION

I believe Latin America may well be on the threshold of a great upsurge of economic development. Generally speaking, attitudes are changing rapidly, and understanding of problems and priorities is growing along with determined efforts to engage with them. The current meeting of leaders from five Latin American countries in Bogotá, Colombia, is an important example. I think also that there is improving international understanding within the Americas and that possibilities for mutual planning and action are increasing. Areas of sensitivity persist, of course, and it is critically important that all concerned try to understand and to act reasonably, logically, and fairly in the realization that what is good for one nation is good for all nations and that a strong, prosperous, and united Pan-America is an essential step toward the attainment of world peace and prosperity.

Principles for Progress in World Agriculture

I predicate these remarks on the assumption that there is general agreement that the problem of uncontrolled population increase is real and becoming more critical year by year. And, unless prompt and substantial progress is made toward population stabilization, any prognosis that during the years ahead we will be able to produce enough food to satisfy the nutritional requirements of the entire world is unrealistic.

The best evidence of this fact is that even today, with our present population, total world food production and its distribution are far from being in balance with human requirements. We operate now from a deficit position, and unless we can be vastly more successful in applying production technology, while bringing about significant reductions in average birth rates throughout much of the world, the situation will worsen rather than improve. If we fail, the best predictions indicate that there will be a severe world food shortage by 1986, perhaps of the magnitude of over 200 million metric tons in grain equivalent—approximately equal to the total annual production of grain in the United States.

I do not suggest that the challenge to humanity lies only in this race between procreation and food production. We are faced also with the issue of whether we can preserve and improve the quality of life and the richness and variety of our environment in order that our world may more universally offer those opportunities and satisfactions which make life an increasingly meaningful experience. Belatedly, we must now press forward with greater efforts to resolve urgent problems which, because they were not clearly understood, have been allowed to reach alarming proportions.

Speech presented at the 33rd Annual Meeting of the National Agricultural Chemicals Association at White Sulphur Springs, West Virginia, September 8, 1966

Recognizing the needs of the developing countries, the United States declared for foreign aid and technical assistance nearly 20 years ago. We undertook to be helpful to many countries as an expression of our sympathy, generosity, and an enlightened national interest. Early in our foreign assistance efforts, there was a tendency to oversimplify the problem and to believe that the answer lay in transferring to the less developed countries what we chose to call our own "know-how," with the aim of achieving rapid "breakthroughs" which would quickly solve agricultural and other developmental problems. Bitter experience has taught us the fallacy of this belief. Large-scale efforts, if unrelated or not soundly conceived, breed confusion and are no substitute for identifying the real bottlenecks and attacking them with logic and competence in a sustained and progressive fashion. Unhappily, now, after some 20 years of experience with foreign aid, there is little evidence that many major economic tides have been turned within the developing nations.

In my judgment the highest form of help is assistance to those who wish to help themselves toward realistic and important national goals. Surely, the objective of every sovereign nation is to develop to the maximum its own human and natural resources, free from dependence upon alms from abroad. National pride is not unlike individual pride, which is a valuable component of human dignity. Debtor nations inevitably have a feeling of mortification concerning their dependence, and are often fearful that they will be obliged to repay gifts and loans from abroad with allegiance —if not subservience. And, although it could be reasonably expected that generous understanding on the part of one nation of the plight of another might engender expanding good will, this has not always occurred. More often than not, the recipient nation may exhibit toward the donor what seems to be a perverse independence, which may well be the result of the desire to reaffirm national sovereignty and political freedom.

We have already seen some of the results of one nation trying to assume the burdens of other nations. The habit of complacent acceptance of "hand-outs," especially when they are labeled "surpluses," can become ingrained. Indeed, some recipient nations may even feel that the flow of benefits is in the reverse direction, since the surplus nation is being relieved of embarrassing accumulations of agricultural commodities and the high costs of storing and preserving them. Some countries have based their long-range national economic plans on the expectation of donations from abroad to supplement their own current underproduction patterns. The application of foreign aid in the form of unwisely donated agricultural commodities may insulate the recipient country from economic realities and discourage greater indigenous effort.

FOCUS ON SELF-HELP

To me it is unwise, undesirable, and could be ultimately catastrophic to think that the productive capacities of the highly developed nations of the world should be used deliberately to produce large surpluses to be donated over indefinite periods of time to countries in a state of underproduction. I do not suggest the cessation of emergency foreign aid at times when needs are critical. I do suggest, however, that when foreign assistance is provided it should be focused sharply on national self-improvement and increasing independence from the need to seek charity abroad.

Currently we are in the midst of an upsurge of ideas, plans, and activities calculated to get at and finally to resolve the total problem of an inadequate world food supply. The solutions offered are myriad and bewildering, often with each proponent claiming highest priority for his own discipline. Somehow we are going to have to concentrate our efforts and resources on immediate and apparent needs, and build future programs upon accomplishment.

What, then, is the answer to the grave question of how the food-deficit nations can improve their agricultural productivity?

I am convinced that it is possible to redesign the international machinery of food production and distribution so that vastly larger quantities of foods and feeds can be rapidly and economically produced and fed into distribution channels. The tools, methods, and materials are all available and their uses are sufficiently understood so that, with suitably planned programs, areas of underproduction can be increasingly converted to full agricultural potentials. The task is neither simple nor easy. Its success depends upon understanding, progressive attitudes, knowledgeable leadership, and continuing sense of purpose on the part of all concerned.

Reduced to simplest terms, it is possible to combine three ingredients to create a formula, which when applied will lead to early and progressive improvement in agricultural production almost anywhere. These are: (1) the mobilization of modern technology, (2) the production, distribution, and opportune application of essential agricultural chemicals, and (3) the provision of timely and appropriate economic incentives to agricultural producers.

Technology—National leaders almost everywhere are keenly aware of the identity of the most immediate and pressing obstacles to overcoming national agricultural underproduction. And it is not difficult to sit down with the local political and scientific leadership of a developing nation and arrive at general agreement as to the nature of the basic problems. It usually becomes quickly apparent that the first step in removing barriers is to bring modern technology into play. We have today at our disposal a vast body of knowledge growing each year in quantity and quality as the results of continuing and essential research pour in. And these are available for the benefit of all who care to utilize them. Application requires the establishment of a body of competent scientists who will immediately go to work on the various problems associated with underproduction. Among these may be the absence of efficient varieties of food crops capable of producing high yields of quality products, the presence of diseases and pests which annually take heavy tolls of food crops, excessive competition with weeds, inadequate seedbed preparation, and wasteful or inefficient water utilization. These are problems of technology, and such problems can usually be overcome through the application of modern science by persons of competence.

Agricultural chemicals—In nations with the most advanced agricultural technologies, the regular use of chemical fertilizers and plant and animal protectants is now taken for granted as essential to full production. Although their importance is not everywhere understood, it is absolutely essential that plant nutrients be regularly added to most agricultural soils if we are ever to have anything approaching maximum productivity. Major emphasis on the production of chemical fertilizers and their appropriate distribution and application could have added millions of tons of food to world food supplies during the past two decades. If, during the same period, pesticides, fungicides, and herbicides had been produced in increased quantities and appropriately distributed and applied, additional millions of tons of food could have been made available.

Economic Incentives—To a degree, most farmers are entrepreneurs. The entrepreneur functions most efficiently when appropriate incentives are available to him. If the farmer is to produce more, he must be provided with the incentives which will stimulate him to exert his maximum effort for food production. These vary with circumstances, but certainly one of the most basic is the ready accessibility of markets where his products can be sold at attractive prices. The farmer must be able to sell the fruits of his labors at prices which will enable him to improve his operation and to provide the amenities of life for himself and his family. In some cases, subsidies for fertilizers, pesticides, or the purchase of farm machinery are "start-up" incentives. Easy credit for sound investments is critically important in helping the farmer to establish and maintain a competitive position. Preferential tax treatment often serves as a further stimulus to agricultural production. We learned long ago that a nation cannot have both cheap food and enough food if "cheap" means that the market price of the food produced locally falls below the cost of producing it. If our own experience has anything to tell us, it is that a highly efficient agriculture can be achieved only by managing the agricultural industry as a sound business investment.

One of the greatest successes of American agriculture has been the development of extension services at both the federal and state levels. The county-agent system plugged the farmer into a network which provided him with advice, information, and, on many occasions, some of the materials essential to his business. The support of research and the training of an increasing number of agricultural scientists and others in the service of agriculture become truly meaningful only when new knowledge can be translated into a growing and improving agricultural economy. In the last analysis, the responsibilities for actual production are vested in the farmer himself, and all of the economic and scientific inputs must reach him to result in the improvement of his efficiency.

ACCELERATING DEVELOPMENT

Once the basic problems of the agricultural economy of a nation are recognized and steps taken toward their solution, it becomes possible to add certain accelerators which are essential to full development. These can be begun immediately if economic conditions permit; sometimes they may have to follow economic priorities. Typical accelerators are improvements in communications and transportation, the development of marketing systems, the expansion of credit facilities, and the local production of the tools and machinery essential to increasing agricultural efficiency. And these accelerators can themselves be accelerated by means of long-term, low-interest loan funds.

The problem is to convince the nations that the only way they can attain economic stability and independence is to exert a major effort to correct agricultural underproduction. This may quite probably require a period of austerity: the postponement of public works of symbolic rather than productive significance, the limitation of national franchises which require heavy annual subsidy but contribute little to the local economy, and a reappraisal of the need for costly military hardware consistent with the requirements of internal law and order and national security. The price of economic independence must ultimately be paid principally by the people of each sovereign nation. Others cannot long bear the burden in either time or money. I believe that the developing nations must move promptly and more effectively toward increased agricultural production. The more advanced nations can assist in this process through the wise contribution of the appropriate components of technical assistance.

OUTSIDE ASSISTANCE

Thus far I have focused my thoughts on what the governments of the developing nations must do to develop a healthy agricultural industry. However, I fully realize that in attempting to bring their economies and their standards of living up to levels compatible with human dignity these nations will certainly require substantial long-term assistance from without. This aid should be directed to the basic economic and social needs of the countries concerned, with the mutual understanding that, regardless of the period of time involved, it can only be temporary. Under these circumstances it becomes possible to establish soundly-conceived bilateral and multilateral programs under which one nation undertakes to assist others, or a consortium of nations aids its membership.

As national economic development programs are established, it becomes possible for the private sector to participate more constructively and effectively in the economic development of the newer or less developed nations. Among the largest and most important groups of experienced and knowledgeable individuals working in foreign countries within the private sector are the American businessmen. Where business leaders from two nations can sit down together and agree upon an arrangement which will provide funds, experience, and expertise to develop the resources of one country, with fair returns for all concerned, then the country's economy begins to move. The accomplishments of American business abroad, especially in the developing countries, are many, but without doubt the greatest achievements lie ahead as understanding of common interests and goals grows and deepens and as systems of operation that take into consideration the best interests of both parties are continually improved. In my opinion, no group has a greater role to play, especially in the agricultural economy of developing nations, than does the agricultural chemicals industry.

Private philanthropy has participated in stimulating self-help activities in countries where the needs and opportunities are manifest. Since I have been asked to describe some of the work of The Rockefeller Foundation in this presentation, perhaps I can best illustrate our type of effort overseas with one or two case histories. I believe they represent one approach which could be effective in improving agriculture in many areas throughout the world.

MEXICO: A CASE HISTORY

The first has to do with Mexico. In 1941 the Mexican Government asked The Rockefeller Foundation to help improve annual corn yields, since this basic food grain was in seriously short supply. The Foundation sent a small team of three specialists who traveled throughout the country and talked with its political, scientific, and business leaders. Their report urged the Foundation to respond favorably and to begin by working to increase the yields of both corn and wheat by improving varieties, soil fertility, and the control of pests. Accordingly, one Foundation staff member was assigned to Mexico; later, other specialists were added so that their scientific disciplines could be applied to the total problem. From the beginning, young Mexican agricultural graduates were associated with the project as colleague-trainees.

The group of American and Mexican scientists found the main bottlenecks to corn production to be low-yielding, inefficient varieties, losses due to pests and pathogens, and inadequate management. The principal problems in wheat production were found to be the presence in Mexico of virulent strains of stem-rust to which all varieties were highly susceptible and the absence of good management and improved varieties. While the plant breeders, plant pathologists, and entomologists were attacking these problems, soil scientists were improving the systems of soil management and water utilization and advocating the increased use of fertilizers and government assistance in making adequate supplies available at reasonable prices.

Mexico became self-sufficient in wheat production in 1956, just 15 years after the cooperative program was initiated, and the corn gap was closed in 1958. In 1960 the cooperative program was converted into a national effort directed and managed by capable Mexican scientists in the National Institute of Agricultural Research.

Today Mexico can produce all the corn it needs on less land through the use of synthetic hybrid varieties, even though its population has almost doubled since 1943. Furthermore, Mexico now has a wheat surplus and is beginning to devote some of its wheat lands to other food crops. This has been made possible by the development of rust-resistant, dwarf varieties of wheat which make highly efficient use of fertilizers. Obviously, the widespread utilization of improved methods and plant materials depended in large measure upon actions taken by government. The Government of Mexico, with intelligence and perception, provided the incentives which stimulated the Mexican farmers to improve their production methods and technologies as new knowledge and materials became available. These incentives included price supports, agricultural credits, subsidies to help increase supplies of chemical fertilizers and crop protectants, extension of irrigation systems, and improving the network of highways to provide outlets for farm products. It is estimated by Dr. Theodore Schultz, Professor of Economics at the University of Chicago, that the total cost of the program to both The Rockefeller Foundation and the Mexican Government is now being returned to the Mexican economy at an interest rate of at least 400 per cent each year.

I think the Mexican program illustrates the three essential

ingredients I have mentioned—technology, agricultural chemicals, and price incentives—all applied under appropriate leadership. Many other developments have occurred in the interim, and these fall into the category of "accelerators." Broadly, they include support to agricultural education, research, and extension, the establishment of industries which complement and support the agricultural industry, along with the aforementioned improvements in transportation and irrigation systems.

Perhaps the most critically important accelerator to agricultural progress in the developing nations is the human one. Through the training program in Mexico have passed more than 700 Mexican scientists, 250 of whom now hold graduate degrees from abroad. The vast majority are currently engaged in some aspect of agricultural education, research, extension, or private business in Mexico. Education in agricultural science in Mexico has steadily improved, and today the outstanding center for agricultural education, research, and extension, known as "Plan Chapingo," includes also a graduate college which, for the first time, is granting advanced degrees in agricultural science to Mexicans and to other nationals. Well over 200 young Latin American scientists from other countries have been brought to Mexico over the years to participate in the program and have subsequently returned to begin local projects, thus providing another multiplier effect.

THE DIFFUSION OF KNOWLEDGE

Within a few years after the Foundation's cooperative program was initiated in Mexico, it began to attract the interest of other countries. In 1950 The Rockefeller Foundation embarked on a similar program with the Colombian Government. In 1955 work was extended to Chile, and, upon invitation, in 1957 to India. All of these programs exchange information, materials, and personnel. Today the wheat and corn varieties developed in Mexico are being successfully utilized, either in "finished" form or as breeding stock, in improvement programs in Colombia, Ecuador, Peru, Chile, Venezuela, India, Pakistan, the Philippines, and East and West Africa. Currently, both India and Pakistan are building up their major wheat improvement programs, using adapted varieties from Mexico as their foundation; in Pakistan 350 tons of Mexican wheat have now been multiplied and successfully grown, and the seed has been used to plant up to one-half million acres; in India 250 tons of wheat sent from Mexico last year have now been harvested, and 18,000 tons of certified seed wheat have just been purchased from Mexico for a vast extension of this program.

INTERNATIONAL CENTERS

Another example of private philanthropy's assistance to foreign agriculture was begun in 1960 when the Ford Foundation and The Rockefeller Foundation joined forces to establish in the Philippines an international institute to help solve the problems of rice production in the rice bowl of Asia. This Institute has brought together an international group of young, distinguished agricultural scientists working under the supervision of an international board of trustees. In the short time which has elapsed since its inauguration in 1961, the International Rice Research Institute has become an important Asian center and has achieved world renown because of its contributions to the improvement in yield and quality of rice grown not only in the Philippines but elsewhere in Asia. The Institute is engaged in important cooperative activities with Thailand, India, and Pakistan and has relationships also with Indonesia, Ceylon, and Malaysia. This intense focus on the problems of rice production, through a combination of biology and engineering, has now resulted in the production of substantial quantities of the seed of new varieties which yield 5 to 7 times the national average of most countries by reason of their genetic potentials, their dwarf stature, and their response to fertilizer.

The success of these "hub" type efforts suggests the desirability of establishing one or two or three additional centers in order to create a new dimension of indigenous effort toward the rapid improvement of agricultural economies. An international center for wheat and corn improvement is currently being established in Mexico, and two sites for agricultural improvement in the humid tropics are under consideration in Africa and in South America. It is believed that the tropics must contribute increasingly to the world's food budget. Therefore, it is timely and opportune to begin now to learn how to use the tropics for a greater variety of agricultural purposes by developing improved methods and new materials and by training a body of specialists who may eventually find career opportunities in opening up more of the tropics to agricultural production. The two proposed tropical institutes would direct themselves to these tasks, at the same time intensively studying tropical soils and their management and utilization for increasing food, feed, and meat supplies for world consumption.

Experience has already taught that centers of this sort can in no wise replace existing institutions. Rather, they stimulate their functions, complement their training activities, and add to their research capacities. Ultimately, it is expected that these "hub" centers will be built into the national or regional economy and will continue to operate effectively in this context.

CONCLUSION

It is my conviction that many of the undesirable trends in food production throughout the world could readily and quickly be reversed. The first requisite is a desire on the part of the developing nation to correct these trends and then to translate this desire into direct action. This can be effected by vigorous local initiative and enterprise aided and abetted by technical and management assistance from abroad through government agencies, the private business community, private philanthropy, and bilateral and multilateral aid programs, each of which has an important role to play. Support from international development banks has already been and can continue to be a major accelerator of the rate of progress.

There are today signs of a new awakening in many of the developing nations; they are beginning to discover that their destiny depends upon their own efforts and the wisdom with which they utilize their own human and natural resources, in conjunction with needed help from abroad, in moving down the road toward economic independence.

Foundations for the Future

For more than 60 years philanthropic foundations have been one of the most important and most effective instruments for social progress in this country. At the same time, they are one of the least known and least understood of our social institutions. At various times they have been both sharply castigated and heartily applauded. But perhaps the most common public response has been indifference, an attitude in large part the result of philanthropy's apprehension that in publicizing its efforts on behalf of scholarship, science, and education it might seem to be seeking applause. Indeed, many of our earlier foundations appeared to be most mindful of the Biblical admonition, "When thou doest thine alms, do not sound a trumpet before thee in the street."

This policy of inconspicuous public service was developed long before the federal income tax was instituted. The setting up of a foundation originally had absolutely no relationship to government revenue, potential or actual. However, the year 1913 ushered in the era of the income tax, and most of the more than 15,000 foundations we now have in this country were born, so to speak, in its shadow. Today, all foundations are charged with the responsibility of continually re-earning their franchise as tax-exempt institutions before the bar of public opinion.

Society is indebted to the accomplishments of private foundations over the past 60 years much more deeply than it realizes. Their achievements in medicine, public health, education, the agricultural sciences, the social sciences, and the arts and humanities have contributed incalculably to the well-being of all mankind.

Address presented at the Seventeenth Annual Conference of the Council on Foundations, Denver, Colorado, May 11, 1966

The following are but a few examples of the early initiative of private philanthropy: the conquest of malaria, hookworm, and yellow fever; improvement of higher, professional, and general education throughout the nation; the modern development of such basic sciences as genetics, biochemistry, microbiology; the establishment of the original agricultural extension service; the founding of free public libraries; early support of radio-astronomy and nuclear physics; as well as a wide spectrum of less spectacular, but equally valuable, efforts in support of the social sciences, technical assistance to foreign countries, international education, humanities, and the arts. Many of these pioneering activities established patterns for subsequent public action and without doubt saved untold quantities of public funds.

The total impact of foundations on the entire scientific, social, and cultural development of this country is so large and so extensive as to be difficult to comprehend. Here again, the picture would be much clearer if the foundations themselves had regularly, fully, and interestingly reported their programs. However, the transition from modesty and reticence to complete and objective reporting has been a slow process within the foundation community.

A factor contributing to the confusion about foundations is their almost unintelligible taxonomy. The term has been used generically to include general purpose or special purpose foundations, trust funds, memorials, endowments, and all the rest, whether privately endowed, established through public subscription, supported by annual drives, organized by the community, controlled completely by a company, or set up for the support of educational or religious institutions. To complicate the situation further, substantial numbers of so-called "foundations" do not, strictly speaking, come under the foundation rubric but are so called simply because they, like the rest, have established a tax-exempt position. The public lumps them all together indiscriminately and is apt to either praise or censure them as a group. The thoughtful writings of F. Emerson Andrews and his colleagues on this subject have been illuminating and most helpful. I think they serve also to emphasize that an in-depth study of the taxonomy of private philanthropy, resulting in a classification that would identify and illustrate the many and varied types of foundations established by private donors, communities, corporations, educational institutions, religious bodies, service clubs, and fraternal organizations, would be a great blessing to those of us in the field as well as a valuable reference for others.

Perhaps just because of the lack of readily available information concerning their activities, foundations have been subjected to a variety of criticisms, many of which are unwarranted—they are too big or they are too small, they do all the wrong things and none of the right things, they are self-perpetuating and self-dealing, their tax-exempt privilege forces the average citizen to bear a heavier tax burden than he would if they were not exempt, they influence public policy in insidious ways, they are not bold enough as innovators or are too liberal. In a large and heterogeneous foundation community there may perhaps be a degree of truth in some of these criticisms, but some are fallacious and there is a high degree of exaggeration in all.

One result of these and related criticisms, has been the suggestion that private foundations should themselves draw up a voluntary code of ethics to govern their behavior. This proposal does have merit, particularly as it might encourage the observance of strict fiscal responsibility. But there are a number of complexities to be considered. If the result of such a code were to be some sort of foundation "trade association," I think that this would be highly undesirable. Moreover, the bewildering array of foundations, all with diverse programs and procedures, essentially presupposes that there can be no absolute uniformity of practice. Nor indeed is there any valid evidence that uniformity of program and purpose is a necessary virtue for foundations. There are such wide variations in the way they are set up, in the provisions of their charters and by-laws, and in the origins and types of their funds that any strict application of a uniform code might severely hamper not only the established philanthropies with a distinguished record of purpose and achievement but also the new foundations just coming into being.

I believe that the laws currently on the books are clear and can be effectively applied wherever needed. Abuses when identified can be stopped once and for all by withdrawing the tax-exempt privilege. This penalty is absolute in its effect and is the perfect weapon for the purpose. We do know that some agencies set up as foundations have not lived up to their responsibilities and have taken advantage of the philanthropic purpose for private gain. They have been the main provocation for the attacks to which foundations as a group have been subjected. These should be identified, examined, and, if found guilty of abusing their privilege, should be legally expunged from the roster of tax-exempt philanthropies.

I do believe that foundations themselves can help their own cause and protect the interests and purposes of valid private philanthropy. Perhaps the best instrument for this purpose is the Council on Foundations. If the Council were to sponsor a definitive study of foundations, publish the results, and ultimately prepare a statement delineating the highest standards of foundation practice, this could serve both as a model for foundations striving to adhere to the noblest principles of private philanthropy and as a template for measuring the pattern of performance of those whose conduct falls short of the acceptable.

As a final point, I would like to mention the sometimes stated, but to me entirely unjustified, contention that government should now take over all aspects of social welfare. It has been asserted that this is already taking place with the result that private philanthropy is losing out in terms of its usefulness and the quality of its function. I would reject this thesis as ridiculous. This philosophy, if adhered to in earnest, could eventually destroy private philanthropic initiative and substitute a stultifying social system in which government becomes more the master than the servant of the people. I believe that government, as the servant of the people, and the individual donor, alone or in association with the like-minded, are both vital forces to social evolution.

It has become a familiar theory of history that the progress of humanity comes about largely in response to the challenges put to it. To most of us this is more than academic theorizing; it is the mainspring that keeps us, and the institutions that we serve, going. In my judgment, we are currently suffering from no shortage of challenges. Indeed, we may very well be suffering from an embarrassment of plenty in both the dimensions and the number of the challenges before us.

This does not worry me. The foundation community is organized to examine, probe, and test the opportunities to which every significant challenge gives prolific rise, and it is certainly far up in the vanguard of those forces of our time that are constantly pushing forward the frontiers of knowledge and the application of knowledge upon which all progress ultimately rests.

It has always seemed to me a characteristic of foundations—perhaps their most commanding characteristic—that they admit no ceiling on human progress. Depressing as are some of the realities with which we have to reckon every day, ours is essentially an optimistic trade. And when I consider some of the kinds of challenges that are facing us, I see them not as a catalog of despair but as a partial inventory of opportunities, more vast in their implications than any that foundations have encountered before. I am going to mention some of these, as they look to me, not because I think they are the only ones, but because they strike me as broadly and vividly reflecting the kind of world, the kind of society, and the kind of age in which we are going to have to carry out our great tasks for the predictable future.

1. Our life in America today presents a strange paradox. Although we have achieved a standard of living never before attained anywhere, we are assiduously bringing about the rapid destruction and degradation of the three resources without which man cannot survive: our land, our water, and our air envelope.

It seems incredible that in our growing affluence we did not set aside as an absolute necessity for the future an adequate share of our economic and natural resources to assure that the effect of increasing industrialization would not be a deterioration in the quality of our environment. The story of the destruction of our forests, watersheds, wildlife, and recreation areas is an oft-told tale and indeed a tragic one. Although limited progress has been made toward restoration, renovation, and conservation of some of these once rich and often badly utilized natural resources, they continue to be drained through neglect and the pursuit of profit, while those in a position to rise to the defense continue to be apathetic. The natural beauties of our land have all too frequently become ecological slums, and their vital contributions in the form of pure water, wildlife resources, agricultural products, and recreational opportunities may be lost forever to society.

Furthermore, we are energetically doing what we can to make our last resource, the atmosphere, an aerial sewer. We have even begun to clutter up outer space with a variety of discarded or misguided space paraphernalia. Closer to earth we pour into our air envelope every conceivable variety of debris ranging from atomic fallout and the gaseous and particulate by-products of industry to dust, motor exhaust, incinerator smoke, and even rubber worn from tires revolving at high speeds. And the problem is becoming international, as industry, technology, and urbanization become more widespread through the world.

The private sector, especially industry, educational institutions, and foundations, has become increasingly interested in the whole field of environmental science, as has government at the federal, state, and municipal levels. However, unless greater and more imaginative efforts are undertaken and demonstrable success is achieved, the prospects are for even more rapid deterioration of our environment in the future than in the past. I believe that foundations can and indeed should have a vital role in shedding new light on this complex problem by their aid to research and other supporting efforts toward its ultimate solution. Problems in environmental science must be approached through many disciplines, including medicine and public health, agricultural and animal science, engineering, climatology, architecture, economics and sociology, transportation, and jurisprudence.

2. At long last we are seeing with greater clarity than ever the implications of uncontrolled population increase. The threat is obvious, and it is imminent. We know that it cannot be resolved by government action alone, as important as this must be in the long run. Continuing research in demography, human biology, and the physiology of reproduction is of fundamental importance. No less essential is universal awareness of the problem and ways in which it can be attacked. Consequently, we must have further studies of traditional attitudes, cultural philosophies, and the economic and social factors affecting individual decisions on family planning. And we must formulate and organize systems through which there can be more public enlightenment and more widespread response to it. Progress to date has been slow but encouraging; foundations have played a major role, but it has not been enough. Ahead for all of us lies an even greater task. And it will require all the imagination, all the ingenuity, and all the understanding which can be brought by private, governmental, and international organizations to make positive and effective progress toward population stabilization.

3. Closely allied to the population problem is that of inadequate world food production. We are today in a state of chronic and precarious imbalance between a growing population and insufficient food supplies. We must now make important decisions as to who will produce the food for the future, how it will be distributed and utilized, and under what conditions. The distribution of surpluses (now almost nonexistent) and the provision of other types of massive international assistance are, of course, primarily matters for national governments to decide. But, at best, these can be only holding actions. We must look farther ahead and try to solve the problem, not merely treat its symptoms. We need especially to examine and investigate the various possibilities for closing food gaps in the underproducing nations. This requires the concerted effort not only of governmental agencies but of educational and philanthropic institutions, as well as of private enterprise. In the view of many authorities the problem is growing rather than diminishing, and they predict a major world food deficit within 20 years. Therefore, unless prompt, continuing, and successful effort is made to understand and correct the situation, the indications for the future are ominous. Private philanthropy has already played a major role through its efforts to improve the agricultural industry and productivity of new nations. Here again, however, the greatest challenges lie ahead.

4. Many serious problems of public health continue unresolved. Although in this country and certain others extraordinary achievements can be recorded—with much of the earlier impetus coming from private philanthropy—mankind as a whole is still afflicted and harassed by disease. Human pathogens—tricky enemies which lurk and resist subjugation—return to afflict generation after generation. Intensive and continuing research must be conducted on the broad spectrum of critically important diseases attacking man and his domestic animals and on the ecological potential for the control or eradication of major diseases. The problems of public health are particularly pressing in the tropics, yet if man is to satisfy his need for more food, land, and greater economic opportunity, the tropics must one day be conquered. Thus far, however, they have yielded only partially to the onslaught of medical science. Examples of resistance are many: malaria is still with us, schistosomiasis remains substantially the plague that it has been for

centuries, and the multitude of parasitic organisms that prey on humans may well today constitute the greatest single cause of disease, discomfort, and economic loss throughout the humid tropics. Similarly, the health of domestic animals, upon which the inhabitants of the tropics must depend in large measure for protein foods, is menaced by a wide variety of pests and pathogens. Foundations have, of course, been active and successful in making inroads here, but the problem is vast and the progress is slow and fragmentary. Once more the challenge of the future far outweighs the achievements of the past.

5. Human behavior is exceedingly complex and constantly changing, and we have barely scratched the surface of many of its facets. The secrets of the mind are still largely undisclosed and only vaguely understood. In an increasingly complex society the necessity for understanding individual human motivations and actions and man's interaction with other men, both singly and in groups, becomes more pressing and more important.

Challenging opportunities for research are at every hand. The behavioral sciences, a comparatively recent field of study which draws upon all disciplines having to do with human conduct, give promise of shedding increasing light on the mental process. There are also other new and exciting avenues of knowledge that are beginning to open as a result of penetrating studies in the fields of psychology, psychiatry, animal behavior, and molecular neurophysiology, among others. The problems are complex and the research must be sophisticated, but they may one day lead us to greater insight into the individual and social problems which must be solved if future generations are to live full, satisfying, and constructive lives.

6. Our entire educational system is now being seriously strained. Growing numbers of young people must be educated in contemporary terms. Continuing education is everywhere recognized as of growing importance, and our institutions are under constant pressure to host the increasing numbers of students from abroad who seek the educational experiences available here. And the quantitative implications, serious as they may be, cannot be more important than the qualitative aspects of our educational system. We need to educate our youth to serve as effective members of a society in a state of flux; we need to develop the creative talent which will

expand the horizon of knowledge or produce works of artistic merit which will heighten the quality of human existence. We must produce the leadership which will guide our future destinies into desired pathways. Our educational institutions at all levels must be constantly re-examined to insure that they are fulfilling these manifold functions, and helped to achieve their goal of providing the best education for all Americans.

The current ferment on the campus is indicative of fundamental problems which must be identified and ultimately resolved if the university is to serve its function as an instrument for the development of the individual student and to increase its services to social and scientific progress. Here again, private philanthropy can play as great a role in the future as it has so effectively in the past.

7. Another factor contributing to the social eruption we are witnessing today is that certain minority groups are suffering from serious social and economic disadvantage, the consequences of which affect our entire population to some degree. These stresses are serious and their implications are alarming. Overly slow in the past to bring about appropriate changes, we now face onrushing forces which threaten to bring about increasing strife and chaos in various parts of our nation. During the years ahead the search for greater understanding, improved communication, and the undertaking of specific programs directed toward the relief of social tension and the resolution of longstanding problems require attention, resources, and leadership. Private philanthropy has a long and distinguished record of achievement in the area of providing equal opportunity for all citizens. This experience can stand us in good stead in the time ahead. The secret of success may well be the skill with which all sectors of society are knitted into a fabric of interaction and self-help and equal opportunity as contrasted to relief and legal compulsion.

8. A greater part of our most serious challenges of the future will be directly, or indirectly, associated with expanding urban life. We have seen the development of urban complexes with huge populations, the subsequent deterioration of the center or core areas, and the flight of the inhabitants to the suburbs, which often become infected with the same problems as the older areas or develop new ones. We have not yet discovered how to prevent the social decay in our cities, which creates congestion, tension, and outbreaks

300

of violence accompanied by the breakdown of the fabric of law and order. If our cities are to become better places in which to live and work rather than a tangled conglomeration of humanity, vehicles, and waste, we shall have to work unceasingly for a greater understanding of what has to be done to bring about the desired changes and to obtain the public support necessary for any permanent improvement. It is not to be expected that private philanthropy alone can undertake to resolve the gigantic problems created by mass crowding into urban complexes. We can, however, stimulate the support of study and research, community action, and the reform necessary to a gradual reversal of current trends.

9. One aspect of the situation is the apparent breakdown of the family and the resulting increase in psychological and social problems. Many factors may account for this: the rapid tempo of progress and change, the burgeoning of new technologies, the increased mobility and wider contact made possible by speedier transportation and communication, and unprecedented affluence. All these factors appear to have changed patterns of family life with bewildering rapidity in ways with which we are not prepared to cope, and have led to the deeply rooted restlessness, resentment, resistance, and revolt of youth. A major and intricate facet of this situation is the persistent problem of juvenile delinquency. Some may assume that we are passing through only a temporary phase. But this solace may be rooted in a tragic misconception. It is far better that we try now to ascertain the facts and take action rather than wait until too late to learn of our error.

We need to know more and to do more about the increasing number of promising lives being broken by the harmful effects of narcotics addiction, alcoholism, illicit drug experimentation, and the rejection of well-established social mores of proven value.

From prehistoric times religion has been the greatest single force in the behavior of man. The evolution of civilization and the evolution of religion have been inseparable. However, in this country, and indeed in others, questions are being raised more often as to the role of religion and religious leaders in the great issues so critical to continuing social progress. Many have asked whether the churches have held back when they should have led, have remained silent when they should have spoken up, and have compromised when they should have stood fast. Whatever the facts, there

301

are important and increasing opportunities to re-examine and strengthen the vital role of religion in a fast-changing society. All these factors require study, understanding, and action if we are to retain the values which we have long cherished and which, in order to have equal validity and relevance today, must be adapted to the complex of the contemporary human experience.

10. We live in this country in a highly technological society, now passing through a phase of fast and accelerating automation, which leaves many with more free time and leisure than they ever had before. This development, in the face of a growing population, increasing affluence, and changing standards of taste, highlights the necessity of providing new impetus to multidimensional cultural development, as, for example, making available to the entire society much of the best in the creative and performing arts. I think we are realizing as never before the need for giving people of all ages and in all sectors of society access to the enriching experience of hearing and seeing works of artists and artistic performers. There are great opportunities for innovations in this area, and by selective and imaginative support of the arts and the humanities the foundations can contribute uniquely to the cultural enrichment of this nation.

11. Many of the ills of mankind are compounded by the difficulties which we have in communicating with our own kind. Linguistics, semantics, cultural traditions, and many other factors are all involved. Surprisingly enough, in spite of the destructive wars of the past, which have brought about death, conquest, human deprivation and suffering, and some of the worst examples of man's inhumanity to man, we have not yet been able to learn from these experiences how to prevent similar and perhaps vastly more destructive conflicts in the future. Political ideologies, embodying varying concepts of power structure and privilege, have effectively placed barriers to achieving that now almost forgotten hope, "peace and prosperity for the world." Nor can we ever aspire to that hope as long as nations seeking to improve their economic development are at the same time intent on destroying their neighbors. Although, quite obviously, this is one of the most difficult and persistent problems of mankind, every effort must be made to find the keys to unlock the doors to understanding between individuals, groups, communities, and sovereign nations. The re-

search, experimentation, and pilot operations required are enormous and must be continuously improved and intensified. Here is an ideal area for the utilization of private resources for intellectual accomplishment leading to improved communication and better understanding among men and nations.

12. Finally, we cannot escape the fact that we are part of a world community and that the problems of any sector of the globe become, to some degree, our problems. In a world where hunger and famine stalk some lands each year, where ignorance is unresolved in too many areas, and where the struggle for decent standards of living prohibits the development of democratic institutions, the more advanced nations face what is perhaps their greatest challenge—the challenge to assist the less developed nations to achieve levels of economic and social progress which will enable them to take their places in the community of nations. The needs are enormous and the spectrum of opportunity is unlimited. Foundations, because of their resources, experience, and flexibility of action, are signally qualified to participate in a constructive fashion in the many facets of foreign assistance to the developing areas. The past record of the contributions of private philanthropy is a brilliant one. In the fields of education, medicine, public health, and agriculture it has contributed immeasurably to the well-being of millions who would have been unable to resolve fundamental problems without such assistance. In view of past achievements it is reasonable to expect that within the broad field of foreign aid the private sector, and foundations in particular, will continue to find new and telling ways of helping the underdeveloped areas and their peoples create a better life for themselves.

Private philanthropy has pioneered in all of these troubled areas, and in these and many others it must continue in the future to play a key and initiatory role. Although foundations vary widely in their resources and size, money does not necessarily determine quality. Large and small, if they apply imagination, experience, and, hopefully, wisdom to the use of available resources in good causes, they are all important contributors. The small but significant community and civic project, modest aid to educational and health projects—each is part of the pattern and content of the philanthropic enterprise. In this every foundation can share. Our resources, though limited, are significant in terms of money and expertise, and they pave the way for the investment of vastly greater public funds in good cause. And we have the strength of a lively and affirmative tradition behind us. Nevertheless, if we are to make the most of our opportunities, we must help advance a wider understanding of the changes that are essential to a healthy, progressive society in which all members contribute on the basis of equality and individual ability.

In conclusion, the question confronting foundations today is not whether there is still validity in their existence, or whether public funds have made them unnecessary. On the contrary, private philanthropy, of which foundations are one of the major forces, is needed now more than ever before and is faced with even greater challenges in solving contemporary problems. The question really is how imaginatively and effectively can we select our roles and goals and how rapidly can we move toward them in the service of all society. There should be no relaxing of our total efforts toward the great objective.

Survival or Fulfillment

It would be a melancholy paradox if all of the extraordinary social and technological advances that have been made by man were to bring us to the point where society's sole preoccupation would of necessity become survival rather than fulfillment. Until quite recently, most Americans lived with the happy if unrealistic faith that there would always be new land to develop and untapped natural resources to exploit. We thought of the abundance of nature as being inexhaustible and treated it with abandon and without regard for the future. And while we, along with others, proclaimed our intentions to make the world a better place in which to live, we have at the same time been acting vigorously, if perhaps unconsciously, to bring about the opposite, ignoring all the danger signs until clear and imminent threats to our well-being have forced themselves upon our consciousness.

Forces other than overconfidence and inexcusable carelessness have effected dramatic changes in our society and in our ways of thinking. The impact of two world wars and unparalleled advances in education, communication, and transportation have resulted in enormous exchanges of students, scholars, scientists, businessmen, and tourists, with the result that the earth no longer seems vast nor does any part of it appear remote. We are now acutely aware of international problems that once seemed scarcely of any concern to us. The comfortable isolation which we enjoyed in the past has disappeared, and serious problems in any part of the world inevitably involve our own interests.

An address delivered at the California Institute of Technology Conference on The Next Ninety Years, March 7, 1967

Since the end of the Second World War we have seen the emergence of almost 60 new nations. The earlier balance of political power has changed, and our nostalgic hope that we could concern ourselves mainly with achieving progress and prosperity in an atmosphere of peace has gradually faded away. In fact, nearly half of the present population of the United States have spent their entire lives in the tense atmosphere of the cold war.

There is a tendency to oversimplify the present politico-economic situation by dividing the world into the rich nations and the poor nations—the haves and the have-nots—and to hold the more fortunate group responsible for the development of the other. Furthermore, the developing nations are impatient, often demanding. Their ambitions are high; many want to make the great leap forward without fully recognizing that any forward movement—and especially a leap—must be made from a solid base. And while they are insistent in their demands, they are often inconsistent in their political philosophies.

We are presently caught up in an extraordinary surge of activities on a world scale, involving food supplies, population stabilization, economic development, education, and even military action. The social and political forces of our modern world, having brought about these various geo-political phenomena, now look to science and technology to provide the practical solutions to the problems of an uneasy world. However, unless certain difficult decisions are made and prompt action taken to implement them, any solution, scientific or otherwise, will be impossible.

POPULATION

It is a fundamental fact that, next to world conflict, the greatest single threat to mankind is that of explosive population increase. To date, neither the disadvantaged countries nor those who would help them have been able to limit the vast increase in numbers. The evidence of this situation has long been before us, but appropriate action to overcome it has been woefully slow. This has not been because science and technology have failed to develop the information and necessary materials. Rather, there has been failure throughout all sectors of society to recognize the critical nature of the problem. And today, although the informed public is becoming increasingly aware of the situation, some of our leaders and spokesmen are re-

306

luctant to face up to the long-range implications of unrestrained population growth. And while the debate rages, wave after wave of new citizens join the world's ranks at the rate of 65 million a year. Although millions of these individuals are unwanted, unplanned for, and cannot be properly fed, clothed, housed, and provided with educational and other opportunities, we have thus far been unable to stem the tide. Unless this situation is universally recognized and programs gotten under way to resolve it promptly, survival may well become our chief concern, with attendant degradation of the human condition.

The desire to be blessed with many sons is deeply imbedded in the mystique of all societies from their earliest origins when infant mortality was high and the life span short. And thus, under adverse circumstances, the ancient injunction to multiply and replenish the earth underscored man's basic need to insure the perpetuation of his species. Thus, since the dawn of medical science a major emphasis has been upon successfully bringing new individuals into the world and stretching out their life spans.

It is tempting to blame science for emphasizing death control while neglecting birth control. And it is true that if it had been possible, beginning several generations ago, to include family planning within the spectrum of public health and medical care, the rate of population increase might today be more nearly within reasonable bounds. However, the humanitarian concerns of the time were to alleviate human suffering and protect life. There was no public interest in population stabilization. Indeed, when attention was called during the last century to the ultimate dangers of uninhibited population increase, the warning went unheeded. Those who sounded the alarm were often labeled as prophets of doom in a world where the prevailing climate was belief in the eternal abundance of nature and the inevitability of human progress.

Science and technology are, at best, tools and instrumentalities. They are amoral and can be used either for the benefit or detriment of mankind. The ultimate decision for social action is fundamentally a moral choice, falling within the jurisdiction of religion, politics, ethics, and philosophy. The leaders in these fields, in association with the scientific community, have the combined responsibility for the direction which social evolution will take. The question can properly be raised whether our religious, political, and social leadership has responded adequately to major moral problems and whether or not decisions have been diluted by expediency, selfishness, apathy, or ignorance. Even today in much of the world the people are ahead of their leaders in understanding the dangers of an uninhibited population increase and in desiring to bring about family planning for their own well-being. The leadership must take increasingly vigorous action in the dissemination of information, the organization of appropriate programs of family planning, and the continuing and growing support of the entire movement. Otherwise, we may be unable to close the floodgates in time to apply our intelligence, energy, and resources to the satisfactory accommodation of an already overextended population.

Within the more highly industrialized nations the products of science and technology have been astonishing in their variety, brilliant in their conception, and miraculous in their achievement. We have a plethora of power instruments which work for us and obey our command, and our achievements in agricultural and engineering technology dominate the landscape and contribute efficiently to our well-being. Unhappily, we and other nations have also developed engines of war and destruction whose construction and maintenance drain our economic lifeblood and whose worldwide distribution is a potential threat to our civilization.

But even in these more advanced nations there are many accelerators which interact to bring about worsening conditions in a time of unrestrained population growth. The pressures on land, resources, and technology to satisfy all the requirements of society are ever expanding. In response, there is a growing drain on land, water, soil, and subsoil resources; increasing strains on our cities, suburbs, and even rural areas; and heavier demands on our professionals, scientists, technologists, and the producers of the enormous varieties of goods and services which are required today.

We do not know the carrying capacity of our total environment, but it is perfectly clear that as now constituted our systems of production and distribution are inadequate even to the present task. Under the most favorable circumstances these cannot conceivably improve more rapidly than the current rate of population growth. We can already identify areas in which the stark struggle for survival is in progress. The most dramatic example is to be found in India, over which looms the threat of famine unless its position of agricultural underproduction can be corrected. In the interim India must depend upon contributions of food from sympathetic nations. These food contributions cannot be provided indefinitely, and the prevailing production deficiencies, even if corrected, will be insufficient to feed the population of the future if present levels of increase persist.

FOOD

There are forces which can be marshaled to improve human nutrition substantially throughout much of the world. Initially, these forces, applied in concert, can help us buy much needed time to mount an effective population stabilization effort. If and when there are significant gains in reducing the population increase, then we may be able to begin to close the food gap.

The technology of conventional food production has reached such high levels of efficiency that, if applied generally to agrarian systems, world food-grain production could be readily doubled or trebled. If the political, social, and financial leadership of a nation interacts to develop and support a modern agricultural industry, it is quite possible to mobilize the necessary technology, obtain improved biological materials, apply appropriate agricultural chemicals, and utilize essential implements to reverse the now widespread pattern of agricultural underproduction.

Highly efficient varieties of food crops and breeds of domestic animals have been developed; more are on their way. On the basis of current advances biologic engineering of plant and animal species offers exciting new promise for the future, and a wide variety of opportunities exists, not only in improving the quality of conventional agricultural products but in adding to the quantity through nonconventional methods involving algae, fungi, and bacteria, which manufacture protein substances from inorganic components. There is undoubtedly a growing need for protein food supplements, and technology can on an increasing scale find ways to utilize sources of food now thought of as having limited economic possibilities.

There are no technological secrets in agricultural production, and all nations with the will can find the way to take advantage of modern knowledge and methods. Currently there are striking examples of accomplishment by developing nations seeking to improve their own food production systems. Mexico, the Philippines, and Pakistan are but three countries which are now making notable progress in the significant annual increase of basic food crops. And their example can be followed by others.

Self-help must be the central thrust of all the hungry nations as a matter of responsibility and pride in the face of growing need. Assistance from without must, on an increasing scale, be designed to accelerate rather than to replace the self-help process. Here again, the danger signals are clearly evident to those who will see them, and they indicate that more developed nations cannot for any considerable period of time or in any significant dimension feed portions of the world which remain static in terms of their own food production efforts. Unless this is clearly understood and maximum efforts are made to reverse systems of underproduction wherever they exist, survival will, indeed, become man's chief concern in much of the world.

HEALTH AND DISEASE CONTROL

Thanks to the efforts of many national and international organizations, the status of world health is better than ever before, although still far from ideal. We have not everywhere eliminated or even contained malaria; schistosomiasis continues to plague millions who dwell in the tropics, dysentery is still a great killer of the very young, and the incidence of venereal disease, even in the more developed countries, rises and falls according to our alertness and effort. And we must remember that improvements in public health must go hand in hand with population stabilization and increased food production. Unless advances in these three areas are made simultaneously and in an integrated fashion, the central purpose of life—that of human fulfillment—cannot be achieved. The health of our own population is perhaps at its highest level, although at times it seems as though we have simply exchanged the old well-known vulgar diseases for more exotic ones, the products of affluence. Indeed, if current trends continue, it may be possible to keep a man alive indefinitely just as we did the Model-T in years gone by when we replaced it bit by bit until nothing was left of the original but the radiator cap. It would be an interesting situation when the average man knows that at least several of his organs were once working for someone else.

310

EDUCATION

The pressures on all of the world's educational facilities continue to grow apace, even though the differences may be extreme. In some cases the greatest immediate need is to provide merely the basic rudiments of education; in others it is for more and better education, at least through the secondary school level; and in many of the industrialized nations the most urgent demand is for an expansion of undergraduate, graduate, and professional continuing education.

In our own country the pressures that we originally ascribed to the postwar "baby boom" have now become a permanent fact of life. Each year vastly larger numbers of students must be accommodated throughout the educational network. Indeed, the current requirements of life in our country imply that education through the baccalaureate level is essential today for most of our citizens. The logistics of numbers alone are extraordinarily difficult, as is the problem of financing the vast educational mechanism of this nation. Equally difficult, perhaps, is the continuing adjustment of institutions of higher education to the changing scene. Students who experience the intense pressures of modern life and who are witnesses to the succession of failures in man's efforts to promote world peace and prosperity, inevitably become concerned and feel that they must rise in protest. Some of this activity, conceived in perplexity but founded on intelligence and carried on in good faith, is a healthy sign of the students' interest in their country and in the world around them. Inevitably, however, some of this rising tension and confusion is utilized advantageously by those who would destroy our form of society rather than work constructively to improve it.

Current evidence suggests that in the education of burgeoning numbers of our youth we are going to face more rather than less difficult situations in the future. It will not be possible forever to go on increasing the numbers and dimensions of those institutions required to provide mass educational activities at central locations. We may have to disperse this effort, extend public secondary education by two or even four years, and utilize more fully the primary and secondary school facilities which are now in service for only a limited part of each year. Our universities might then be able to devote themselves to the graduate education that is becoming more and more necessary and available. This would give us the time to plan for a future where even this system and structure will be inadequate to take care of the numbers to be educated. Ultimately, we may one day have to call again upon the technologies related to engineering and education to provide educational service on a plug-in basis in the home, along with all the multiple other services we receive in this fashion.

OUR NATURAL ENVIRONMENT

Today all the training and education we have provided for ourselves have failed to give us an awareness of what we, either by our passivity or by our actions, are doing to our environment and, ultimately, to ourselves. In response to population pressures and in conjunction with increasing affluence, we have destroyed much of what we like to call the great American heritage. Most apparent has been the damage to many of our great water systems, both through neglect and through direct action. Now that we have permitted untold billions of dollars worth of damage, we are beginning to realize that we will have to spend further billions to correct the mistakes of the past. Otherwise, we face the probability that these water assets so important to us will be destroyed to the point of no return. We have already ruined many of our prime watersheds, silted and polluted our lakes and rivers, eliminated their wildlife, and spoiled them for human recreation.

Few would believe today that rivers such as the Hudson, Merrimack, and Chattahoochee were once sources of inspiration for a school of landscape painters, for Thoreau, and for Lanier. Nor would they recognize in the lyrical descriptions of Lake Erie penned at the turn of the century that body of water now declared biologically moribund as a result of man's tender ministrations.

We now realize that the long-range effects of air pollution on the health of people can be far more drastic than water pollution. In this country such terms as "greenhouse effect," "particle load," "thermal inversion," "blowby device," and "discomfort level" have become part of the vernacular. Hospital and medical records indicate increasing numbers of patients with asthma, bronchitis, emphysema, and allergic reactions that are aggravated by the air they breathe. In the plant kingdom the leafy vegetables have reacted to irritating pollutants in the air to the extent that on occasion they become unmarketable because of resultant blemishes. Doubtless, other indirect and insidious threats to the health of man and plant and animal life lurk in our immediate atmosphere.

Water pollution may often extend beyond national boundaries, but air pollution is inescapably international. Just as the expansion of our cities has caused a spectacular concentration of people and industry into urban areas, which are now growing toward each other, so their accompanying smog cover is becoming a single umbrella which, as a result of air movement and topography, spreads out and extends over an ever-widening area. The smog areas on our eastern seaboard are closely linked, as are those on our west coast. Already, over parts of Northern Europe atmospheric pollution has become an international problem, and we may expect similar situations beyond our own borders in this hemisphere if this menace to mankind increases.

The past lack of understanding and imagination and unwillingness to pay the costs of protecting the future have caused us to reach the point where water pollution, soil pollution, and now on an increasing scale, pollution of our air envelope have caused our environment to deteriorate. It is virtually intolerable in several places, barely tolerable in others, and growingly intolerable wherever there are concentrations of people, their waste products, and the so-called "by-products" of their industry. Actually, there are no by-products, but only materials that are discarded as uneconomic and for which we have not yet had the ingenuity to develop an economic use. As a result, untold wealth has been lost through the wasteful process of extracting a single material of commercial value, while, through ignorance and lack of imagination, discarding others potentially many times more valuable.

So, along with too many people and too little food, we now have environmental pollution. As these problems grow and interact, we have every reason to expect that unless there is drastic and prompt improvement, mere survival may well become our main preoccupation in the not-too-distant future.

Foresight and wisdom are badly needed. It will not be enough for political leaders, educators, and scientists to come together in an effort to repair the damage of the past, reverse destructive trends, and attempt to build pathways to a better future. Rather, every sector in the national community and the community of nations will have to participate actively and constructively in the total effort if we are to achieve success. Only through vigorous and collective effort can we curb the population explosion, supply the foods to sustain all of the world's citizens, put an end to the wanton destruction of our natural resources and their utilization in ways which often cause further deterioration of our physical environment, and finally, move the specter of war ever further from the contemporary scene. As we approach these goals, we can then use the world's resources to assure that all human beings can enjoy the educational and other opportunities for self-fulfillment to which they are all entitled within the limits of individual potentials.

CONCLUSION

It has been observed that threats to society from the outside often seem more frightening than those from within. The latter, perhaps, are often less perceptible and more insidious, at least until they grow to some visible and obvious dimension. Today we and other nations of the world are faced with a variety of both internal and external challenges, some of which are clearly frightening. It is these challenges—over-population, human hunger, environmental pollution, and social and economic disadvantage—that we must vigorously attack and correct if we are to avoid bringing the world to a condition where we must revert to the harsh principle of the survival of the fittest.

The dangers which now confront civilization are clear and increasingly imminent. It is time to meet them with intelligent, vigorous, and continuing action. Perhaps the first step is to assure that citizens everywhere are aware of these threats and convinced that all must support remedial effort. Then the forces of government, business and industry, labor, education, religion, and private philanthropy can come into play and interact for the benefit of all of society. The strength of a pluralistic society can be dissipated unless there is unanimity of thought and concerted action on those problems which, if left unsolved, will impede and perhaps eventually halt human progress toward universal humanitarian goals.

The purposes of life have always been the subject of great debate. However, most would agree that the ideal human condition is one in which the individual is provided with opportunities to pursue his own destiny to the limits of his own capabilities and to enjoy the satisfactions of family life while using his abilities to contribute to the well-being of the community and society in general. To achieve these human goals man's material requirements must in some reasonable dimension be met; good health and proper nutrition are essential biological components of the desired human condition. Unless these, as well as certain other physical requirements of his existence, are effectively and universally satisfied, man can only revert to an earlier state in which his entire energies were directed solely toward survival.

A very early precursor of modern man has recently earned himself the title *homo habilis*, "tool-maker man." Ever since he lived, almost two million years ago, the genus *homo* has been modifying his environment in ingenious and multifarious ways in order to survive and improve his comfort. If modern man, *homo sapiens*, is really worthy of his *title*, he should be able to find the solutions to our current environmental problems. We can identify the dangers, determine the remedies, and take steps both within and beyond national boundaries to apply appropriate measures to correct adverse trends and ultimately move closer to a condition of peace and prosperity. Unless we do, the next 90 years may be considered as the decline of a golden age and a period fraught with tension, retrogression, and at some point, world conflict.